DRUG USE IN LONDON

DRUG USE IN LONDON

EDITED BY GERRY V. STIMSON, CHRIS FITCH AND ALI JUDD

First published 1998
by Leighton Print

Designed by I J Harris Design (telephone 0956 274 485 or 0171 428 9537).

British Library Cataloguing in Publication Data
A catalogue for this book is available from the British Library

ISBN 1 874676 15 1

Contents

Acknowledgements

The Centre for Research on Drugs and Health Behaviour is core funded by the North Thames Office of the NHS Executive.

Drug Use in London is supported by the Zeneca Group PLC, Esso and London Electricity Board.

(Esso)

Many thanks to I J Harris Design for their flexibility and foresight.

Additional thanks to the following:
Gill Auld (Time Out), John Balding (Schools Health Education Unit), Ann Barber (Home Office), Martin Bardsley (Health of Londoners Project), Jackie Baxter, Kirsty Blenkins (apa Tower Hamlets), Raj Boothroyd (Riverside Substance Misuse Service), Chris Bowden (BMRB International), Mark Brangwyn (Association of Local Government), Chris Budgen (HIV Project), Thia Bunyan (Kingston & Richmond health authority), Penny Butler (Offenders and Corrections Unit, Home Office), Jane Carrier, Rosalie Chamberlin (Kaleidoscope), Lufbuné and Thelma Chapple, Peter Congdon (Barking and Havering health authority), John Corkery, Linda Cusick, Mike Daykin (Crime and Criminal Justice Department, Home Office), Richard du Parq (Performance Information Bureau, Metropolitan Police Service), Ian Edmund, Warren Evans (Performance Information Bureau, Metropolitan Police Service), Steve Fitch, Christine Franey, Liz Gass (Central Drugs Co-ordination Unit), Richard Goldfinch, Mike Goodman (Release), Trisha Grant (Directorate of Public Affairs, Metropolitan Police Service), Maria Griffin, Dick Groves (Metropolitan Police Service), Sarah Hallam, Rob Harnett, Debbie Hart (Imperial College of Science, Technology and Medicine), Denise Herraghty, Joan Heuston (Health Education Authority), Vivian Hope (Public Health Laboratory Service), Amanda Hopkins (Her Majesty's Customs and Excise), Mike Hough (Southbank University), David Huke (Her Majesty's Customs and Excise), Tim Hull (CSN Consultancy), Melany Hunt, Jude Hurley (Performance Information Bureau, Metropolitan Police Service), Martin Jauch (CO14, Metropolitan Police Service), Tim Jennings (Health Education Authority), Les King (Forensic Science Service, Dave Lambert (Office for National Statistics), Don Lavoie, Paul Leahy (Metropolitan Police Service), Alan Leonard (Her Majesty's Prison Wormwood Scrubs), Robert Lilly, Charlie Lloyd (CDPU), John Maggi (Home Office), Hazel Mann, Bertie Mann (Government Office for London), Eileen Matthews (Kingston & Richmond health authority), Pat Mayhew (Crime and Criminal Justice Unit, Home Office), Sylvia Mazabel, Grant McNally, Nicky Metrebian, Rowan Miller (Caravan Project), Rosemary Moore (London Drug Policy Forum), Ciarron O'Hagan (Release), Sandra O'Hagan (Kingston & Richmond health authority), Stephen Parfitt, Tim Parson (City of London Police), Jim Parsons, James Payne, Geof Pearson, Andrew Percy (Research and Statistics Directorate, Home Office), Grant Pettitt (London Research Centre), Michael Pollard, Alan Quirk, Malcolm Ramsay (Research and Statistics Directorate, Home Office), Dave Regis (Schools Health Education Unit), Harry Shapiro (ISDD), Andy Simmons (Hungerford Drug Project), Sarah Smith (Harris Research), Dave Stewart (Leighton Print), Hayley Stolk, Chris Stone (Diatech), Emma and Nibs Taylor, Betsy Thom, Marilyn Toft, Keith Ward (Research and Statistics Directorate, Home Office), Chris Watts (Barking and Havering health authority), Chris Watts (Prison Library Service), Russell Webster, Sian Lloyd-Haywood, G.L. Wilkins (Crime and Criminal Justice Unit, Home Office), Basil Williams (Mainliners).

Foreword

Throughout Britain, it is recognised that large numbers of people have used illegal drugs. No longer a topic of marginal interest or importance, drugs and drug use now appear as regularly on the agenda of local associations and regional bodies as they do on those of national public health and law enforcement agencies. However, until now it has been extremely difficult to obtain information specifically about drug use in the capital.

Everyone involved in the production of this book has done so simply out of the recognition that London is *special*. On most counts of problematic drug use - such as the number of known heroin users, the level of HIV infection among drug users, and the amount of drugs seized - London reports consistently higher levels than anywhere else in the UK. Organisationally, the capital continues to maintain its historic status as the focus for drug treatment and service delivery in the country, and since the introduction of the first national drugs strategy - *Tackling Drugs Together* - now also plays host to one-quarter of England's 106 Drug Action Teams. In addition, London's sheer geographic scale and instutional fragmentation - with its 33 local authorities, 16 health authorities, 27 Drug Action Teams, five Probation Service areas and around 150 drug services - also contributes to its very special character, making the simplest of organisational tasks and interventions instantly more difficult.

The publication of Drug Use in London comes at both an important and intriguing time. With the introduction of the new national drugs strategy, *Tackling Drugs to Build a Better Britain*, those interested in drugs and drug use need to consider how this will be applied in and across London. However, the application of this strategy is likely to be only one of a series of changes taking place in the coming years. Of these, the potential establishment of a London-wide electoral mayor and assembly offers equally intriguing possibilities. If formed, this body could open the way for accompanying pan-London 'public health' or 'drug' strategies targeting issues such as organisational co-ordination, information gathering, and intervention development. Now is an important time then, to begin considering where these two strategic developments could overlap one another. Hopefully, the range of commentaries and statistics offered in each chapter of this book will aid this process, as well as making it easier to identify any debt either strategic move owes to its predecessors.

Drug Use in London only represents a modest step in the wider process of review, consultation and change taking place throughout London and the UK. However, although difficult to predict what the future holds for either drug use or the capital, we do hope that the book will achieve at least one aim: to encourage people to think about how drug-related harm can be reduced on a pan-London basis.

Gerry Stimson, Chris Fitch and Ali Judd

1st May 1998

1

WHY LONDON?

Alyson Morley
London Drug Policy Forum

Sections

London - drugs capital of the United Kingdom

London is one of the world's foremost capital cities. A centre for national and international government, finance, business, entertainment, culture and transport. It is also the drugs capital of the United Kingdom.

Home to just over seven million people, London is culturally extremely diverse and over the years people from every part of the world have settled here. It has some of the oldest established black and ethnic minority communities who have lived here for centuries. It is also home to people who are newly arrived from all parts of the United Kingdom and further afield. However, the very aspects which make London such a diverse, dynamic and attractive city also bring problems. Poverty, unemployment, crime, homelessness, social and economic deterioration, social exclusion and racism are features of life for many Londoners. These can represent both the causes and consequences of problem drug use.

London is a net importer of drug users from other parts of the UK. They are attracted by a number of factors: the anonymity of the big city; a means of escape from problems at home; the guarantee of a plentiful supply of drugs; and a diverse range of drug services. Whatever the reason, London has more than its fair share of drug users originally from other parts of the country.

It is also important to see London as part of Europe and the global community. London has small but well established drug using populations from other European countries. The most notable examples are Irish and Italian problem drug users who have been attracted to London by the 'British system' of substitute prescribing and harm reduction measures not widely available in their own countries. One study in London reported that 26 per cent of a sample of injecting drug users had been born outside of the UK. This group contained 29 different non-UK countries of birth (Advisory Council on the Misuse of Drugs, 1993). Other communities are associated with the use of particular drugs: for example, some people from Somalia and Ethiopia use Khat, a mild stimulant, as part of leisure activities.

> **Key finding**
> In terms of prevalence, even though London had only 12 per cent of the UK population in 1996 (Office for National Statistics, 1997), 21 per cent of all notifications of drug users made to the Home Office Addicts Index in that year were reported from London (Home Office Statistical Bulletin, 1997).

Drugs and crime

London is an important point in the distribution route for drugs bound for other parts of the UK and Europe. The Metropolitan Police Service has estimated that three-quarters of all drug trafficking occuring in the UK takes place within London even though most consignments are en route elsewhere (Metropolitan Police Service and London Drug Policy Forum, 1994).

Profit
The illicit drugs market is highly profitable. Consequently it is highly competitive and violence is not uncommon.

As with other major cities in Britain and America, London has seen a sharp rise in the number of drug-related killings over the past five years. The main reason cited for this trend is the emergence of 'crack' cocaine which is both highly profitable and addictive. On the one hand, some dealers will compete ruthlessly in 'turf wars'. On the other hand, some problem users will resort to desperate means to acquire crack. In areas of high unemployment, where there is little prospect of young people gaining well paid jobs, the attraction of the illicit drug market is clear. Every young person diverted into the illicit market and associated crime represents one less young person available to learn skills and expertise which can contribute to the legitimate economy.

Numbers

Illicit drugs can be expensive and it has been suggested that a number of problem drug users may, at some point, finance their habit through acquisitive crime. Recent research following a group of 1,100 problem drug users showed that in the months preceding treatment the group had collectively committed 70,000 crimes. It is estimated that if the same level of offending continued over a two year period it would cost their victims £34m (Department of Health, 1996). This calculation excludes significant costs to the criminal justice system.

It has been suggested that there are between 40,000 and 80,000 problem drug users in London (Metropolitan Police Service and London Drug Policy Forum, 1994). Indeed, recent estimates by the Home Office suggest that of the 175,000 residents in a typical Inner London borough, around 2,500 of these could be problem drug users (London Drug Policy Forum, 1997). Consequently, the true costs of drug-related crime present a major problem for London's citizens.

Drug services

In response to high client demand, London has developed a wide range of drug services from outreach and syringe-exchange schemes through to high care in-patient detoxification (Chapter 2). According to the 1992 Standing Conference on Drug Abuse (SCODA) directory of drug services, over one-quarter of all drug agencies - statutory and non-statutory, national and local, generic and specialist - were based in London (SCODA, 1992). They, in turn, act as a magnet for drug users from other parts of the country which are not so well served.

Needs

London has a mobile, multi-cultural, heterogeneous population and as one would expect, its drug using population has varied needs. Whilst the most visible problem drug users continue to be white male opiate users in their mid to late twenties, more needs and client groups are emerging. Crack cocaine dependence is a particularly worrying feature in London since not many agencies are able to offer crack users a service that meets their needs. Although indications are that drug misuse is less prevalent among African, Caribbean and Asian people than the white community (Leitner, Shapland and Wiles, 1993), some black and Asian drug users experience severe problems which are often exacerbated by racism and social exclusion. Drug misuse is a rising trend amongst such groups though there are very few services for them.

Any large city with a diverse population is likely to experience similar problems, however it is the sheer scale and range of these problems which distinguish London. Whether it is a drug user themselves, the relative or friend of someone with drug problems, a victim of drug-related crime, a householder faced with mounting insurance costs, or the concerned parents of a child growing up in a neighbourhood with a visible drug culture, drug use will affect the lives of almost all Londoners.

London - a bureaucratic nightmare

Planning in the past

Formerly, drug use was seen as simply a legal or a medical problem and with little, or no communication, between the two. The legal or 'drug misuse' side of the problem would be addressed by the police, the courts, the prisons and the probation services. Meanwhile, the health needs of 'problem' drug users were the remit of statutory, and to a lesser extent, non-statutory drug services. It should be noted, however, that only until relatively recently, local authorities have been willing to address either the needs of drug users or the damage that drug use can cause to communities. Although some good local relationships did exist, there has traditionally been little overall co-ordination or collaboration between different organisations.

In 1985, District and Regional Drug Advisory Committees (DDACs and RDACs) were established to develop joint arrangements between local authorities and health authorities. Despite some success in encouraging multi-agency collaboration, many DDACs and RDACs were perceived to be medically dominated and too narrowly focused on medical needs (London Research Centre and National Local Government Forum on Drug Misuse, 1991).

Planning on paper

The past five years have seen major changes in the way that statutory authorities plan and deal with drug issues. The *National Health Service and Community Care Act (1990)* placed a statutory responsibility on local authorities to prepare and publish plans on the needs of the local population, including those of problem drug users (Chapter 4). It should be noted, however, that local authorities still have no statutory requirement to actually provide these services.

Since 1990, however, there has also been a growing consensus that the problems associated with drug use cannot be addressed successfully by any one agency in isolation. Local authorities, health authorities, the Probation Service, the police, specialist agencies and communities have increasingly promoted the need to work together to address the damage that drugs can do to individual users and the wider community. Present solutions, therefore, concentrate on co-operative and collaborative multi-agency working as outlined in *Tackling Drugs Together* (HMSO, 1995) and realised in the creation of Drug Action Teams (DATs).

Planning in reality

This, however, is easier said than done on a London-wide basis. Although there is growing interest in establishing a number of pan-London bodies, including an elected mayor and assembly, it is not an exaggeration to say that London is still a planner's nightmare when it comes to drugs (Map 1.1 overleaf).

The varying geographical coverage and responsibility of agencies is the main hindrance to joint working, and service provision is still inconsistent across London. Most statutory and non-statutory services tend to be concentrated in Inner London, leaving some Outer London boroughs without local access to specialist counselling advice. Unfortunately, as people with drug problems tend to gravitate towards areas with good services, service purchasers can make the problem 'go away', to an extent, simply by ignoring it.

Responsibility

The mobile and transient nature of many people in London with drug problems can also lead to difficulties in establishing which authority is responsible for meeting an individual's needs. Cash strapped local authorities and health authorities are understandably reluctant to take financial responsibility for someone with acute and ongoing need if there is a question mark over where they actually reside.

Rationale

The extent to which services in London and the UK have been rationally planned is also open to question.

Specialist drug services have developed as much in response to funding initiatives as they have in addressing local needs. According to SCODA records, in 1980 there were just 14 specialist residential and non-residential drug agencies in London (SCODA, 1997). A massive expansion, largely due to the Department of Health's 1984 Central Funding Initiative, ran from 1984 to 1988. By 1992, there were 127 agencies listed in the SCODA directory for the Greater London area. In 1997, it was estimated that there were around 150 drug agencies operating in the capital (Chapter 2).

Many people in the drugs field welcomed this major investment. However, subsequent problems for service planners have arisen. Whilst in the 1980s agencies addressed the drug problems of the day - largely injecting heroin use amongst young, white, working class males - in the decade or so since then drug use has moved on, and is now far more diverse with widely varying needs. Presently, a common problem for service providers is now keeping pace with changing trends in drug use.

Order out of chaos?

Clearly the situation in London is far from ideal. Inevitably, the lack of rational planning means that drug users in need will suffer. However, steps have been taken at strategic, local and national levels to address this situation.

London Drug Policy Forum

In 1991, the London Drug Policy Forum was established. Its genesis lay in a London-wide conference to discuss the threat of crack cocaine. One of the main recommendations arising from the conference was that there should be a pan-London forum to improve co-ordination between statutory and non-statutory agencies on drug issues. The Forum aims to promote greater co-ordination of strategies to deal with drugs, and despite having just one worker for most of its life, has gone some way to improve multi-agency working and provide policy advice for London boroughs, DATs and other statutory agencies. Although it is funded by the Corporation of London and

LONDON - THE PLANNER'S NIGHTMARE

London-wide bodies

There is growing interest in both establishing a number of new pan-London bodies, as well as strengthing and extending the activities of existing organisations. The new London bodies include: a single strategic authority for London (comprised of an elected London mayor and assembly); a single London-wide health authority, and a single police authority for the capital.

33 Local authorities

There are 33 local authorities in London (including The City of London authority). These are responsible for local social services, council housing, education and other amenities. Since the implementation of the NHS Community Care Act in April 1993, local authorities have had responsibility for community care services to local residents, including those for problem drug users. Some forums exist for local authorities to agree pan-London issues relating to drug and alcohol issues. Local authority elections take place every 4 years.

16 Health authorities

These are agencies within the National Health Service responsible for meeting the health needs of at least one, and often two or three, local authority populations. The creation of an 'internal NHS market' in 1991 aimed to separate the purchasing and provision of health services. Service provision became the responsibility of 'NHS Trusts' (comprised of a number of different hospital facilities in an area and managed by an executive committee drawn from these hospitals). Purchasing roles were fulfilled by the existing health authorities and included organising primary care services and issuing contracts to local general practitioners (GPs). GPs can also apply to become 'fundholders', allowing them to directly purchase health services for their registered patients. The NHS is, however, likely to undergo significant change in the coming years. These changes may include the establishment of a pan-London health authority.

63 Metropolitan Police divisions

Unlike any other police force in the country, the Metropolitan Police Service is directly accountable to the Home Secretary. The separate City of London Police are confined to the Corporation of London's 'square mile', while the Metropolitan Police cover an area which extends beyond the borders of London into parts of the surrounding counties. This coverage is divided into 5 policing areas, with 63 divisions. These apply the Metropolitan Police drug strategy according to problems in the local area. Plans for a 'London police authority' are currently being discussed and considered.

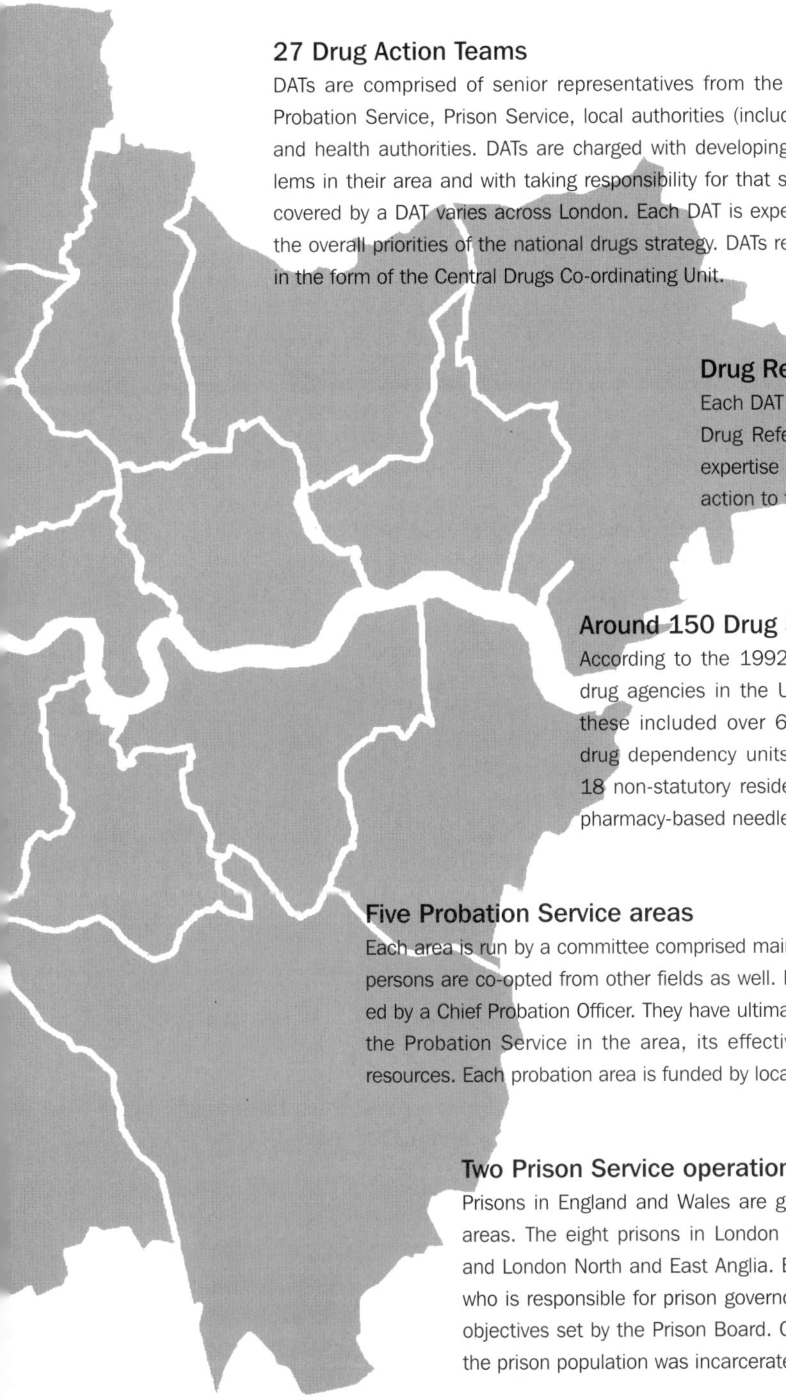

27 Drug Action Teams

DATs are comprised of senior representatives from the police, HM Customs and Excise, Probation Service, Prison Service, local authorities (including education and social services) and health authorities. DATs are charged with developing a strategy for tackling drug problems in their area and with taking responsibility for that strategy's implementation. The area covered by a DAT varies across London. Each DAT is expected to make progress in line with the overall priorities of the national drugs strategy. DATs report directly to central government in the form of the Central Drugs Co-ordinating Unit.

Drug Reference Groups

Each DAT is usually served by more than one Drug Reference Group which provides local expertise and involves local communities in action to tackle drug misuse.

Around 150 Drug Services

According to the 1992 SCODA directory, a quarter of all drug agencies in the UK are based in London. In 1997, these included over 65 community-based services; 13 drug dependency units; 12 structured day programmes; 18 non-statutory residential rehabilitation units; and 229 pharmacy-based needle-exchange outlets.

Five Probation Service areas

Each area is run by a committee comprised mainly of members of the judiciary, but persons are co-opted from other fields as well. Each probation committee is headed by a Chief Probation Officer. They have ultimate responsibility for the direction of the Probation Service in the area, its effective operation and efficient use of resources. Each probation area is funded by local authorities and the Home Office.

Two Prison Service operational areas

Prisons in England and Wales are grouped into 12 distinct operational areas. The eight prisons in London fall into two areas: London South, and London North and East Anglia. Each of these areas has a manager who is responsible for prison governors achieving the targets, goals and objectives set by the Prison Board. On June 30th 1995, 11 per cent of the prison population was incarcerated in London establishments.

Map 1.1

the Home Office it has no statutory or executive powers. Instead, it works by facilitating and supporting initiatives rather than demanding greater co-operation and co-ordination.

Other co-ordinating groups

Other groups have also developed - most notably the Greater London Association of Directors of Social Services, Drugs and Alcohol Purchasers' Group (Chapter 4). This Group was formed in 1993 in response to the rapidly shifting environment of community care. It works to provide some consistency across London in the purchasing of services for drug and alcohol users and in the assessment of their needs. The Group produce an annual directory of residential drug and alcohol services purchased by London boroughs. This also includes information on those service providers offering structured day programmes. The Group hopes to develop core quality standards and a core set of data for the assessment of client needs for inclusion in future directories. Again, the Group has no statutory authority or independent resources but, despite this, has vastly improved relationships between purchasers and providers of drug services.

More recently the Inner London health authorities have established a Drug and Alcohol Purchasers' Group and the non-statutory drug agencies have formed a pan-London Drug Providers' Consortium.

There is real potential for all these groups to make the best of an unsatisfactory situation. All attempts at pan-London co-ordination have been purely voluntary and co-operative. How far these existing arrangements can secure lasting London-wide planning and agreement is open to debate.

DATs

Tackling Drugs Together, the 1995 government strategy for drugs, has resulted in the establishment of DATs to co-ordinate and drive forward the strategy at local levels. The strategy, for the first time, gave equal emphasis to three areas of work: law enforcement and the reduction of drug-related crime and the fear of crime; education and prevention to reduce demand for drugs; and access to effective treatment for drug users. This three-pronged approach has been re-emphasised in the new government drugs strategy, *Tackling Drugs to Build a Better Britain (HMSO, 1998)*.

Of the 106 DATs in England, 27 - almost one quarter - are in London. Current reports indicate that DATs are bringing together the disparate priorities and interests of the agencies involved. These have been recently evaluated and the findings from this will inform future development.

Anti-Drugs Co-ordinator

The current phase of *Tackling Drugs Together* ended in April 1998. Through extensive consultation with those in the field, the UK Anti Drugs Co-ordinator, Keith Hellawell has now produced the successor to *Tackling Drugs Together*. However, it remains to be seen what the outcome of *Tackling Drugs to Build a Better Britain* this new drugs strategy will be for London.

A 'Drug Action Plan' for London?

Local teams and voluntary pan-London arrangements have undoubtedly gone a long way to improving the situation in London. What many planners of drug services now hope for is the development of a Drug Action Plan for London. But what prospect is there of this happening?

Who wants it?

The potential support for a Drug Action Plan for London appears considerable. Currently, 'drugs' are now on the agenda of a number of organisations and groupings that, a decade ago, would have viewed them simply as medical or legal issues. Drug misuse is now widely acknowledged as both a cause and consequence of urban deterioration and social exclusion. Drugs are no longer seen as a marginal issue and the consideration of 'drug problems' now takes place in a bewildering array of settings: tenants associations; environmental committees; community safety projects; leisure and recreation committees to name just a few. Furthermore, this is not just happening at a local level but also between boroughs and other agencies and on a pan-London level. The Association of London Government, London's local authority association, has also attempted to raise the issue of drugs in a variety of contexts and audiences.

Who will do it?

Who though will be responsible for consolidating and compounding this support?

The task is simply too big and complex for the existing London Drug Policy Forum to take on. However, one answer might be in the establishment of a strategic authority for London which has the overview, resources, and, more importantly, the statutory authority to address London-wide problems from a London-wide perspective.

When might it happen?

The Government have now held a referendum on the establishment of both an elected mayor and strategic authority for London. This new body could be established by Parliament as soon as September 1998 and the newly elected mayor and assembly could then begin work in the Autumn of 2000.

It is expected that such an authority will have responsibility for a range of strategic issues such as economic regeneration, planning, policing, transport and environmental policy. If public health is also added to the list then drugs could feature, not as a specific issue in its own right, but as an important consideration in a number of other strategic themes. However, whether this would eventually lead to the development of a concrete Drug Action Plan for London is open to debate.

Drug use in London - what next?

The nature and extent of drug use in London is continually evolving. Whereas in the past, problem drug users - while willing to use the full range of illicit substances - would generally have a primary drug of choice, poly-drug use is now far more common. Similarly, although young white men still comprise the majority of problem drug users, young women and

people from ethnic minority groups are beginning to be represented in significant numbers. Furthermore, where recent research has indicated a rising prevalence of drug use in London, preliminary Home Office indicators now suggest that this prevalence may stabilise, and could even fall amongst certain age groups in the future (Ramsay and Spiller, 1997).

As for the co-ordination of services, DATs are still a relatively recent development. They have the potential to facilitate planning and collaboration which addresses all aspects of the drugs problem. However, their effectiveness and staying power is, as yet, untested and there is also no London-wide DAT. The London Drug Policy Forum has sought to address this by creating a post specifically to liaise with and assist London based DATs to address pan-London issues. There are regular quarterly meetings of both chairs and co-ordinators of DATs to discuss issues of mutual concern in order to promote good practice and consistency.

There are, however, some problems which cannot be addressed by individual DATs working in isolation. How does one address the needs of drug users within the criminal justice system or deal with drug trafficking and dealing? If DATs do develop to adopt a service commissioning role they must also consider the needs of particular groups such as women with children, black drug users and stimulant users on a pan-London basis. Currently, the London Drug Policy Forum is striving to fulfil this role. Time will tell if it can keep pace with demand.

One thing, however, is certain in London - the problem drug users of tomorrow are unlikely to share the same characteristics and needs as the problem drug users of today. Consequently, policy makers, planners, and providers all face a continual task to adapt, develop and invoke new initiatives to meet the changing pattern of drug use in London.

References

Advisory Council on the Misuse of Drugs (1993). *AIDS and Drug Misuse. Update Report.* London: HMSO.

Department of Health (1996). *The Task Force to Review Services for Drug Misusers. Report of an Independent Review of Drug Treatment Services in England.* Wetherby: Department of Health.

HMSO (1995). *Tackling Drugs Together: A Strategy for England 1995-1998.* London: HMSO.

HMSO (1998). *Tackling Drugs to Build a Better Britain.* London: HMSO.

Home Office Statistical Bulletin (1997). *Issue 22/97 Statistics of Drug Addicts Notified to the Home Office, United Kingdom 1996.* London: Government Statistical Services.

Leitner, M., Shapland, J. and Wiles, P. (1993). *Drug Usage and Drugs Prevention: The Views and Habits of the General Public.* London: HMSO.

London Drug Policy Forum (1997). *Drug Users and the Criminal Justice System.* London: London Drug Policy Forum.

London Research Centre and National Local Government Forum on Drug Misuse (1991). *Co-ordinating Drugs Services.* London: London Research Centre.

Metropolitan Police Service and London Drug Policy Forum (1994). *Drugs and Community Safety: Promoting a Partnership Approach*. London: London Drug Policy Forum.

Office for National Statistics (1997). Personal communication.

Ramsay, M. and Spiller, J. (1997). *Drug Misuse Declared in 1996: Latest Results from the British Crime Survey*. London: Home Office.

Standing Conference On Drug Abuse (1992). *Drug Problems - Where to Get Help*. London: SCODA.

Standing Conference On Drug Abuse (1997). Personal communication.

DRUG SERVICES

Annette Dale-Perera
Standing Conference on Drug Abuse

Sections

Drug services in London

London has a plethora of specialist health and social care services for individuals with drug problems (Box 2.1 opposite). Categorising them and estimating their number is problematic as the nature and extent of these change constantly. This is partly due to the diversity of funding bases, service locations, and types of service delivery used within the capital, with many organisations providing a wide range of interventions and activities for drug users (as well as training for other health and social care professionals) from a single site.

The terms 'service' and 'intervention' have been used in this chapter to distinguish between the organisational base from which interventions are delivered (the 'service') and what is actually provided from the service (the 'intervention'). It should be noted, however, that there may be some overlap between a service and an intervention. Some dedicated or 'stand-alone' drug services, for example, may offer only a single intervention (such as needle-exchange). Where this is the case these are discussed under specific interventions.

Who provides services for problem drug users in London?

The estimated 150 distinct drug services in London can be grouped into the following categories: community-based services (non-residential); hospital based services; residential services; generic services; and self-help and peer-led initiatives. This section considers the different types of service falling within each of these groups. Information on the specific interventions provided by each of these service types is discussed later.

Community-based services (non-residential)

Over one-third of the drug services in London are community-based. These provide a range of services including advice, counselling and treatment to problem drug users in the local population. They are usually out-patient or non-residential, and there is provision in both the statutory and non-statutory sectors. Individuals can normally refer themselves to these services. There are

two main types of community-based service: community drug teams (CDTs); and street-based agencies.

Community drug teams (CDTs)

CDTs are statutory community-based services which provide a wide range of treatments and interventions for drug users within a particular geographical area. CDTs are mainly comprised of multi-disciplinary teams including psychiatric nurses and social workers (MacGregor, 1991). They are usually active in encouraging 'shared care' work with local GPs (general practitioners) whilst identifying and referring those individuals with complex needs to more specialist services. They also offer advice, support and joint work with specialist drug services and GPs.

CDTs were established in the 1980s (Box 2.2 overleaf). They were initially intended to help problem drug users gain access to generic health care, and to train and enlist generic community services (such as GPs) to respond to

Box 2.1
An overview of
drug services and
interventions in
London

An overview of drug services and interventions in London

Drug services and interventions can be divided into specialist and generic

- Specialist - specialise in treating problem drug use.
- Generic - offer a wide range of help to the general population including help for those with drug problems.

However, drug services in London do not easily fall into neat typologies (as will become apparent), and it should be noted that some generic services do offer specialist treatment or services for problem drug users.

There are a range of drug services and interventions in London

Specialist
- Fifty-three needle-exchange schemes providing services through dedicated outlets, community-based services and outreach schemes.
- Over sixty-five community-based services providing health care to the local population affected by problem drug use.
- Twelve structured day programmes (SDPs) offering community-based support through a fixed weekly programme of activities.
- Thirteen drug dependency units (DDUs) offering a range of usually out-patient services with a focus on prescribing substitute drugs and providing health care.
- Eighteen residential rehabilitation units providing intensive support to those individuals unable to address their drug problems in a domestic setting.

Generic
- Twenty-one pharmacy-based needle-exchange schemes each involving a number of pharmacy outlets.
- Nearly four thousand general practitioners (GPs) in London.

It should be noted that a single service may offer more than one of the above interventions.

Changes in health purchasing mean the statutory, non-statutory and independent sectors are no longer entirely separate

- Statutory sector services - usually part of National Health Service Trusts. However, services provided by social services (such as residential rehabilitation) or the Probation Service (specific community-based services for offenders) are also in the statutory sector. Similarly, although the majority of statutory services have a medical input, some non-statutory agencies offer prescribing services.
- Non-statutory services - normally locally founded or are part of a larger national organisation. The majority restrict activities to information and advice giving.
- Independent sector agencies - private businesses whose services generate income.

drug problems. The establishment of CDTs was in response to a general move away from 'specialist models' of care for drug users and towards an 'integrated' model of care (Strang and Clement, 1994). In short, this meant that specialist services were no longer considered to be the only health care option for managing drug users. However, the aim of increasing the involvement of GPs and other generic agencies in working with drug users was not always achieved. Consequently, many CDTs later took on the direct delivery of care to clients, thus ironically re-creating the specialist care model. There is considerable overlap between CDTs and street-based agencies.

Street-based agencies

Street agencies have traditionally been run in the non-statutory sector. However there are a number of local authority and health authority based schemes. Street agencies originally began in the 1960s as a response to the then emerging drug problem. Most were non-statutory organisations, sometimes linked to Christian churches and based in central London. They frequently offered outreach, counselling, advice and information.

Currently, street-based agencies offer services to all types of drug users, although in many cases the options for non-opiate users may be limited. They usually offer a smaller number of interventions than CDTs and these often include counselling, health education advice around drugs, alternative therapies, and referral to prescribing services (such as DDUs) or residential services. Some agencies offer structured day programmes and housing, legal and welfare advice. In addition, they may also offer an outreach service. Street agency staff team are often from a variety of disciplines including drug workers, nurses or community psychiatric nurses, outreach personnel and non-statutory workers.

Hospital based services

These are usually provided by specialist NHS facilities.

Drug dependency units (DDUs)

There are thirteen drug dependency units in London. This figure includes those DDUs which are part of larger specialist statutory drug services such as the Maudsley Hospital, Riverside Mental Health Trust Substance Misuse Service, and West London Health Care NHS Trust.

DDUs are statutory specialist services which offer assessment and treatment of problem drug users on an out-patient basis in a health service setting. They characteristically offer treatment to opiate dependent drug users and are staffed by a specialist multi-disciplinary team directed by a consultant psychiatrist.

Key finding

DDUs were first established in 1968, and mainly in London (Chapter 3). They were set up on the recommendations made by the Brain Committee in their review of the rapid national increase in drug use (Second Brain Report, 1965). Subsequently, services for drug users moved away from general practitioners to specialist services, creating the original specialist model of care.

The role of a DDU will vary according to the network of drug services in the local area and the competencies of the staff team. The bulk of interventions are focused around the prescription of substitute drugs and general health care. The range of interventions provided by DDUs are designed to enable work with individuals who have difficult or complex

Box 2.2
Recent history of
drug service devel-
opment in London

Recent history of drug service development in London

1960s
Street agencies begin to emerge.
Therapeutic communities cross the Atlantic
and come to Britain.

1968
Move away from limited GP care with the
establishment of specialist DDU clinics.

1972
SCODA formed to provide an organisation
for non-statutory sector agencies (today,
SCODA deals with *all* drug services).

1980s
General move away from 'specialist' to 'integrated' models of care is reflected in the
establishment of community drug teams.

1982
ACMD report Treatment and Rehabilitation
recommends that GPs play a more important role in treating drug dependency.

1984-1988
Central Funding Initiative injects new
money into the development of treatment
and rehabilitation services. Results in many
new occupational groups being drawn into
working with problem drug users.

1987-1990
In response to HIV, prevention of AIDS
becomes more important than the prevention of drug use. Growth in needle-
exchanges, health education activity and
methadone prescribing

1990
National Health Service and Community
Care Act 1990 introduces a 'needs-led'
approach to the provision of drug and
alcohol services (Chapter 4). These
reforms separated out responsibilities for
providing and purchasing health care leading to a 'market place' for health care.

1995
Tackling Drugs Together (HMSO, 1995)
provides a general strategy for dealing
with problem drug use over a three year
period. This leads to planning and co-ordination at a local level by London's Drug
Action Teams (DATs). The remit for the
group is to create action plans to address
local health need.

1996
National Treatment Outcome Research
Study (Department of Health 1996) supported the Task Force Review. Following
1,100 patients undertaking different treatments, its brief preliminary reports indicated
that even short periods in treatment and
rehabilitation were effective - particularly in
reducing levels of drug-related crime. Peer
reviewed papers still awaited.

1996
Task Force to Review Services for Drug
Misusers (Department of Health, 1996)
reports that 'treatment worked'. The first
national review of treatment effectiveness.
Made recommendations on good treatment practice and the provision of services for all drug users.

1998
The New NHS (Department of Health,
1998) document states that teams of local
GPs and community nurses will work together in new primary care groups to purchase
services. However, little specific mention of
drug and alcohol services.

1998
Will the successor to Tackling Drugs
Together result in a different emphasis on
intervention in a 'post-AIDS' era?

care needs. These may include pregnant women, drug users with severe physical and mental health problems, and problem drug users living with HIV and AIDS.

Many DDUs have access to hospital in-patient beds for in-patient detoxification. In response to the threat of an HIV epidemic in the 1980s, DDUs moved towards longer-term substitute prescribing and away from detoxification. Recent developments have seen attempts to link the operation of DDUs into local networks of drug services. In certain areas, the DDU will work alongside the community drug team and other services - both in hospital and community settings - to provide a range of specialist interventions, advice and information.

In-patient detoxification units

These are in-patent units attached to NHS hospitals and usually form part of a DDU. They are either 'designated' (a unit specifically for detoxification) or 'non-designated' (having allocated beds within a psychiatric ward). A range of detoxification packages are available in the units to drug users wishing to withdraw from their drug of dependence. Non-statutory, community-based residential projects also run in-patient detoxification units.

Residential services

Residential rehabilitation units or 'rehabs' offer services for problem drug users requiring interventions which cannot be undertaken in the community or that require long-term support. Such services have been operating since the mid 1960s and have traditionally been provided by both the non-statutory and independent sectors.

Clients may be able to self refer to such services but in some cases a professional referral is required. A number of rehabs have been set up in the non-statutory sector, providing a wide range of residential support. These are based on a number of different philosophies with the length of residency varying according to the programme (but usually falling between two to eighteen months). The majority of drug users in rehab will be expected to enter rehab drug-free, having already completed a community or in-patient detoxification.

Whilst problem drug users can be referred to any of the hundred or so residential services in England and Wales, many local authorities will favour local rehabilitation units. London has some of the longest established residential services together with many innovative models of residential care. The support given can range from highly intensive and structured residential care, to semi-supported living schemes, to services providing the equivalent of hostel accommodation. Interventions offered include: detoxification; ameliorative prescribing for the after-effects of crack cocaine use; health care; vocational training; alternative therapies and specific interventions designed for different groups of problem drug users.

Residential services in the UK have diversified during the past ten years (Table 2.3). As indicated in the national SCODA survey of 53 residential services, programmes are now generally shorter and encompass a broader range of services.

There are five main types of residential services in London and the UK: twelve step programmes; Christian-based programmes; therapeutic communities; semi-supported living schemes; and crisis intervention services.

Interventions offered	%
Detoxification	42
Ameliorative prescribing	32
Alternative therapies	40
Primary health care (on-site)	38
NVQs or other qualifications	40
Basic education	60
Computing skills	48
Targeted support for those with HIV/AIDS	52
Free access to fitness facilities	74

Source: SCODA (1997a).

Notes: NVQs are National Vocation Qualifications.

Twelve step programmes

'Twelve step' or 'Minnesota Method' programmes are based upon the principles of Narcotics Anonymous (NA). Each programme views problem drug use as a 'disease' from which only incremental improvements or 'steps' can be made. Continued and total abstinence from all mind altering substances is the aim.

Steps one to five deal with changing the problem behaviours and beliefs of the client, whilst steps six to twelve concentrate on sustaining this change (Keene, 1997). Residential programmes using the Minnesota Method commonly base treatment on only the first five steps. Clients then follow the remaining steps by attending NA self-help networks.

Christian-based programmes

These programmes follow a Christian edict (where the client is required to follow the faith) or use Christian teachings solely to motivate staff.

Therapeutic communities (TCs)

In the UK, the therapeutic community approach grew from at least two strong traditions: the Maxwell Jones approach (which developed in England and provides a model of dealing with behavioural or psychiatric problems);

and the Synanon or 'Concept House' approach (which developed in the American addiction field in the mid-1960s and came to Britain in the late 1960s). The major difference between the two is that the Maxwell Jones model tends to adopt a more democratic approach to rehabilitation. Residents are usually encouraged to vote or express an opinion during decision-making processes.

In both TC approaches, peers are encouraged to support and constructively confront each other in order to facilitate behavioural change. Residents also engage in individual development: undertaking additional responsibilities and earning further privileges and status throughout their time in the TC. For example, in order to avoid relapse, residents are initially confined to the TC itself, or are only allowed out with an escort. However, as they take on further domestic responsibilities and later engage in voluntary work or education, they are granted additional privileges and freedoms.

Examples of therapeutic communities in London exemplifying the two broad categories above include Phoenix House (Concept House) and the Richmond Fellowship Crescent House (Maxwell Jones approach). Many Concept Houses, however, have modified their approaches over the last ten years. This is mainly due to both the impact of HIV (where a less confrontational and stressful atmosphere is believed to avoid the premature onset of AIDS) and the introduction of community care legislation requiring an increased emphasis on clients' rights and individual planning (Chapter 4).

However, as noted previously, services do sometimes deviate from standard theoretical models. In some TCs, for example, the philosophy underlying service provision will stem from the founder of the community, and their original concept will be reflected in the skills of staff, the interventions offered, the range of problem drug use amongst clients, and the characteristics of any other residents in the community. The Elizabeth House Association in West London, for example, is a TC which bases its programme around problem drug users learning to live with others, and deliberately shifts the focus away from their problem use. In three houses (originally donated by local nuns), eighteen former drug users live alongside twelve staff and fourteen other residents who do not have drug problems. Staff provide twenty-four hour cover.

Semi-supported living schemes

Many residential rehabilitation units provide a network of semi-supported living schemes. These are schemes where clients are required to take some responsibility for their own programme of recovery. The Gatehouse in South London (part of the Phoenix House project) offers clients input into the content of their treatment programme. Residential care from staff is also only provided for twelve hours a day, encouraging clients to address and solve any problems arising outside of these hours themselves.

Crisis intervention services

Individuals may - for reasons ranging from medical or drug-related emergencies, to emotional traumas, forthcoming legal action, and physical threats - require immediate treatment. Although some interventions can be obtained from local hospital or psychiatric units, some residential rehabilitation services will also provide 'crisis' interventions. These services are usually either located in a dedicated unit or in separate facilities within a larger residential unit.

At City Roads, a twenty-one day programme of treatment is provided to clients before they are referred onto other services for longer-term care. It offers immediate access over a twenty-four hour period, and a range of interventions including detoxification, primary health care, psychiatric assessment, food and rest, alternative therapies, and help with legal, housing and social care problems. Prior to its closure, Turning Point's ROMA (Rehabilitation Of Metropolitan Addicts) offered a different model of crisis intervention by providing residential care to chaotic barbiturate and opiate drug users unable to stop using drugs. ROMA facilitated long-term reduction and provided maintenance prescriptions of substitute drugs to those residents still addressing other problems in their lives. ROMA also catered for pregnant problem drug users and individuals living with HIV.

Generic services

Problem drug use is not only managed by specialist dedicated drug services. A wide range of generic services are increasingly providing services to drug users. They include GPs, pharmacists, the police, and other criminal justice agencies.

General practitioners

GPs are significant providers of care for problem drug users in both London and the UK. They are one of the most frequent points of first contact for problem drug users, providing both general and specialist care (Department of Health, 1996).

In 1982, the Advisory Council on the Misuse of Drugs recommended in their report *Treatment and Rehabilitation* that GPs could play an important role in the treatment of drug dependency (ACMD, 1982). Since then, there has been increasing encouragement from the Department of Health for GPs to provide care for drug users. In response to a rise in problem drug use, and the resulting growth in demand for treatment places and the increasingly long waiting lists for specialist drug services, the Department of Health also recommended in a number of further reports that an increase in the numbers of drug users receiving treatment in primary care settings should occur (HMSO, 1995; Department of Health, 1996; Department of Health 1997).

GPs are in a good position to identify and offer advice to problem users who may not already be in touch with specialist services. GPs can offer a number of services including substitute prescribing of methadone and tranquillisers, harm reduction advice, distribution of condoms and general health care. GPs also occupy an important role in the provision of shared care and treatment to drug users.

Key findings

A 1992 survey of London injectors found that 78 per cent were registered with a GP, with 62 per cent reporting a visit to a practitioner in the last three months (Donoghoe, 1997). In the last three months, the same survey found that 43 per cent had been prescribed drugs by their GP and approximately half of these had received a prescription for methadone and half for tranquillisers.

A survey of over 200 female injectors in London in 1996 found that the main service utilised during the previous six months was general practice (Macleod et al, 1998).

Shared care

Some GPs and community-based services - mainly within the statutory sector - operate shared care schemes. These are schemes defined by the Department of Health as 'the joint participation of specialists and GPs in the planned delivery of care for patients with a drug misuse problem, informed by enhanced information exchange beyond routine discharge and referral letters' (Department of Health, 1996).

With the help of a liaison worker, GPs and community-based services produce a joint plan of care for a client. Models of shared care vary enormously across the capital, reflecting the ranging needs of clients, the GPs' skills and the network of local drug services (Beaumont and Janikiewicz, 1997). Schemes can include: informal agreements where GPs and services simply keep in touch about a client; a worker from the drug service running a clinic with clients in the GP's premises; or the GP providing substitute prescribing and general health services. The apa community drug team in Tower Hamlets claim to be one of the first in London to develop and introduce a shared care protocol.

Pharmacists

Many pharmacists provide clean needles to drug users through the 21 needle-exchange schemes operating in the capital (these schemes are comprised of a number of distinct needle-exchange interventions). They may also be dispensing prescribed substitute drugs to problem drug users. The Department of Health has continued to encourage pharmacists to work with drug users, and has been working together with specialist drug services or GPs in the dispensing and supervised consumption of prescribed oral methadone to opiate users (Department of Health, 1996).

Police

Most police forces operate a form of 'arrest referral' scheme (Chapter 6). The aim of these is to 'use the opportunity provided by arrest to encourage drug users to seek treatment'

(Department of Health, 1996). While schemes vary across the capital, they typically involve individuals detained at police stations being provided with details of local drug services. This information, in the form of a card or leaflet, may be given only to those people arrested for drug-related offences, individuals suspected of being a problem drug user, or simply to each individual detained. Some arrest referral schemes have drug workers on-site, whilst others have drug workers on-call. Such schemes are normally implemented in a partnership between the police and local drug services. Reflecting the need to modify services to local health problems, the Blenheim Project operates an arrest referral scheme where first-time offenders are given details of the project, and if they agree to undergo a course of counselling this is taken into account by any criminal justice bodies involved.

Other generic services which provide services to drug users include the Probation Service, the Prison Service, the Youth Service and hospital accident and emergency departments.

Self-help and peer-led initiatives

Narcotics and Cocaine Anonymous
Narcotics Anonymous is the largest self-help network for current and former problem drug users in England. NA views drug use as a 'disease' which affects mind, body and soul. 'Twelve step' programmes are commonly used to improve health and make amends in attitude and lifestyle with the ultimate goal of abstinence from drugs and alcohol. NA is financially self-supporting and has an estimated London membership of approximately 3,000. Members are encouraged to attend support groups on a daily or more frequent basis. Cocaine Anonymous (CA) offers a similar programme of support, but with a smaller membership base.

Drug user support groups
There are a number of support groups and services managed by current and former drug users. Mainliners was originally established by users and former users who had HIV. It now provides a comprehensive network of services to drug users affected by HIV including: outreach; HIV prevention initiatives; a drop-in service with meals; alternative therapy groups; individual and group counselling; training events; and a newsletter. Other drug user groups include the West London organisation FIRM (Fun in Recovery Management). This has also been set up by former drug users with the assistance of local authority support. The group currently run a drop-in centre where the aim is for former users to meet and support each other in abstinence. Individuals may also engage in acupuncture, meditation sessions and social events.

What types of specific drug interventions are services providing ?

Describing the number of interventions related to problem drug use in London is not easy, partly due to the absence of a pan-London body to monitor what is going on. In addition, defining what an 'intervention' is an equally arduous task as there is often little consensus and definitions are subject to rapid change.

This chapter therefore tentatively describes the main interventions provided by some of the services outlined in the previous section.

Outreach

Providing help and care to problem drug users involves both contacting and attracting them into services. Services such as the Hungerford Project and the Cranstoun Drug Services (formerly known as the Cranstoun Projects) operate outreach programmes in an active attempt to contact 'hard to reach' problem drug users.

Outreach can be defined as any community-based activity which attempts to contact individuals or groups out of contact with existing services (either through problems of access or the user not wishing to seek help from these services). Outreach teams work with problem drug users in their own communities and local settings and provide both advice and information on safer drug use and safer sex. They will also provide clean injecting equipment and condoms to reduce the risk of transmission of HIV and other blood borne viruses. Outreach falls into one of three main categories: 'detached' outreach (in non-agency settings such as streets, squats and bars); 'peripatetic' outreach (in organisational settings such as prisons, GP surgeries and youth clubs); and 'domicillary' outreach (undertaken in the homes or core settings occupied by target individuals).

The Hungerford Project in Central London has a growing reputation for undertaking outreach work such as needle-exchange with homeless problem drug users. They also operate satellite services at Centrepoint's Night Shelter and the London Connection. The Cranstoun Drug Services have funded a black outreach team called SAFE since April 1997. This team targets stimulant users and young people in the London borough of Wandsworth, and female sex workers across Wandsworth and the additional Merton and Sutton areas. The Blenheim Project run an established outreach programme in local schools, youth clubs, and nightclubs.

Needle-exchange schemes

Needle-exchange schemes in London fall into three basic models: 'dedicated' or 'stand-alone' services whose main function is needle-exchange; those run by community-based drug services (either in-house or via outreach), HIV services or hospitals; and pharmacy-based schemes (Chapter 3).

> **Key finding**
> It is estimated that over six million syringes are distributed each year by syringe-exchange schemes in London (this figure excludes sales of syringes in pharmacies) (Parsons et al, 1997).

Dedicated needle-exchange schemes typically supply clean injecting equipment (including a range of syringes), syringe disposal containers (cynbins) and condoms. They often also provide harm reduction advice on safer drug use and safer sex. An example of such a dedicated scheme is the Cleveland Street needle-exchange in Central London.

Most community-based services offer needle-exchange as part of their general programme of work. A large number of services provide this intervention through peripatetic outreach in generic or community-based settings (such as in GP premises). Others will distribute packs of injecting equipment during detached outreach work in a range of locations including streets, squats and outdoor music festivals.

Pharmacy-based needle-exchange schemes have grown rapidly over the past five years and there are now 21 schemes in London with around 229 outlets (Map 2.4 opposite). Each scheme is implemented and co-ordinated on a health authority or local authority basis. For example, the health authority of Ealing, Hammersmith and Hounslow have 23 retail pharmacists particpating in their needle-exchange scheme. Most areas in London also have networks of pharmacists who, supported by the same co-ordination schemes, distribute packs of injecting paraphernalia from their premises.

Structured day programmes

Following the introduction of the *NHS and Community Care Act* in 1993 - which had major consequences for the provision of residential care for drug users (Chapter 4) - many services reacted by developing structured day programmes (SDPs). Such programmes were thought to be attractive both to service purchasers and service users as they offered the promise of effective intervention without the additional cost and disruption of time in a residential placement. London now hosts twelve of these initiatives.

Most SDPs provide interventions on either a three or five day a week basis. A holistic approach to rehabilitation is adopted, promoting: life skills and vocational training; sessions on building and restoring personal independence and responsibility; and helping to maintain drug users' links with their families and social support networks. Some SDPs also employ a 'rolling programme' of activities which allow individual clients to negotiate a customised timetable for their rehabilitation. Some programmes

also accommodate drug-free and current problem drug users.

Twelve step SDP

London has the only SDP with a twelve step Minnesota Method philosophy - the Self-Help Addiction Recovery Programme (SHARP). The eleven week programme follows the first three steps of NA and Alcoholics Anonymous (AA), with group therapy, videos, and 'life story' presentations by clients. Clients are encouraged to use the NA and AA self-help networks of support during the programme and for aftercare.

Vocational SDPs

Some SDPs provide drug users and former drug users with vocational skill sessions. These interventions range from basic literacy and numeracy skills, to practical workshops to improve an individual's chances of either gaining employment or progressing into further or higher education.

The Milton Skills Centre provides such sessions through both residential and SDPs for drug-free and current problem users (in two separate programmes). The Centre boasts a computer suite, professional audio video facilities, and an art centre with kiln. Education and training are provided on a range of topics and clients can qualify for National Vocation Qualifications (NVQs). The centre is currently arranging an accreditation scheme for these NVQs with the London Open Colleges Federation. The Base (Cranstoun Drug Services) in South London also offers similar activities and skills training which are accredited with Richmond College.

Aftercare for residential rehabilitation

Some residential units operate SDPs to provide 'aftercare' services to former residents. Residential aftercare aims to

LOCATION OF PHARMACY-BASED SYRINGE-EXCHANGE SERVICES IN LONDON, 1997

Map 2.4

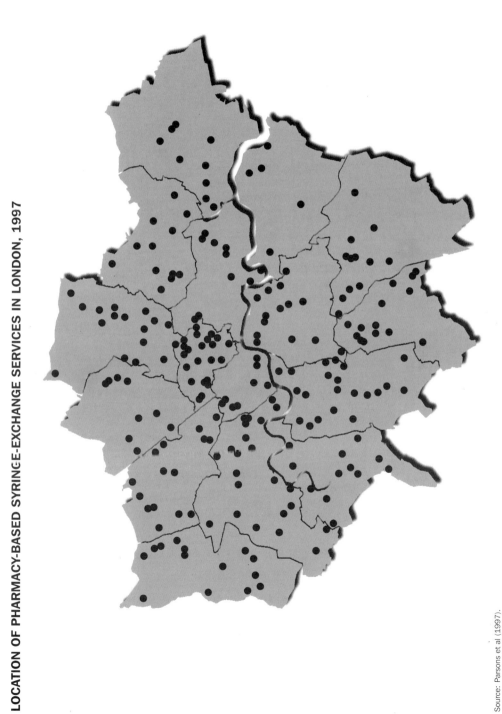

Source: Parsons et al (1997).

Notes: Map based on data collected from pharmacy syringe-exchange co-ordinators during April 1997.

ease the transition of former residents into independent living, whilst maintaining the gains made through previous treatment. There are numerous ways in which this may be done. Some SDPs, for example, try to co-ordinate their services with other treatment schemes managed by the rehabilitation unit. Crescent House in West London has a drug-free flat specifically for former residents who are encouraged to continue attending the main treatment programme for a time period as aftercare. The Milton Skills Centre provides aftercare in the form of a 'drop-in' clinic. Here, both former clients and new clients from the Islington and Camden area are equally welcome.

Counselling

Counselling forms a core intervention in many community-based services and is thought to be flexible enough to respond to all problem drug users. Counselling aims to either bring about behavioural change (helping the individual to examine and solve their own problems) and/or to give support and advice. The types of counselling used include: 'person centred' counselling (derived from the Carl Roger's approach); and cognitive behavioural counselling which combines the principles of learning theory (behaviour theory) and cognition (knowledge and understanding used to control thoughts and behaviour). This technique is most commonly used in relapse prevention (stopping people returning to drug use) and motivational interviewing (a tool to help individuals recognise and do something about their problem). There are a variety of other types of counselling including twelve step counselling and relationship and family therapy.

Detoxification and methadone reduction

Detoxification is the process whereby an individual dependent on a drug is taken off that drug to eliminate physical dependence with minimal discomfort from withdrawal symptoms. This can be done either abruptly or gradually. Usually the drug the individual is dependent on (or a substitute drug) is administered to them in gradually decreasing doses. Detoxification can be undertaken in community-based contexts (through a CDT, DDU or GP) or through in-patient settings (in-patient unit).

Methadone reduction programmes typically reduce an individuals drug use gradually over six to eight weeks with the aim of total abstinence. In reality, these programmes vary in duration from six weeks to six months. There are also particular forms of rapid detoxification available. This method - 'rapid opiate detoxification' - is commonly undertaken in the independent sector.

Maintenance prescribing

Long-term prescribing of a substitute drug aims to maximise stability and encourage harm reduction (Chapter 3). Typically this involves the prescribing of oral methadone to opiate dependent drug users. Maintenance prescribing may be delivered by a specialist NHS drug service or through a GP.

Recently, structured methadone maintenance programmes have emerged. These are on-site structured methadone dispensing coupled with psycho-social interventions. The Maudsley Hospital and Riverside Mental Health Trust Substance Misuse Service operate structured methadone maintenance programmes. Some London

DDUs, such as the Chelsea and Westminster Drug Treatment Centre, also prescribe injectable opiates (both methadone and heroin) to a small number of opiate dependent drug injectors who have tried and failed previous oral methadone treatments and are unable or unwilling to give up injecting. Their aim is stabilisation and the reduction of drug-related harm.

Alternative or complementary therapies

Some community-based services offer auricular acupuncture, homeopathic teas (which are used in the detoxification process and to help problem users 'sleep' during difficult periods of withdrawal) and shiatsu massage. The status of such therapies varies across the capital. The Blenheim Project, for example, use complementary therapies extensively in their work with problem stimulant users as they are thought to help users to relax and reduce any 'craving' for stimulants. However, in other sites such therapies are of a secondary status, and are often the first interventions to be dropped from the overall programme of work when funding shortages occur.

Education, prevention and advice

London has both local and national twenty-four hour telephone help-lines. These include the National Drugs Help-line (established in 1995 and offering advice all year round) and the City Roads twenty-four hour 'crisis intervention' information line. Release has a twenty-four hour help-line offering advice for criminal and legal emergencies and information and advice on drug use. Most community-based services also provide advice and

support during office hours by phone. Examples of these are the Blenheim Project's general enquiry and advice line. These services receive calls both from London and the rest of the UK.

London agencies have also developed written materials giving drug education and prevention advice aimed at problem drug users. Information packs have been produced in a variety of languages which utilise images from different cultural and ethnic groups. In addition, information is also targeted at different groups who may come into contact with drug use. A good example of this is the 1997 *London Dance Safety Campaign* (Chapter 8), which was supported by the 27 London Drug Action Teams and the London Drug Policy Forum. This provided information to: the wider public (through a poster campaign on London Transport); individuals attending dance venues (leaflet campaign in London clubs); and staff and management of dance venues (via the dissemination of health and safety guidelines) (Branigan et al, 1997).

Peer education

Peer education is the targeting and selection of members of a particular group or social network to inform them and encourage them to pass on accurate information to others with similar characteristics (Ward et al, 1997). The ultimate aim is to influence commonly held beliefs within the community so that behaviours which minimise the risks associated with problem drug use become the 'norm'. A common aim of drug-related peer education might be to encourage drug users to pass on information on safer drug use and injecting practices to produce safer and healthier drug use.

The Angel project in Kings Cross operates a peer education scheme for drug users in the local area. The apa

CDT in Tower Hamlets also operates a peer education scheme for Bangladeshi youth. This scheme is run by an Asian worker with local connections, insight and knowledge.

Services for specific groups

A common criticism of service provision in London has been that the majority of drug services have targeted white, male, opiate users. However there are also services who provide treatment to specific target groups.

Black and minority ethnic groups

The Brixton Drugs Project and the Maya Project actively target black drug users. Both agencies ensure the presence of black and ethnic minority staff on their teams and use positive multi-cultural images in any distributed health information. Other services, such as Crescent House and the Westminster Drug Project conduct black drug user groups within the wider remit of the agency. These two services also conduct outreach work in agencies with black and Asian links (as do the Cranston Drug Services and the SAFE outreach team).

Young users

Most drug services are adult orientated and are neither skilled nor suitable for working with a younger age group with different needs. Services for young drug users (defined as those under 17 years of age) are required to operate within the Children's Act of 1989. This requires detailed monitoring procedures and the involvement of local Child Protection Committees and social services' Child Protection Teams if a child is deemed to be 'at risk' from their problem drug use.

Kaleidoscope in Kingston specialises in providing a network of health and social care services for those users aged under 25. Lorne House (Turning Point) also offers a residential service for those between 15 and 25 years of age. Young people undergo detoxification upon admission and are expected to remain totally drug-free whilst in residence.

New models of service provision also include 'one stop shops' - drop-ins which provide a range of services for young people. For example, the Hot Orange Project in Woolwich provides a drop-in service for under 25s with advice and counselling on a range of topics including sexual health and drugs.

Primary crack users

New approaches are increasingly being developed to respond to the needs of crack users. These include ameliorative prescribing regimes, alternative therapies, relapse prevention, and stress management techniques. In addition, London has two SDPs for crack users. The Blenheim Project's SDP operating in West London is cognitive in focus and offers a twelve week programme for around twelve clients. Alternative therapies are also provided including

> **Key findings**
> Two in seven 15 year olds in London have used illicit drugs. This compares to just over one in three 15 year olds in the rest of England and Scotland.
> One in ten 15 and 16 year olds have used amphetamine, falling to one in 25 for ecstasy, and one in 100 for heroin (Chapter 10).

auricular acupuncture and 'detoxification' and 'sleep' homeopathic teas to counter the effects of withdrawal. Vital, which is part of the Newham Drug Project in East London, runs a women's group which is mainly crack orientated but also includes other stimulant users.

> **Key finding**
> Around one in a hundred 16 to 24 year olds in London have used crack at some time (Chapter 10).

Co-existence of mental illness

Those with substance misuse and mental health problems are a diverse client group and present particular challenges (Chapter 4). In London, many of these clients may also be homeless and/or involved with the criminal justice system. This group falls between two specialist providers - drug services and psychiatric mental health services - and are frequently not well catered for by either, with neither service willing or able to take the lead in providing treatment. In-patient and crisis services can provide a period of detoxification from illicit drugs and assessment over a number of weeks. In addition, residential rehabilitation services, as indicated previously, are beginning to widen their remit and may accommodate those who may require psychiatric medication.

HIV and AIDS

London has a number of specialist services for drug users with HIV and AIDS. These include Mainliners who provide information and support, and the Griffin Project (Turning Point) in West London which provides both respite care (short-term care for patient whilst their main carer has a break) and terminal care for problem drug users with AIDS. In addition, many drug services may have a specialist HIV worker as part of their staff team.

Drug using offenders

Other drug services such as Crescent House also run specific groups which address problem drug use and offending behaviour. In addition, peripatetic outreach is used both in probation and bail environments. Under the *Criminal Justice Act 1991*, drug using offenders are liable to receive 'community sentences' where they can be ordered to attend either an SDP or residential rehabilitation unit as part of their punishment (Chapter 11). SDPs for drug using offenders are often part funded by probation services and commonly include probation officers as staff. This investment may be necessary if a recent study indicating that one-third of the London probation population are problem drug users is representative (Beaumont and Janikiewicz, 1997).

SDPs for drug using offenders tend to employ a 'cognitive approach' to both problem drug using and offending behaviour. This involves encouraging clients to understand the reasons why they use drugs in a problematic manner and consider the ways in which they could change this behaviour.

The Community Drug Project SDP in South London has modified a cognitive approach especially for drug using offenders called 'Reasoning and Rehabilitation'. This has been in operation since 1994, with an eight week programme which offers clients sessions on problem solving, critical reasoning, emotional management, social and negotiating skills. The approach encourages clients to question the motivations behind previous offending, and address how they may have been coerced into believing this to be the right course of action.

Prisoners

A range of treatment and helping services are available for drug users in prisons in London, including detoxification, counselling and twelve step programmes. Most are provided by prison staff or community-based drug agencies. Services are normally commissioned directly by the Prison Service or are provided as a part of mainstream drug services.

In London, Holloway and Pentonville prisons both have structured drug treatment programmes. Holloway prison has a 33 bed short-term rehabilitation programme and a 33 bed detoxification unit. Pentonville operates a 49 bed programme with a twelve step approach. Cranstoun Drug Services also manage the Prisoners' Resource Service (PRS). This provides advice, counselling and referral to specialist services for both remand (awaiting trial) and sentenced prisoners. This is achieved through regular 'information surgeries' held in prisons. Telephone contact and help through written correspondence is also undertaken.

Homeless users

The Hampstead Road Centre offers a satellite service in Rathbone Place to drug users of no fixed abode. This offers a reduction programme where methadone is prescribed over time in gradually decreasing amounts. Some community-based services will provide outreach to homeless drug users. As previously mentioned, the Hungerford Project specialise in such activities, and a GP practice in Victoria (together with a CDT) offers specialist drug treatment for homeless problem drug users.

Pregnant users

In addition to problems associated with problem drug use, pregnant women are at risk of obstetric complications. This can be related to their drug use, often resulting in poor health and late or infrequent antenatal care (Gerada et al, 1990). A few services have community maternity liaison nurses. In West London, Riverside Mental Health Trust Substance Misuse Service has a specialist 'liaison nurse' who acts as the focal point between drug and alcohol services, antenatal services, and health visitors representing problem drug using women in the area who are pregnant. In South London, the Lands Clinic offers a specialist service for pregnant women and their partners with concerns about their drug and alcohol use.

Families

Services for the relatives and carers of drug users are normally based in the non-statutory sector. One exception is England's only family therapy service for drug and alcohol users, based at St Mary's in Paddington. London also hosts a national self-help network for relatives of drug users, Adfam. This provides a range of services, including a telephone help-line and training for family support groups. Rehabilitation units providing residential services for drug using couples or parents and their children include the apa Maya Project in South London, Rachael House and Elizabeth House.

How do London's drug services work?

Funding

Funding for drug services is directly available from a number of sources (Box 2.5). However, funding for drug and alcohol services will vary according to the status of the provider.

The NHS has traditionally been the largest statutory provider of drug services, receiving money from health and local authorities. The non-statutory sector tends to have a more eclectic funding base with money being drawn from the commercial and charitable sectors, but additional income is obtained from health and local authorities, and central government. Local authority social services (within the community care legislation) and the Probation Service (within the *Criminal Justice Act 1991*) provide 'top-up funding' for residential rehabilitation services. Although most residential care is funded from local authority community care budgets, 'unregistered' residential services can be funded through housing benefit payments (Chapter 4). Many non-statutory services actively seek funding to generate income, whilst independent sector agencies largely generate their own income (although this distinction has blurred with the introduction of the NHS internal market).

While GPs do not purchase drug services there are a number of pilot projects underway to involve GPs in the shared purchasing of NHS services in partnership with health authorities. Health authorities are increasingly funding the costs of prescribing methadone through general practitioner drug treatment programmes.

Box 2.5
Funding resources for drug services

Funding resources for drug services

- Special National Health Service funds - the Drug Misuse Services Special Allocation for health authorities. This is not ringfenced.
- Hospital and Community Health Service monies - mainstream budgets can provide money for drug users; monies for the development of primary and community services can include provision for the development of shared care for drug misusers.
- HIV/AIDS - for HIV prevention or health promotion work. Purchasers can use the prevention budget for HIV positive drug users, where drug use is a local priority, but not the treatment budget.
- Mental Health Challenge Fund - EL (96) 109 makes it possible to bid for services targeting people with mental health problems associated with substance use.
- Section 28a, including joint finance - funding allocated to health authorities under S28A of the NHS Act 1977 (including payments to local authorities, non-statutory sector organisations and housing associations for social service and housing purposes).
- Community care funding - local authority purchasing of substance misuse services is for the most part covered by general community care funding.
- Drug and Alcohol Specific Grant - local authorities can fund non-statutory sector service providers through bids for specific grant funds. The grant enables local authorities to pay organisations to expand and/or to improve local community care services in accordance with community care plans.

Source: Department of Health (1997).

Catchment areas

Although some community services operate under an open-access policy where there is no geographical criteria determining who can use a service, for others access is restricted to those living within the local health authority area. This is known as a 'catchment area'.

The process of an individual gaining access (referral) to a residential service is almost entirely overseen by an applicant's local authority. This consists of each applicant undergoing a community care assessment carried out by the local authority social services department, a decision being made on whether the applicant's 'needs' are great enough, and the local authority finding a suitable placement for successful applicants.

The extent and quality of provision differs across London and reflects funding resources and investment. Community-based services and NHS services are usually 'block funded', meaning that those individuals living within a service's catchment areas are automatically eligible to receive treatment from them.

Professionalism

The majority of staff in specialist NHS or non-statutory drug services have professional qualifications (usually in nursing). However, it is unclear whether these are relevant to working with drug users.

Staff usually enter the drugs field from a wide range of backgrounds and some have no formal qualifications. However, the majority will usually go on to gain a professional qualification of some kind and the demand for these has steadily increased. Drugs workers and counsellors are more likely to receive training in counselling than any other member of staff, whilst nurses are less likely to receive any further training (Boys et al, 1997). There are still no widely accepted standards of practice for staff working with drug users.

Management

Purchasing guidelines from the Department of Health affecting health, social and probation services have enforced new professional standards of management and care (Department of Health, 1997). Consequently, services are now required to include 'quality assurance' as part of their contract with purchasers. This simply means that agreed performance indicators relating to the structure, processes and outcomes of a service are monitored and evaluated.

SCODA have facilitated and supported this process in two ways: firstly, National Quality Standards for drug and alcohol treatment have been issued (SCODA, 1998); secondly SCODA have also offered guidance to service providers to increase the quality, range and value for money of services (SCODA, 1997).

Drug services in London: the reality

Although impressive on paper, the reality of service and intervention provision is somewhat different.

The downside

The potential benefits of local partnerships and treatment coherency agreements between service providers has been arguably compromised by the competitive nature of the 'provider market'. This has forced most drug services to face financial difficulty at some point, and some smaller, and hence more vulnerable, non-statutory community-based drug services have been forced to close.

Ringfencing

Ringfencing has played a significant part in the fortune of London's drug services. The removal of ringfencing of drugs and alcohol money in 1992 put drug services at a distinct disadvantage, forcing them to compete with other services such as those for the elderly and mentally ill (Chapter 4). In addition, these cuts in community care funding also had a knock-on-effect on social care services. Consequently, community care allocations in some of London's local authorities could not meet the placement demand for services in 1996/97.

HIV funding has been instrumental in the expansion of UK drug services since the late-1980s (and in the development of harm reduction approaches more generally). Until 1996/97, a broad consensus existed amongst purchasers of health care services that it was legitimate to use funds from one particular HIV-related budget ('AIDS treatment and care') to subsidise the development of drug services. However, in 1996/97 ringfencing around this budget was removed, meaning that health authorities no longer *had* to spend these funds on HIV-related services. This situation was complicated further by the introduction of expensive triple combination therapy for people with HIV/AIDS, meaning that existing resources were squeezed even further. In short, drug services faced a situation where funding was scarce.

This has all taken place in a scenario where general NHS overspending in certain health authorities has already plunged some drug services into crisis as grants have been cut back. In addition, residential services have been adversely affected by changes in housing benefit, cuts in Transitional Special Needs Management Allowance and also reductions in the Probation Accommodation Grant.

Organisation

While the setting up of DATs to develop and co-ordinate local action plans for drug services has been welcomed, they have not always achieved their full potential. In some areas, for example, it has been unclear what their actual role should be in influencing the funding of drug services. Furthermore, in other areas of London there has been little co-ordinated planning of services. Organisations have had different planning cycles, often contradictory agendas and diverging priorities - all of which makes the joint commissioning of services difficult.

Quality controls and emphasis on purchasing effective services (stemming from the *Community Care Act 1990*) have had negative and positive effects. While purchasing requirements have led to better quality services being delivered to drug users, the overall number and range of services being provided has been reduced. This is partly accountable to the tendency for health authorities to provide short-term funding. Although still welcome in a climate where funding is difficult to obtain, the typical funding 'window' given to services of around one year, is not enough time for new services to either develop or demonstrate their effectiveness.

Marginalisation

London is unique compared to other large UK cities: it has a larger, transient population; pronounced homelessness; a mix of ethnic groups; and the highest prevalence of HIV among drug users in England and Wales (Chapter 13). However, some drug users are still marginalised from drug services. There are still not enough treatment places, for example, for problem drug users under the age of 17. Similarly, services for minority ethnic groups remain underdeveloped in many London boroughs and non-opiate services (such as those for crack users or those with complex care needs) are minimal.

> **Key finding**
> In a survey of access to community care, while approximately 70% of community care assessments for drug users resulted in a placement, the process of assessment and funding was found to be compounded by: delays of up to three months; restrictions on the choice of residential unit; and end of year funding problems (SCODA, 1996).

On the up-side?

Recent changes in NHS policy (Department of Health, 1998) have outlined grand plans: the deconstruction of the NHS 'internal market'; an emphasis on partnership between providers and purchasers; and the formation of national evidence-based bodies. However, although the white paper has indicated that teams of GPs and community nurses will form local Primary Care Groups with the ability to 'shape' service provision, there is little other hint of the future for either mental health or drug and alcohol services.

Some London regions do, however, seem likely to benefit from a new Department of Health formula for allocating health monies in 1998. The formula will allocate funds according to the population aged between 15 to 44, the proportion living in rented accommodation in 1991, and a market forces factor (MMF) which reflects geographical variations in service costs (Thomson and Bellis, 1997).

Policy

Now at the end of its three year programme, *Tackling Drugs Together* (HMSO, 1995) has initiated the planning and development of drug services in London. As a result, drugs have always been kept on the agenda in health and local authorities. The appointment of Keith Hellawell as the UK Anti-drugs Co-ordinator, the new drugs strategy and the increased emphasis likely to be placed on Drug Action Teams in both the revised national strategy and the general strategic planning of drug services for London, should ensure the provision of better co-ordinated and effective drug services for problem drug users in London.

References

Advisory Council on the Misuse of Drugs (1982). *Treatment and Rehabilitation*. London: HMSO.

Beaumont, B. and Janikiewicz, S. (1997). Working with other agencies. In Beaumont, B. (ed.) *Care of Drug Users in General Practice*. Guildford: Radcliffe Medical Press.

Boys, A., Strang, J. and Homan, C. (1997). Have drug workers in England received appropriate training? 1995 baseline data from a national survey. *Drugs: Education, Prevention and Policy* (4), 297-305.

Branigan, P., Kuper, H. and Wellings, K. (1997). *Posterspotting. The Evaluation of the London Dance Safety Campaign*. London: London School of Hygiene and Tropical Medicine.

Department of Health (1996). *The Task Force to Review Services for Drug Misusers. Report of an Independent Review of Drug Treatment Services in England*. Wetherby: Department of Health.

Department of Health (1997). *Purchasing Effective Care and Treatment Services for Drug Misusers*. London: Department of Health.

Department of Health (1998). *The New NHS*. London: HMSO.

Donoghoe, M. (1997). Personal correspondence.

Gerada, C., Dawe, S. and Farrell, M. (1990). Management of the pregnant opiate user. *British Journal of Hospital Medicine*, 43.

HMSO (1995). *Tackling Drugs Together: A Strategy For England 1995-1998*. London: HMSO.

Keene, J. (1997). *Drug Misuse Prevention, Harm Minimisation and Treatment*. London: Chapman & Hall.

MacGregor, S., Ettore, B., Coomber, R. et al (1991). *Drug Services in England and the Impact of the Central Funding Initiative*. ISDD Research Monograph No 1. London: Institute for the Study of Drug Dependence.

MacLeod, J., Judd, A. and Hunter, G.M. (1998). Provision of care for alcohol and drug misusers [letter]. *British Journal of General Practice*, 48, 1004-1005.

Parsons, J., Turnbull, P. and Sheridan, J. (1997). Personal communication.

Standing Conference on Drug Abuse (1996). *The Eye of the Needle*. London: SCODA.

Standing Conference on Drug Abuse (1997a). Personal communication.

Standing Conference on Drug Abuse (1997). *Enhancing Drug Services*. London: SCODA.

Standing Conference on Drug Abuse (1998). *National Quality Standards for Drug and Alcohol Treatment*. London: SCODA.

Second Brain Report (1965). *Drug Addiction*. London: HMSO.

Strang, J. and Clement, S. (1994). The introduction of community drug teams. In Strang, J., and Gossop, M. (eds.) *Heroin and Drug Policy: The British System*. Oxford: Oxford University Press.

Thomson, R. and Bellis, M. (1997). No quick fixes. *Health Service Journal*, October, 30-31.

Ward, J., Hunter, G. and Power, R. (1997). Peer education as a means of drug prevention and education among young people: an evaluation. *Health Education Journal*, 56, 251-263.

3

SUBSTITUTE OPIATE PRESCRIBING AND PHARMACY SERVICES

Michael Farrell, Janie Sheridan, Paul Griffiths and John Strang
Maudsley Hospital and National Addiction Centre

Sections

Substitute opiate prescribing and pharmacy services

This chapter focuses on the prescribing of substitute opiate drugs and the activities of community pharmacists in London. These are dealt with together because both activities are related through the prescribing and dispensing of drugs for patients with drug problems, and both are involved in HIV prevention activities (one through prescribing and advice, the other through supplying needles, syringes and advice).

What is substitute prescribing?

Substitute prescribing is where a drug considered harmful for an individual is replaced by a relatively less harmful drug. However, the decision to substitute prescribe is rarely as simple as assessing the innate harms or effects of each drug. Instead, a range of other wider factors are taken into consideration (Box 3.1)

As the majority of substitute prescribing in London and the UK is opiate orientated and generally involves the substitution of oral methadone for heroin, this provides a natural focus for this chapter. However, other treatments are available and include the substitute prescription of oral diazepam (for tranquilliser misuse) and oral dexamphetamine sulphate (for problematic amphetamine use).

Substitute prescriptions are normally prescribed by general practitioners working in a local practice, or doctors and psychiatrists working in a community drug team or drug dependency unit (Chapter 2). These prescriptions are then dispensed at selected community pharmacies which can include small local pharmacies, larger 'high-street' outlets and pharmacy counters at selected supermarkets. A number of drug services in London also dispense prescriptions through on-site 'pharmacies'.

Box 3.1
Why is substitute prescribing used?

Why is substitute prescribing used?
• Increasing the ability to attract problem drug users into treatment settings by offering a stable prescription of substitute medication. This can potentially reduce the chance of the user being involved in acquisitive crime or consuming adulterated substances.
• Encouraging individuals in treatment to stabilise and reduce their problem drug use through 'maintenance doses' of substitute drugs.
• Promoting behavioural change amongst users in treatment to reduce injecting behaviour and the risk of adverse health consequences such as HIV, hepatitis, overdose or skin infections.
• Meeting longer-term clinical goals such as abstinence.

Prescribing, policy, practice and London - the 1950s and 1960s

Although developments in prescribing, policy and practice are influenced by factors on a nation-wide level, London has always played a role in this process. Prior to the 1960s there were no specialist drug services in London or the UK. Instead a handful of general and private practitioners prescribed drugs - mainly pharmaceutical heroin and cocaine - to treat drug dependency. Doctors wrote prescriptions for the drugs which were dispensed by community pharmacies.

Due to a growth in the illicit trade of prescribed drugs in the 1950s and 1960s - notably centred around the over-prescribing activities of a few London doctors - the *Dangerous Drugs Act of 1967* ruled that general practitioners could no longer prescribe heroin or cocaine for treating drug dependency without possessing a special licence. Instead, specialist drug dependency units were established in 1968 to take over the prescribing role of such controlled drugs. General practitioners, however, could continue to prescribe methadone.

This legislation resulted in just under a thousand individuals in London (and around three thousand patients in   the UK) being brought into such specialist services over a short period of time (Spear, 1994; Strang and Gossop, 1994; Stimson and Oppenheimer, 1982). With the establishment of around 15 out-patient clinics - compared to a smaller number of clinics in the Home Counties and very few elsewhere in the UK - London had the heaviest concentration of specialist units and patients in the country (Connell and Strang, 1994).

The new specialist prescribing services continued the separation of prescribing (by doctors) from dispensing (by pharmacists) - unlike the US methadone maintenance system which brought these together for on-site consumption. In the UK, off-site dispensing was favoured as it was thought to prevent addicts congregating daily at drug dependency units.

The 1970s

Cocaine prescribing virtually ceased after the creation of the specialist clinics, and methadone was increasingly prescribed for opiate misuse at the end of the

1960s and the early 1970s. Combined with a lack of central direction over the specialist drug clinics, the growing use of methadone resulted in discussions amongst clinics about the respective merits of prescribing the now three main drug forms - injectable heroin, injectable methadone and oral methadone.

By the late 1970s, most clinics introduced a policy that only oral methadone would be made available to patients, those who had attended pre-1975 were now retained on maintenance supplies of injectable drugs. However, the publication of a study conducted at a London drug clinic at the end of the 1970s continued to fuel discussion over the merits of prescribing injectable or oral formulations (Hartnoll et al, 1980).

Today, there is considerable variation in the balance between injectable and oral methadone prescribing in the UK with some regions reporting up to 10 per cent of prescribing in injectable form (such as London) and other regions reporting minimal injectable prescribing (Farrell et al, 1996). In 1996, only 106 UK doctors were licensed by the Home Office to prescribe injectable heroin. Thirty-nine of these doctors worked in London and all but one of the London doctors were working in the National Health Service (Metrebian et al, 1996).

The 1980s and onwards

In retrospect, the establishment of specialist clinic prescribing appears to have been a reactive policy initiative without either a coherent long-term treatment or service policy to underpin it. Although the limitations of this particular organisation of services became apparent early on, the slow development of drug problems in the community meant that services remained marginal. However, this began to change with an increase in heroin use in the late 1970s and early 1980s, in turn highlighting problems of limited provision, reduced accessibility and a lack of flexibility and adaptability.

Service expansion

Such agitation about gaps in service provision for heroin users resulted in a number of policy initiatives. In 1982, the Advisory Council on the Misuse of Drugs recommended the expansion of community-based services. The 1984 Central Funding Initiative, which provided central government funding for local drug service development (MacGregor et al, 1990), resulted in a major expansion with over 50 per cent of funding going to community-based services. Sixty-two per cent of this expenditure was for statutory services and 38 per cent for non-statutory services. In London the former North-West Thames region was the most successful in bidding for funds, while South-East Thames was less successful.

HIV

The mid 1980s also saw the advent of serious concern about the spread of HIV infection. The Advisory Council on the Misuse of Drugs report on *AIDS and Drug Misuse* (1988) was influential in shaping the style and priority of service development. This report introduced the concept of *flexible prescribing* - prescribing that might have a number of aims in addition to abstinence. It emphasised the importance of engaging and retaining problem drug users in contact with services, with the aims of helping them to modify their risk taking behaviour and improve their health and social well being without necessarily achieving total abstinence from drugs. It also supported increasing the availability of clean syringes and injecting paraphernalia to drug injectors.

The *Task Force to Review Services for Drug Misusers* (Department of Health, 1996) reported similar benefits from the provision of opiate substitution. It came to this conclusion on the basis of a review of international literature, and also preliminary data from the National Treatment Outcome Research Study.

Methadone prescribing

Policy changes over the last decade or so have resulted in significant rises in the prescription of methadone.

The UK now has a wide network of methadone prescribing in mainstream drug services and in primary care.

Any medical practitioner may prescribe methadone for the treatment of addiction, but prescriptions must be written in accordance with the *Misuse of Drugs Regulations* (1985). The Home Office Dangerous Drugs Inspectorate, with the help of the police, inspect community pharmacies to ensure that these regulations for prescribing and dispensing are complied with by both doctors and pharmacists. The regulations are mainly concerned with record keeping and the practical storage and dispensing procedures of controlled drugs such as methadone. It should be noted, however, that although general treatment guidelines do exist, there are currently no specific guidelines for methadone prescribing in the UK, and doctors are free to exercise their clinical judgement and to vary the dispensing regime.

Prescribing and dispensing

Methadone is prescribed as tablets, as oral mixture (most commonly 1mg of drug per 1ml of solution, but other strengths are available) and as ampoules for injection. Probably 95 per cent of the methadone which is prescribed is dispensed at community pharmacies.

Prescriptions are written for the patient by a general practitioner, or doctors or psychiatrists working in a community drug team or drug dependency unit. NHS prescriptions for methadone normally provide a fortnights supply and the drugs are dispensed by community pharmacists in accordance with Misuse of Drugs Regulations. The methadone is usually dispensed as a 'take home' dose, although some types of methadone prescriptions are also consumed under the supervision of the pharmacist. Private practitioners may also write prescriptions.

It is recommended that in the early phase of treatment all drugs are dispensed on an instalment basis (normally daily 'pick-ups' with weekend supplies).

NHS instalment dispensing from community pharmacies requires the pharmacist to be paid by the NHS for each instalment dispensed. There are no dose limits, but practitioners generally prescribe doses between 20 and 100mgs in the form of oral methadone mixture. Because consumption is not

Key finding

An annual 1.3 fold increase in the overall consumption of methadone has occurred in the UK for each of the past six years.

usually supervised, there appears to be considerable diversion of prescribed medication resulting in a large black market, where oral methadone sells at about £10 per 100mls. To date, diversion has not been a political issue, but there are rising numbers of first service contacts reporting methadone use only (Chapter 12), and there have been reports of deaths from non-dependent methadone use.

Volume of prescribing

Data are not available on the number of people to whom methadone is prescribed and over what time period. However, data are available both on the *form* in which methadone is dispensed (oral mixture, ampoules and tablets) and on the *amount* dispensed (as a percentage of general practitioner prescriptions in London and England in 1993).

As Table 3.2 shows, over one-fifth (21.6%) of all oral methadone dispensed against general practitioner prescriptions in England took place in London. This compares to one-third (36.5%) of HCL 1ml ampoules (50mg/ml), and one-fifth of Physeptone tablets (22.4%).

Data on prescribing suggests that 20 to 22 per cent of national general practitioner prescribing of methadone occurs in the 16 London health authorities.

Drug type	London as a % of England
Methadone HCL injection (50mg/ml 1ml amp)	36.5
Methadone HCL injection (10mg/ml 5ml amp)	24.2
Methadone HCL injection (10mg/ml 1ml amp)	11.7
Physeptone injection (10mg/1ml amp)	19.3
Physeptone tablets (5mg)	22.4
Methadone HCL oral mixture (1mg/ml)	21.6

Table 3.2 Oral methadone, methadone tablets[1] and injection ampoules, dispensed in London as a percentage of general practitioner prescriptions in England, 1993

Source: Howes et al (1997).

Notes: 1 Physeptone is a brand name for methadone tablets.

The community pharmacy dispensing of controlled drugs, and other pharmacy services

Given the problems of estimating the scale of substitute prescribing and dispensing, a national survey of community pharmacies was conducted in 1995. This was carried out as part of the Department of Health's *Task Force to Review Services for Drug Misusers* (1996). This used a one in four sample stratified by health authority, and had a 75 per cent response rate (n=1,984 pharmacies). The survey was designed to assess the level of service provision by community pharmacies for problem drug users in the context of HIV prevention.

> **Key finding**
> In 1995, there were 10,500 community pharmacies in England and Wales. 1,850 of these community pharmacies were in London.

Community pharmacists are required by law to keep detailed records of all the methadone, diamorphine (heroin) and amphetamine prescriptions they dispense. Pharmacists were asked by the survey to provide details of the drugs dispensed and whether the prescription was private, or from a hospital or general practitioner.

Two caveats need to be considered before interpreting data on dispensing. Firstly, because not all pharmacies dispense, there will be a tendency for patients from one prescriber to go to a limited number of pharmacies. Therefore the clustering of prescriptions around particular pharmacies in terms of source, drug, dosage and instructions should be expected. Secondly, it does not necessarily follow that

prescriptions dispensed from, for example, London pharmacies actually originate from London prescribers. It is possible, with some prior organisation, for a patient from Birmingham to redeem a prescription in London.

Controlled drugs in England and Wales

The most commonly dispensed controlled drug in England and Wales was methadone, comprising 91.8 per cent of all opiate and amphetamine prescriptions dispensed, followed by amphetamine (4.4%) and diamorphine (1.6%) (Sheridan et al, 1996). To date, these data provide the most detailed picture of opiate and amphetamine prescribing in the England and Wales region.

Controlled drugs in London

For purposes of comparison, the sample of community pharmacies in London health authorities were put into two groups (Box 3.3 overleaf). This used the categories employed in the King's Fund report on London's Mental Health (Johnson and Lelliott, 1997).

> **Key findings**
> In England and Wales:
> 50 per cent of pharmacies dispensed controlled drugs for treating addiction.
> 35 per cent sold injecting equipment to known or suspected drug injectors
> 19 per cent were involved in a needle-exchange scheme (Sheridan et al, 1996).

Box 3.3
National survey
of community
pharmacies (1995)
categorisation of
London health
authorities

Categorisation of London health authorities

• *Inner Deprived London*: Kensington & Chelsea and Westminster; Camden & Islington; East London and The City; Lambeth, Southwark & Lewisham (n=93 pharmacies).

• *Other London*, comprised of Mixed Status London: Brent & Harrow; Ealing, Hammersmith & Hounslow; Redbridge & Waltham Forest; New River (now Enfield & Haringey); Merton, Sutton and Wandsworth; along with High Status London: Barnet; Hillingdon; Barking & Havering; Bromley; Croydon; Bexley & Greenwich; Kingston & Richmond (n=217 pharmacies).

Pharmacies dispensing

It should be noted that pharmacies in urban and city centre environments are located more closely together thus allowing customers and patients a greater choice. They also tend to be open longer hours. With regard to the provision of services for problem drug users, it might then be expected that a smaller proportion of the total number of pharmacies in London would need to be service providers to give the same accessibility to services as that needed in more rural areas. However, almost 50 per cent of London pharmacies were found to be dispensing controlled drugs, which is the national average. A greater proportion of Inner Deprived London pharmacies (nearly 60%) were providing this service than Other London ones (Figure 3.4).

Drugs dispensed

The most commonly dispensed drug in London was methadone (92.6%), followed by diamorphine (2.7%) and amphetamine (2.6%). The rest of the prescriptions were for other opioids, stimulants and benzodiazepines. Overall, the profiles are very similar to the whole of England and Wales, but amphetamine prescribing featured slightly less strongly in London, and diamorphine slightly more. For methadone specifically, 54 per cent of methadone prescriptions were from Inner Deprived London and 46 per cent from Other London.

Type

Almost 11 per cent of London prescriptions were for tablets of methadone, 9.7 per cent for injection ampoules and 79.6 per cent for oral methadone. Again this is very similar to the profile for England and Wales (at 11%, 9.3% and 79.6% respectively) (Strang et al, 1996). The mean daily dose was 52.4mg with a range from 2 to 250mg (median 45mg).

Pharmacies in Inner Deprived London dispensed a slightly higher proportion of prescriptions for tablets than either Other London pharmacies or pharmacies in England and Wales as a whole (Figure 3.5 overleaf).

Figure 3.4
Pharmacies dis-
pensing controlled
drugs by location,
1995

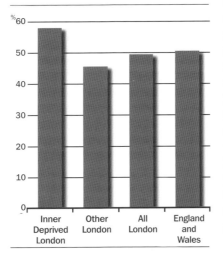

Figure 3.5
Methadone prescription dispensed by type and location, 1995

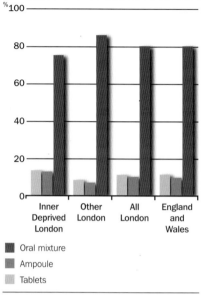

Oral mixture
Ampoule
Tablets

Source

Just over one-third of all London prescriptions were from general practitioners, the remainder were from specialist drug services attached to hospitals. Other London had fewer prescriptions from general practitioners than Inner Deprived London and England and Wales (Figure 3.6). Pharmacies in Inner Deprived London and in England and

Figure 3.6
Methadone prescriptions by type of prescriber and location, 1995

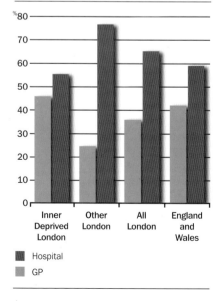

Hospital
GP

Wales had similar proportions of general practitioner and hospital prescriptions.

The vast majority of prescribing in London was done by NHS practitioners (94.1%), the rest being from private practitioners (Figure 3.7). London as a whole has much of the private prescribing in England and Wales. Inner Deprived London also had by far the highest proportion of prescriptions from private practitioners: 7.5 per cent compared to 3.9 per cent for Other London and 1.5 per cent for all the pharmacies in England and Wales (Strang et al, 1996).

Figure 3.7
Methadone prescriptions by type of prescription and location, 1995

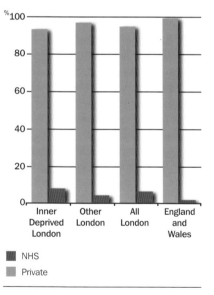

NHS
Private

Pharmacy syringe sales and exchange in London

Of those London pharmacies surveyed, 42 per cent reported selling injecting equipment (Figure 3.8). This was higher than the national average for England and Wales (35%). A further 34 per cent indicated a willingness to do this if

**Figure 3.8
Pharmacies
providing a needle-
exchange service
by location, 1995**

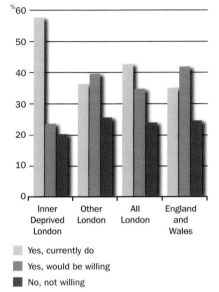

Yes, currently do
Yes, would be willing
No, not willing

**Figure 3.9
Pharmacists'
attitudes towards
operating needle-
exchanges by
location, 1995**

Although almost the same percentage of London pharmacies were dispensing controlled drugs as in the rest of England and Wales, this provision of services for problem drug users does not extend to needle-exchange schemes. The figure for involvement in a needle-exchange scheme for England and Wales as a whole, was reported to be 19 per cent (Sheridan et al, 1996). However, this could reflect the concentration of pharmacies in London and the fewer pharmacies needed to provide adequate cover to similar size areas.

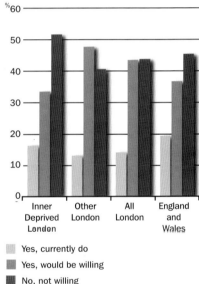

Yes, currently do
Yes, would be willing
No, not willing

there were sufficient local demand, whilst 24 per cent reported that they were unwilling. Interestingly, Inner Deprived London pharmacies were more likely to be providing this service.

Fourteen per cent of the London pharmacies surveyed were already involved in a needle-exchange scheme, and 43 per cent indicated a willingness to participate in the future (Figure 3.9). Pharmacies from Other London were more likely to report a willingness to provide a needle-exchange scheme, than those pharmacies located in Inner Deprived London.

The future of substitute prescribing services in London

During the past decade, substitute prescribing services have become an increasingly important part of overall service provision in both London and the UK. However, although the role and cost effectiveness of substitution services now appears to be recognised, it is becoming apparent that further study is required in two key areas: mapping current service provision and evaluating its effectiveness.

Mapping

It is widely agreed that there is limited information on current treatment and other interventions offered to problem drug users in London. Elsewhere in this book (Chapter 12) are data on the number of people treated by different kinds of services for problem drug users. In this chapter we have tried - with limited available data - to look at the kinds of prescribing and pharmacy services provided. Overall, the emerging picture indicates a considerable similarity between London and the rest of England and Wales. However, the percentage of private practitioners prescribing drugs in London is strikingly higher, whilst the proportion of pharmacies delivering needle-exchange appears to be lower within London. There is clearly a need for more detailed monitoring and surveillance so that the activities of the different services can be properly compared (Chapter 14).

Evaluation

There is also a need for further research into the most effective ways to deliver such substitute prescribing services in order to determine which style of treatment has the most impact on the quality of life of service users. Generally, there is likely to be a continued struggle to find a balance between minimising the diversion of prescribed drugs such as methadone onto the illicit market, whilst maximising user access to substitute prescribing services. Given current concerns about diversion, there is likely to be an expansion in London of pharmacy-based supervised methadone consumption (where individuals collect and consume their methadone under the supervision of a pharmacist). However, the eventual balance between such service provision and current methods of provision will be influenced by forthcoming Department of Health clinical guidelines on the management of problem drug users.

Acknowledgements

The authors would like to acknowledge the help of Emily Finch, Sarah Welch, John Marsden, Alison Nobel and Samantha Howes.

References

Advisory Council on the Misuse of Drugs (1982). *Treatment and Rehabilitation*. London: Department of Health.

Advisory Council on the Misuse of Drugs (1988). *AIDS and Drug Misuse Update Part I*. London: HMSO.

Connell, P. and Strang, J. (1994). The creation of the clinics: clinical demand and the formation of policy. In Strang, J. and Gossop, M. (eds.) *Heroin and Drug Policy: The British System*. Oxford: Oxford University Press.

Department of Health (1996). *The Task Force to Review Services for Drug Misusers. Report of an Independent Review of Drug Treatment Services in England*. Wetherby: Department of Health.

Farrell, M., Sell, L., Neeleman, J. et al (1996). Methadone provision in the UK. *The International Journal of Drug Policy*, 7 (4), 239-244.

Hartnoll, R., Mitcheson, M., Battersby, A. et al (1980). Evaluation of heroin maintenance in controlled trial. *Archive of General Psychiatry*, 37, 877-883.

Howes, S., Farrell, M. and Sheridan, J. (1997). *Report to Department of Health* (unpublished).

Johnson, S. and Lelliott, P. (1997). Mental Health Services in London: Evidence from Research and Routine Data. In Johnson, S., Ramsay, R., Thornicroft, G. et al (eds.) *London's Mental Health*. London: Kings Fund.

MacGregor, S., Ettore, B., Coomber, R. et al (1990). *The Central Funding Initiative and the Development of Drug Services in England*. University of London: Birkbeck College.

Metrebian, N., Shanahan,W. and Stimson, G.V. (1996). Heroin prescribing in the United Kingdom: an overview. *European Addiction Research*, 2, 194-200.

Sheridan, J., Strang, J., Barber, N. et al (1996). HIV prevention, drug misuse and the community pharmacist: findings from the 1995 national survey in England and Wales. *British Medical Journal*, 313, 272-274.

Spear, B. (1994). The early years of the British system in practice. In Strang, J. and Gossop, M. (eds.) *Heroin and Drug Policy: The British System*. Oxford: Oxford University Press.

Stimson, G.V. and Oppenheimer, E. (1982). *Heroin Addiction: Treatment and Control in Britain*. London: Tavistock

Strang, J. and Gossop, M. (1994). *Heroin Addiction and Drug Policy. The British System*. Oxford. Oxford University Press.

Strang, J., Sheridan, J. and Barber, N. (1996). Prescribing oral and injectable methadone to opiate addicts: data from the 1995 national survey of community pharmacies in England and Wales. *British Medical Journal*, 313, 270-272.

4

COMMUNITY AND SOCIAL CARE PROVISION

Terry Bamford
Royal Borough of Kensington and Chelsea Housing and Social Services

Sections

What is community and social care?

The dividing line between health and social care is never easy to draw. In the field of substance misuse, 'social care' is used to describe those community-based services which are not staffed by health service professionals such as doctors and nurses. It includes mainly residential rehabilitation services and some community-based advice, information and counselling services (Chapter 2). Social care provision may be offered by local authorities, the non-statutory sector, or the private sector. These services will normally all have close liaison with health care agencies.

There are 33 local authorities in London (including the City of London) which have responsibility for community care services to their local residents, including those for problem drug users. These authorities fund residential stays for those in rehabilitation from problem drug use and support some community-based services. London also has 16 health authorities charged with purchasing healthcare to meet the needs of their resident populations. However, substance misuse is only a small part of a local authority's wider community care responsibilities.

Health needs do not follow geographical boundaries and a highly specialised service may meet the needs of problem drug users across London. A day programme for crack users, for example, will often draw individuals from a geographical radius wider than the local authority the service is located in. This can often make it difficult for local authorities to address purchasing issues or to identify gaps in local service provision. The move to pan-London purchasing has mainly developed as a response to this problem.

The NHS and Community Care Act 1990

Prior to the *NHS and Community Care Act 1990* the costs of financing residential placements were often met by central government through social security payments. This funding was provided according to the demand for a particular service. Such a financial strategy facilitated an explosive growth in the private and non-statutory sector provision of residential care. While most of this growth was in the provision of care or nursing homes for older people, drug services also benefited from a secure source of income. As many clients using the services were on income support, their placement fees were met by social security. At that time, assessment of client need was undertaken by those providing the residential care service.

The introduction of the *NHS and Community Care Act 1990* on the 1st of April 1993, was in large measure dictated by the Treasury's desire to cap these rapidly escalating costs. The act had three main consequences.

Firstly, all clients were now to be funded from local authority community care budgets, rather than from social security coffers. Secondly, funding was now allocated on the results of an assessment process conducted by the local authority. Placements were now granted according to an assessment of client need and eligibility, rather than the 'demand-led' system that existed before. Thirdly, social services had to take on new responsibilities and roles in which they had little experience. These included: assessing which

individuals needed residential rehabilitation; finding a suitable placement to
meet the clients' needs; and arranging
finance for that placement.

Significantly, although the *NHS and
Community Care Act 1990* required local
authorities to publish plans outlining the
provision of community care for their residents, there was still no statutory
requirement for the local authority to
provide services for problem drug users
(London Drug Policy Forum, 1993).

Resulting problems of the Act

The Act was met with misgivings by
many in the private and non-statutory
sector. Local authority social services
departments also voiced concerns,
highlighting the relative inexperience of
their staff in providing services to people with drug and alcohol problems.
However, nowhere was tension more
acute than amongst the ranks of drug
and alcohol rehabilitation providers.
Until now, the great majority of their
placements had been funded by central
government funds.

Ringfencing

In 1991, the Government did initially
acknowledge these misgivings by
agreeing to 'ringfence' drug and alcohol funding for a period of three
years. In theory, this meant two
things. Firstly, that a set amount of
money was 'ringfenced' or allocated
from central government funds specifically for drug and alcohol service provision. Secondly, that by doing this
the full impact of the *NHS and
Community Care Act 1990* would be
postponed for three years - allowing
local authority social services departments time to develop strategic plans
for problem drug and alcohol users. In
practice, however, although social services departments remained the 'pay-
masters' - being able to allocate residential placements as they saw fit
(usually on the basis of demand
rather than assessment) - they had
little control over the total volume of
expenditure available.

Ringfencing revisited

In September 1992, a surprise
announcement was made by the
Government: *all* community care funds
were now to be ringfenced. This ruling
provided social service authorities with
a secure funding framework for community care. However, because drug
and alcohol funding was not ringfenced
within this framework, these services
lost the financial protection which
they had been previously promised.
Attempts at a judicial review and a
sustained campaign failed to reverse
this decision.

In addition, organisational changes
within some London authorities resulted in a split between those individuals
now responsible for commissioning
services and those for providing them.
This caused particular problems for
the small numbers of personnel with
specialist expertise in substance misuse. Traditionally, they had spanned
both responsibilities but now found
themselves subsumed into wider areas
such as HIV and AIDS services. This
made it difficult for individual authorities to define a separate strategic and
commissioning priority for substance
misuse services. Seeking a pan-
London response was, therefore, a
logical development for hard pressed
local authorities.

The pan-London response

The changed world of community care resulted in three pan-London responses.

Firstly, the formation of the Greater London Drugs and Alcohol Purchasers' Group in 1993. Secondly, the creation of the London Drug and Alcohol Services Purchasing Directory in 1995. Thirdly, the development of the Drug Service Providers' Consortium in 1995.

Drugs and Alcohol Purchasers' Group

In 1993, the Greater London branch of the Association of Directors of Social Services set up a group of staff with lead roles in commissioning and purchasing substance misuse services - the Drugs and Alcohol Purchasers' Group. This body was formed to tackle two inter-related problems: costs and funding.

Costs and funding

Social services departments in London knew from their experience of recruiting foster parents how easily costs could escalate in a situation where demand for residential placements exceeded supply. They were anxious to avoid a situation where one authority would pay a higher price for the same placement than its neighbour. Furthermore, information gathered for the failed judicial review indicated that the total resources going into drug and alcohol services from social services departments, particularly in Inner London, were likely to be lower than levels of funding previously available from central government. Significantly, if this drop in funding meant that there was to be a contraction in the overall number of places available, purchasers were anxious that the process should be managed in such a way as to guarantee access to a minimum range of services.

Decisions

In 1993/94, the purchasers group took a series of decisions designed to control such costs. The group took the view that social service departments should not exceed the available budget for funding drug and alcohol services. In order to stay within this budget they attempted to set limits on residential placement costs at the former social security level. They then sought to restrict the length, and hence total cost, of placements to a maximum of 12 weeks with reassessment at that time.

Both approaches were, however, flawed. Firstly, the Group failed to appreciate the complex mix of funding of residential rehabilitation provision. Some projects in London received financial assistance not only from their local authority, but also from the London Boroughs Grants Unit, Home Office Probation funds, or through the charitable status of the project. Secondly, although the attempt to curtail the length of placements was designed to limit expenditure, it overlooked the real issue: effective drug and alcohol placements meant keeping people in placement for the duration of a treatment programme rather than them dropping out too early due to issues of cost.

Outcomes

Nevertheless, the initiative did have two effects. It served to draw purchasers together in a common interest and it resulted in a shift in the balance of residential rehabilitation from long-term placements towards shorter more focused care. That shift has continued and few social services departments nationally, and perhaps none in London, would now be willing to fund placements in excess of a year on therapeutic grounds (as happened prior to 1993 when social security was meeting the cost). The Drug and Alcohol Purchasers' Group continue to meet in 1997 and are currently looking to appoint staff to strengthen their pan-London purchasing function.

In practice the diversity of funding of residential rehabilitation placements meant that the attempt to fix prices at the former social security level never really took hold. By the end of 1994, purchasers faced the dilemma of either watching their attempt to secure some regulation of the market collapse, or adopting a more proactive stance.

Drug and Alcohol Purchasing Directory

In discussion with providers, London purchasers agreed in 1005 to launch the first edition of the London Drug and Alcohol Services Purchasing Directory. This aimed to provide basic information about the philosophy, staffing and regime of drug and alcohol projects and also a recommended price for services. Prior to this, purchasers rarely had sufficient information about the accounts and funding base of providers to enter into realistic negotiation.

Although difficult to hold providers to a recommended price each year, the exercise served three important purposes. Firstly, it greatly increased the knowledge of local authority care managers about the individual projects in which they were placing individuals. A repeated complaint from providers had been the level of ignorance of care managers about their project and its purpose and the problem of negotiating individually with each care manager. Secondly, it reinforced purchasers' concern about the different funding base of projects and the progressive withdrawal of funding from the London Boroughs Grants Unit, Probation Service and the Housing Corporation, leading to increased costs for the local authority as purchaser. Thirdly, it raised the issue of quality and outcomes of treatment more forcefully than previously, whilst stressing the importance of trying to secure an agreed framework between purchasers and providers for that discussion.

Drug Service Providers' Consortium

The attempt by the GLADSS Drugs and Alcohol Purchasers' Group to secure greater co-ordination and consistency was mirrored in 1995 by the development of the Drug Service Providers' Consortium. This consortium engages in dialogue with purchasers on behalf of its diverse and sometimes competitive constituents. The issues discussed have ranged from protocols in relation to the negotiation of the Directory prices to quality standards and outcome measurement.

The interests of purchasers and providers are not identical and a degree of tension is inevitable. What both groups continually seek however is a framework which will maintain a broad range of both generic and specialist services, and will give providers a reasonable degree of financial security.

Mapping community and social care provision

In 1996 there were 32 drug and alcohol residential rehabilitation providers operating in the capital. These varied in philosophy from an overtly religious orientation through to twelve step models and therapeutic community approaches (Chapter 2). These projects also ranged from those encouraging abstinence to those working on minimising harms from drug use, in price from £240 to £1,820 (recommended gross weekly charge), and in size from six to 31 places.

De-registered care

The two years following the introduction of community care witnessed a loss of some 25 per cent of the residential rehabilitation beds previously available in London. Whilst some residential rehabilitation services were forced to close due to limited community care funding from local authorities, other services avoided this by 'de-registering' their premises. Effectively, this meant that residential rehabilitation services redefined their working identity and practice in two main ways.

Firstly, the services stopped providing a full 24 hour residential service and began operating on a partial 'bed and breakfast' basis. As community care funded placements had to be provided by law from registered residential or nursing homes with 24 hour provision, this process of 'de-registering' allowed these services to seek financial support outside of the community care sphere.

Secondly, these services then secured funding through housing benefit, which was often at a higher and more readily available level than previous community care support. Although recent changes in social security regulations have questioned the wisdom of this move, services such as Alcohol Recovery Projects have benefited from substantial support in this way over the past three or four years. In 1995 there were 35 bed spaces in such non-registered provision.

Those services which remained in 'registered' premises faced an insecure and uncertain future with continuing financial pressure. They also had to cope with 33 different local authorities each with their own assessment criteria, their own care managers and their own contracting procedures. The only element in common was a desire by local authorities to pay the lowest possible price for service.

Day care

The pressure on residential resources was quickened by the rapid development of 'day care' provision. 'Day care' describes everything from drop-in day centres to five days a week, full-time, structured programmes. Rehabilitation programmes delivered in a day care setting were attractive to both purchasers and to service users as they offered the promise of effective interventions without the additional cost and disruption of time spent in a residential placement. Consequently, Drug and Alcohol Specific Grant funding in 1995/96 was targeted at this area of development.

The range and type of day care services developed in London varied immensely. Some residential providers, for example, sought to develop their own day programmes as part of an 'aftercare' package. Others, meanwhile, saw the day programmes they already offered as part of residential rehabilitation being extended to users living in the community.

Funding community and social care provision in London

1995 and 1996 saw local authorities becoming more directly engaged with funding a range of local prevention initiatives. This is evident from the shift in local authority funding from 1994/95 to 1995/96. It is also evident that the increased investment has gone largely to non-statutory sector grants, rather than for community care placements. Figures drawn from 14 of London's 33 authorities illustrate this general trend (Table 4.1).

The increase in placement expenditure happened despite fears by providers that drug and alcohol clients would be marginalised. The commitment shown by local authorities to increase investment in this area is striking. While the investment in in-house services is noteworthy, the need to improve the quality of assessments undertaken by local authorities is a consistent theme from providers and has been reflected in staffing improvements.

Table 4.1 London local authority community care expenditure for drugs and alcohol, 1994-1996		£'s spent on community care placements	£'s spent on drug and alcohol in-house staff	£'s spent on grants to non-statutory sector	Total
	1994-5	£3,123,600	£632,900	£1,762,500	£5,519,000
	1995-6	£3,327,700	£831,600	£2,009,600	£6,168,800
	% increase	6.5%	31%	14%	11.8%

Dual diagnosis and social care

There is increasing concern about the numbers of people with substance misuse problems who also have mental health problems, or whose scale of misuse has resulted in homelessness. The community psychiatric teams set up as part of the Department of Health's report on the Homeless Mentally Ill Initiative suggest that over one-third of their clients present with drug or alcohol problems. Many of these clients show a pattern of opportunistic and occasional misuse.

The traditional clinical separation of mental health from drug and alcohol problems has militated against the involvement of the National Health Service with this group of clients, and has made it more difficult to achieve an

integrated pattern of provision. Mutual training, holistic assessments, avoidance

Key findings

A study of schizophrenics in an Inner London area found that one-fifth had alcohol or substance misuse problems. This rose to 44% when only those under 36 were examined (Duke, Pantelis and Barnes, 1994).

Research with over 700 young homeless people in Central London found that 88% were currently using at least one drug (Flemen, 1997).

Drug use amongst the young and homeless is at least twice as common as among their non-homeless peers (Flemen, 1997).

of multiple referrals and dissemination of good practice initiatives are starting points for a better service to this group of users. The increasing awareness of both purchasers and providers of the particular needs of this group may unlock additional resources.

Community care - still more problems than answers?

Several years into the community care changes, one can see clear trends emerging in London. Despite the overall contraction of the market, the majority of services have survived with a consolidation by the major providers - apa, Turning Point, Cranstoun Drug Services and Phoenix House. Local authorities have maintained their level of investment in drug and alcohol services, and reflecting their increased awareness of substance misuse problems, are investing more heavily in this area. The creation of Drug Action Teams has involved senior management in social services in the development of overall strategy. This should further reinforce the commitment of local authorities at senior level to develop these services further. The report of the *Task Force to Review Services for Drug Misusers* (Department of Health, 1996) is a further spur to the re-examination of the impact of residential rehabilitation.

Gaps

Unfortunately, gaps still remain in existing services, and financial pressures threaten to expose these further. Using resources effectively is therefore critical. Health commissioners and local authority commissioners are now meeting regularly, and joint commissioning both at a local level and on a London-wide basis could improve co-ordination and value for money. However, chaotic users, young people, women and children, and black users still have such an under-developed service framework that new investment will be required rather than recycling existing resources more effectively.

References

Department of Health (1996). *The Task Force to Review Services for Drug Misusers. Report of an Independent Review of Drug Treatment Services in England*. Wetherby: Department of Health.

Duke, P.J., Pantelis, C. and Barnes, T. (1994). South Westminster schziophrenia survey. Alcohol use and its relationship to symptoms, tardive dyskinesia and illness onset. *British Journal of Psychiatry,* 150, 328-329.

Flemen, K. (1997). *Smoke and Whispers.* London: Hungerford Drug Project.

London Drug Policy Forum (1993). *Drugs and the Community - What Local Authorities Can Do.* London: Corporation of London.

DRUGS PREVENTION AND EDUCATION

John Dunworth and Steve Tippell
North-West and North-East London Drug Prevention
Teams

Sections

Drugs prevention and education - a renewal of interest

Recent years have witnessed important changes in the nature and extent of drug use in the UK. Accompanying these changes has been a renewal of interest in the role of prevention and education in tackling drug use. This was publicly consolidated in the 1995 Government White Paper, *Tackling Drugs Together* (HMSO, 1995). This re-iterated the need for a renewed national emphasis on prevention and education, whilst calling for this to be translated into effective action at a local level.

Since 1990, the Home Office Drugs Prevention Initiative (DPI) has been working in London and elsewhere to develop and test new approaches to community-based drugs prevention. Although drugs education in schools and other settings comprises an important element of this work, the DPI has embraced work within wider communities and neighbourhoods. The DPI also continues to target certain groups, such as South Asian youth, who may benefit from specialised drugs education and prevention work.

This chapter considers the need in London for community-based drugs prevention and education programmes. It also traces the development of the DPI in the capital during the last eight years, and describes work recently conducted by the three London DPI teams. In addition, consideration is also given to the likely future of drugs prevention and education on both a national and pan-London stage.

The need for a community response

Until the rapid increase in drug use - particularly heroin - in the early 1980s, the main thrusts of government policy were essentially reactive: to reduce the supply of drugs (through law enforcement) and to provide health and socialcare for problematic drug users. As the number of users was relatively small at the time, the problem was consequently perceived to be mainly the responsibility of law enforcement and drugs agencies.

The need
The expansion of drug use in the early 1980s brought problematic users increasingly into contact with the wider community. As a result, car crime, burglary and street prostitution quickly became synonymous in the public conscience with drug use. At the same time, 'recreational' use was also reported to have become an accepted part of mainstream youth culture, fuelling media and parental speculation that drugs were as much of a problem for London's suburbs as for its inner city areas. As existing drug service providers were primarily occupied with individuals and had little time or expertise to address wider community issues, it became clear to the Government that these factors required a specialist community response.

The response
To complement its response to combating crime and promoting community action through neighbourhood watch schemes, police consultative committees and the Safer Cities Programme,

Box 5.1
What are drugs
prevention and
drugs education?

What are drugs prevention and drugs education?

Definition

The terms 'drugs prevention' and 'drugs education' are often used interchangeably. However, drugs education generally has a specific focus - be it a particular topic area or target group - and has outcomes which can, to some extent, be measured (such as increased awareness or knowledge). These outcomes may also have a preventative effect in themselves. Drugs prevention has a much wider remit and approach - often with drugs education comprising one element of this approach - which attempts to prevent or change certain behaviours by taking into account wider community contexts, influences and interactions.

Application

The terms 'drugs prevention' and 'drugs education' are often used to describe a range of activities and purposes which aim to:
• Raise awareness of drugs and the effects of drug use.
• Help people to make informed choices about drug use.
• Advise people where they can get help and information about drug use.
• Discourage people from ever starting to use drugs.
• Persuade those already using to stop.
• Discourage those already using from progressing to other more harmful, drugs.
• Persuade those already using to do so more safely ('harm reduction').

This often involves:
• Providing information on drugs and drug misuse.
• Emphasising the importance of personal skills and values.
• Developing the skills needed to avoid 'risk situations' which could lead to drug use.
• Promoting and offering alternatives to drug use.
• Using members of the target group to spread information/resources about drug use to other members ('peer led approaches').

Problems

Drugs prevention and drugs education approaches in London face a number of problems:
• The potential target audience for primary prevention activities - individuals, families or communities that already have, or may come into contact with, drugs and drug use - is much wider than approaches aimed at specific target groups.
• It can be difficult to measure the effect of prevention efforts.
• New 'partnerships' are often needed between agencies (such as non-statutory drug treatment services and bodies such as the police) to carry work forward. These can be difficult and time-consuming to arrange.
• There is a shortage of proven prevention and education models for informing effective local intervention.
• The question of who is responsible for providing and paying for drugs prevention and education is by no means clear.
• Prevention and education still carry the stigma of early attempts which promoted now discredited health slogans in an attempt to change attitudes and behaviour.

Source: Burgess (1997).

the Home Office established the Drugs Prevention Initiative in 1990. The DPI was charged with promoting community-based drugs prevention, and discovering which drugs prevention approaches were most effective. Although intended to complement other government drug programmes - including the Department of Health's publicity campaigns and the Department for Education and Employment's (DfEE) work in providing drugs education programmes in schools - it aimed to base its prevention efforts firmly within communities. This reflected a growing governmental interest in tackling root causes and helping local people to prevent local problems before they happened, rather than simply reacting to crises.

The DPI Phase I : 1990-1995

All of the problems outlined above were writ large in London. Consequently, the first phase of the DPI resulted in six of the twenty national teams being established in London. These were in Brent, Lewisham, Newham, Hackney, Lambeth and Southwark. Although the areas were centrally identified as having problems associated with drug use, the teams were established with the full co-operation of their respective local authorities. Each of these teams had at least three staff and received a grants budget of £75,000 per annum. This funding was used to 'pump-prime' the project (an initial amount of funding allowing the project to be fully established and run in the short-term, whilst longer-term finance was sought from other sources).

Local concerns

The work undertaken by the teams fell into two distinct categories: firstly, the development of local projects and initiatives; and secondly, the promotion of local partnerships and strategies. As there was no pre-set agenda of work, the teams established local advisory groups and began to identify local concerns and formulate programmes with which to address these. These grant funded projects involved many people who, although affected by drug misuse, had never been involved in drugs prevention before, such as parents, tenants groups, churches, local employers and businesses. In essence, Phase I concentrated on exploring the possibilities and scope for prevention, discovering the needs of particular areas, identifying how progress could be made, and more fundamentally, gauging the potential for community involvement.

Projects

Several hundred projects were grant aided by the DPI in London between 1990 and 1995, including telephone information lines, arrest referral schemes, competitions, 'fun-runs', community fetes on housing estates, and localised training courses.

The six London teams also performed a significant role in providing a focal point for prevention activity by pulling together new partnerships. These partnerships helped bridge existing drug agency boundaries and allowed issues relating to problem drug use to be approached from a wider angle. Examples of this work in London were the partnerships formed around the Brixton Drugs Project in Lambeth, Southwark's arrest referral scheme and Hackney's Kingsmead Estate project. In all of these partnerships the six teams played a significant co-ordinating and supportive role.

Evaluation

Much of the DPI's work was independently evaluated and much of the good practice identified from this has been disseminated in a series of DPI papers available from the Central Drugs Prevention Unit. However, these reviews also indicated that more time was needed to develop larger projects over a longer time scale in order to identify more precisely what worked. These ideas and projects were refined into a prevention agenda which formed the basis of Phase II of the DPI's programme of work.

Phase II: 1995-1999

To achieve the core aims of the Phase II agenda by 1999 (Box 5.2), the DPI had to decide which mechanisms and configuration of teams would be best employed to deliver a national programme with a budget of £5.9 million per annum. In London this meant extending cover to all the Inner London boroughs. Consequently, there are now three teams, each with an annual grants budget of £150,000 (Box 5.3 overleaf).

Each of the London teams has three or more major projects within the DPI programme. Deciding which projects to initially pursue was based on the expertise and interest within the teams, community and local authority concerns, opportunities for learning with specific agencies, as well as the willingness of local Drug Action Teams (DATs) and Drug Reference Groups (DRGs) to work with the DPI. However, in all three teams, the overall objective was the same: to develop and sustain the drugs prevention and education elements outlined in *Tackling Drugs Together*.

Box 5.2
The DPI Phase II agenda

The DPI Phase II agenda

The core objective of Phase II is to:

'establish whether and how different combinations of approaches, targets and settings can have a positive impact on young peoples' knowledge, attitudes and behaviour in relation to drugs misuse. The preventative impact may take the form of continued abstinence; delayed onset of evidence of escalation; or reduced misuse, including a return to abstinence'.

Its ultimate aim is to show, by 1999, what local people working together with others in their communities can do to prevent young people from misusing drugs. This includes:

• What parents can do to reduce risks to their children, and what support for parents will assist in this work?
• What community groups can do to reduce drug misuse in their neighbourhood?
• What support the community can provide for schools-based drugs education?
• How best to engage young people in drugs prevention activities outside school?
• What impact criminal justice agencies can have on problematic drug use?
• How best to access and engage people from ethnically and culturally diverse groups?
• Whether integrating different approaches to drugs prevention increases the overall impact?

Each team has continued this work by providing practical assistance to local agencies and organisations, and ensuring that local people are fully engaged within this process. In addition, all the DPI teams provide advice to DATs and DRGs in their areas, as well as a wide range of other agencies and community organisations. This consultancy work is supported by a small grants budget which is often spent 'working up' local ideas and initiatives.

All of the local projects throughout the DPI are brought together nationally in Corporate Learning Groups (CLGs). There are 13 national CLGs which meet regularly to ensure that the DPI programme, as a whole, is continuing to address the questions set by the programme of work, and to share experiences and learning.

Box 5.3
Phase II London
DPI teams (1995-
1999)

Phase II London DPI teams (1995-1999)

- **South London**: Wandsworth; Lambeth; Southwark; Lewisham and Greenwich.
- **North-East London**: Camden; Islington; Haringey; Hackney; Tower Hamlets; and Newham.
- **North-West London**: Brent; Ealing; Hammersmith; Kensington and Chelsea, and the City of Westminster.

Phase II: South London

The South London team has concentrated on developing two demonstration projects. These cover interventions in: the criminal justice system; and community education, information provision and training.

South London drugs referral project

The South London team has built on the foundations of an 'arrest referral' scheme (Chapter 2 and 6) originally set up in Southwark. The team has aimed to facilitate the referral of individuals in contact with criminal justice agencies to drug treatment and information services. In practice, this has meant establishing and co-ordinating multi-agency partnerships across South London between drug agencies, probation services, police stations, courts, prisons and local health authorities. The project is steered by representatives from the South London region who have obtained funding for six dedicated criminal justice workers. Each of the five boroughs covered by the South London team has at least one dedicated criminal justice worker, with Wandsworth employing two workers.

Police and courts
A police arrest referral scheme has been operational across all five boroughs since May 1997, whilst the development of court referral schemes has been guided by survey results from the Western and Camberwell Green Magistrates' Courts. This survey proposed that a range of court staff should receive basic referral training as opposed to employing a dedicated court referral worker. Early indications suggest that the larger number of trained staff has improved the rate of 'hard to reach' offenders - those who might otherwise evade the attention of criminal justice staff - being referred to appropriate treatment and care agencies.

Probation and prison

Probation referral, aimed at people serving community sentences, has been operational in all five boroughs during 1997. Negotiations with South London prison representatives from Brixton, Belmarsh and Wandsworth have resulted in the establishment of a prison referral service. Target groups for this project have included remand prisoners (those awaiting trial or sentencing), those serving sentences of under twelve months and those due for release.

Key finding

By the 30th of September 1997, 291 referrals had been received by the South London Drugs Referral Project. The number of enquiries received by the project for information and advice was almost twice this figure.

South London education, information and training project

This project comprises a library and resource centre, a community education and arts project, and training courses.

Library Resource Centre

The Library Resource Centre has now been established, providing community agencies and individuals with an easily accessible database of drug-related materials and resources.

Drugs Scenes

The 'Drug Scenes' community education and arts project, seeks to complement drugs education and prevention taking place in schools by offering additional opportunities for 'information giving' within the community. The project also attempts to evaluate the value and outcomes of young people receiving the same information from two different sources.

So far, the project has produced two different forms of information: a 'parents handbook' (which offers a variety of resources that parents can use to talk realistically and comprehensively to their children about drugs and solvents); and a youth workers handbook (explaining how a balance can be struck between client confidentiality and the wider care of a young person).

During 1997, the project also offered training, information and support to teachers, parents and youth workers wishing to use 'Drugs Scenes' as a vehicle for drugs education. This took place in selected schools and youth centres across the team's five boroughs.

Training

The team and its partners have also developed an induction training pack for local partnerships wishing to become involved in planning and implementing drugs prevention projects and strategies. The pack includes: good practice guidelines for planning and implementing a training course; exercises on basic drugs knowledge, attitudes and the law; a 'how to work in partnerships' and 'undertaking needs assessment' guide; and post-course evaluation. The pack is designed in such a way that courses can be modified according to the requirements of the particular target group.

Phase II: North-East London

The North-East London team have concentrated on developing local information campaigns, supporting drugs education in schools, and integrating drugs prevention into wider local programmes of social and economic regeneration.

Information action

The team is developing a series of information campaigns on the theme of young people, drugs and the law. This is in response to concern expressed by local police and youth services about the large number of young people arrested for drug-related offences. It was felt that the deterrent of the law was reduced simply because young people were not aware of the penalties involved. Phase one of the project confirmed this initial insight. Research conducted for the team in East London by Middlesex University, found that although most of the five-hundred 13 to 17 year olds questioned reported having a good understanding of the law, they tended to significantly under-estimate the legal penalties associated with a number of commonly used drugs.

The findings of this research have been used to develop information campaigns which employ 'quiz cards' relating to aspects of the law on drugs. Subsequent research with sample groups exposed to these campaigns has indicated significant improvements in knowledge levels. The findings from this are now being used to inform the second phase of the project which focuses on young people 'at risk' and those individuals who can influence young peoples' opinions about drugs. The ultimate aim of the project is to provide clear guidance to DATs on how to develop effective local drugs information campaigns across a range of issues.

Drugs Education Teams

The team has established a multi-agency Drugs Education Team in two boroughs (Hackney and Haringey) to provide practical assistance to schools in developing both their drugs education programmes, and policies for dealing with drug-related incidents. The team recognised that although many agencies, including the police and drugs services, already provided some drugs education in schools, these efforts were not co-ordinated. As a result, pupils sometimes received inconsistent messages from a number of different sources, while teachers tended to rely on outside speakers rather than developing their own expertise in delivering drugs education.

Role

The project has addressed this problem by inviting community-based agencies to work in schools as part of a Drugs Education Team. Team members include police officers, drugs service staff, school nurses and sessional workers. These are trained to deliver specially designed programmes of drugs education based on best practice and in line with DfEE guidance. Teachers remain in the classroom and take part in these sessions so that they can conduct follow-up lessons. Drugs Education Teams are now extending their role to offer schools a wider range of services, including in-service teacher training, sessions with parents and advice on policy development.

Coverage

The Drugs Education Teams have mainly concentrated on work in primary schools but also work in secondary and special needs schools. Since January 1995, the Hackney Drugs Education Team has worked in 61 of the Borough's 72 schools and more than 6,000 pupils have taken part in its programmes. The Haringey Drugs Education Team, which was implemented in February 1996, has entered 52 of the Borough's 62 schools, reaching over 5,000 pupils in its first year of operation. These schemes are run and funded in partnership with the health and education authorities in the two boroughs.

'Together We Can'

The team has also established a community-based drugs prevention project on the Aberfeldy housing estate in Tower Hamlets. This draws on the 'Together We Can' model used in the United States to tackle drug-related problems as part of a wider community regeneration programme. This has been developed in partnership with the Tower Hamlets DAT and local authority.

The project has brought together residents and local agencies to develop and implement action plans which tackle the area's social and environmental problems, including measures to prevent drugs misuse. This has lead to a series of community initiatives including: a drugs education programme in a local primary school; a support group for parents; improved recreational facilities for young people; initiatives to reduce traffic nuisance; and an environmental improvement scheme. These measures run alongside planned housing and improvement programmes and schemes to improve training and job opportunities for local residents.

Phase II: North-West London

The team has focused on four projects which in turn address: supporting school policies; targeting young people excluded from school; information and communications needs of specific target groups; and training for professionals.

Supporting school policies

In 1995, the DfEE published the circular 'Drugs Prevention in Schools. (DfEE, 1995) This recommended that every school should develop a drugs education policy which covers the teaching of drugs education and the management of drug-related incidents. Recognising the difficulties that some schools would face in doing this, the North-West London team responded in three main ways.

Firstly, the team considered drugs education and prevention issues evident in each of its five areas, resulting in the production of local guidelines for schools. Secondly, to complement this work, external consultants were

funded by the team to work with selected schools to produce 'model drugs policies' which could be replicated across all the schools in each borough. This programme began in September 1996 and was planned to finish in April 1998. Thirdly, a further project, 'The Family Fact File', expands upon many of the themes outlined in the school drugs policies and aims to encourage parents to engage in discussions with their children about drugs. This has been operational in Hammersmith and Fulham, Ealing, Hounslow, Brent and Harrow.

School exclusions

The team also works with eight Pupil Referral Units across the region, providing a series of interventions for young people excluded from school for a variety of reasons including drug misuse. These interventions include: an assessment process for teachers and project workers looking at the beliefs, motivations and behaviour of young people in the units; a drugs education and life skills programme for pupils at the units; and a diversionary package for placing young people in training and potential work placements.

The team ultimately aim to develop the education programme and diversionary package into models of 'good practice'. These models will be used with Pupil Referral Units and other services in order to discover which interventions are most effective in engaging young people in drugs prevention. A significant revision to the package has been the introduction of course modules which lead to Youth Achievement Awards. The availability of such awards provides opportunities for individuals to access a range of vocational and leisure activities.

Information and communication

Given the high profile of the Department of Health's information campaigns, the North-West team identified target groups deemed to be 'high risk' in terms of drug use.

The project for 9 to 11 year olds is an audio cassette which uses a soap opera format to discuss and explore problems and dilemmas around drugs, sex, bullying and moving school. For this project, the team is working in partnership with the National Society for the Prevention of Cruelty to Children, National Children's Homes and Childline. The project has been piloted in one school and discussion arising from this looks likely to result in the project being extended to reach a wider audience.

A piece of formative research has also been commissioned to look at the perceptions of drugs by 11 to 14 year old South Asian boys and to highlight how drugs and drugs information are perceived by their parents. Consequently, the research will consider on how best to target such a campaign within Asian communities.

Training for professionals

Given the partnership approach adopted by the DPI, discussions with other related professionals revealed a gap in focused training for two important players in the drugs field: social workers and teachers. Consequently, the team developed two training programmes which integrate drugs within the demands of these larger professional frameworks.

Firstly, although it is recognised that a high percentage of case work in all divisions of social work practice has a drugs and alcohol dimension, there is very little drug input in the Certificate of Qualification in Social Work (CQSW) basic training. The team, in partnership with the University of North London and the Royal Borough of Kensington and Chelsea, has developed a Post Qualifying Award in working with drug using parents. Of the five modules comprising this award, one is devoted purely to drug issues.

Secondly, as a means of supporting drugs education within schools, the team (in conjunction with Roehampton Institute) have also created a drugs education course aimed at teachers and other drug educators. The course, which began its second year in January 1998, critically examines the theory behind drugs education and helps participants construct a drugs education course for their particular school.

Drugs education and the DPI

In Phase II of the Drugs Prevention Initiative, drugs education remains high on the agenda. This follows on from Phase I, where the DPI frequently became involved in drugs education issues in response to the local concerns expressed through partnership work with schools and Local Education Authorities (LEAs). This work generated a number of local drugs education and policy guidance materials, with schools acting as a focal point for community activity and information dissemination.

However, while drugs education is an important part of the national DPI strategy, it should not be mistaken for prevention which goes much wider. Drugs education is a specific discipline, with distinctive characteristics and outcomes, such as increased awareness and knowledge, which are worthwhile in themselves and may have a preventive effect.

Background

Drugs education as a focused activity began in the mid 1980s with the Department for Education's response to a noted increase in heroin use by young people. Through the provision of the Education Support Grant, LEAs were able to employ drugs education co-ordinators who worked with a number of local agencies and provided advice, drugs training and support to teachers and youth workers.

At the time, however, concern was voiced that focusing on drugs as a single issue was perhaps counter productive - instead, it was claimed, drug use education should be integrated into the general health context of young people's lives. This meant relating drug misuse to issues such as sexual health, HIV/AIDS, alcohol and tobacco misuse.

The Department for Education responded to this by introducing the Grant for Education, Support and Training (GEST) programmes. These grants supported the wider aspects of health education. In turn, this was supported by additional grants for in-service training for professionals on drug related issues.

Integration

The move towards the integration of drugs education into a wider educational programme was deepened by the introduction of the National Curriculum and the National Curriculum Council (NCC) 'Curriculum Guidance 5 Health Education' (NCC, 1990). This gave guidance to educators on planning and implementing drugs education programmes and stated what should be covered at all four key stages of a young person's education (ages 7, 9, 11 and 16). Although firmly placed within the realm of science teaching, this was important in making drugs education a statutory requirement in all schools.

Funding

GEST funding was only ever intended as a 'pump-priming' grant, requiring LEAs to fund further educational activities through existing school resources or other alternative sources. Furthermore, the increasing establishment of drugs education within the teaching curriculum - rather than as a special or 'one-off' lesson - meant it now had to compete for existing resources with other subjects within the school curriculum.

The 1996/97 GEST money was open to competitive bids from LEAs and, in order to win such money, LEAs and schools had to increasingly rely on local alliances with health authorities, health promotion departments, the police and other drug service providers to deliver appropriate and cost-effective drugs education programmes. Although the DfEE have now replaced GEST with the 'Standards Fund', it remains to be seen whether the allocation of a set amount of money to each school will reduce the previous reliance on such external alliances.

Quality

Presently, a vast sea of drugs education materials and resources are available, all of which promote a slightly different focus and agenda. However, even with NCC and DPI guidance, no real quality standard exists to help schools judge which of these materials are appropriate and effective. Furthermore, all the materials in the world cannot substitute for good teaching, and such teaching needs to be linked to the wider issue of Personal Health and Social Education (PHSE). Arguably, the real challenge for the future of drugs education is raising the status of PHSE to an integral part of the core curriculum.

Prevention and education: end of term report

This chapter has highlighted how the changing nature and extent of drug use has prompted the need to re-evaluate how drug issues are viewed and responded to. The DPI, in adopting a wider outlook and community approach to the problem, has formed an important part of this new response. It is hoped that this programme of work will continue to provide important indicators on the effectiveness of such an approach.

In terms of London, the DPI 'experiment' has concentrated much of its resources and time on assisting schools and local authorities to construct effective drug policies and provide drugs education at all four key stages of the curriculum. This work has been complemented further by wider community initiatives which seek to instil a stronger sense of individual and social responsibility about drug use. The experience to date of the three London teams described above, highlights not only the demanding philosophy and nature of this community approach, but also what can be achieved through the creation of new partnerships.

The future challenge

Already, considerable amounts of money have been spent on drugs prevention and education, and the number of departments currently funding initiatives is impressive (Box 5.4 opposite). Consequently, the challenge for the short-term is clear: how to make the best use of these available resources and past experiences, and to ensure that these are developed into coherent and effective prevention approaches across London and the UK.

However, the long-term challenge is not as clear. As the detail and practice of the succesor to *Tackling Drugs Together* unfolds it will be interesting to see if this document re-iterates and extends the role previously allocated to drugs prevention and education in *Tackling Drugs Together*. Furthermore, with the expiration of the DPI contract in 1999, the further question to be answered by the new strategy is not

Box 5.4
The DPI's funding
base

The DPI's funding base

- DPI's £5.9 million per annum.
- Department of Health (through the Health Education Authority).
- Department for Education and Employment (through GEST and the Standards Fund).
- Government Offices for the Region (through the Single Regeneration Budget Challenge Fund).
- National Lottery Charities Board.
- Drugs Challenge Fund (enabling DATs to fund prevention activities).

only '*how*' drugs prevention and education will be sustained in the future, but also by '*whom*'? The answers to these questions will have significant repercussions for the future of drugs prevention and education both on a national and pan-London basis.

References

Burgess, R. (1997). Deconstructing drug prevention: towards an alternative purpose. *Drugs: Education, Prevention and Policy*, 4, 271-284.

HMSO (1995). *Tackling Drugs Together: A Strategy For England 1995-1998*. London: HMSO.

DfEE (1995). *Drugs Prevention in Schools*. Department for Education and Employment Circular 4/95.

National Curriculum and the National Curriculum Council (1990). *Curriculum Guidance 5: Health Education*. York: NCC.

ASPECTS OF POLICING: HARM PRODUCTION OR HARM REDUCTION?

Geoff Monaghan
Strategic Analysis Unit, Directorate of Intelligence,
New Scotland Yard, Metropolitan Police Service

Sections

Beyond crime and punishment

Although the enforcement of the law is still the primary responsibility of both the Metropolitan Police Service (MPS) and the City of London Police, drug-related policing in the capital goes far beyond the commonly accepted notion of crime and punishment. This chapter attempts to cover some of the many aspects of the capital's policing story.

Section one of the chapter gives an overview of the enforcement aspects of drug-related policing in London and outlines the capital's policing resources and structure. Section two then describes the development of a formal policing drugs strategy in England and details how this was translated to the MPS area. Section three concludes by re-addressing a number of themes familiar to many in the drugs field - harm reduction, intervention development, and relevant legal issues - from a police perspective. By 'turning the tables' this section provides an unusual variation on familiar themes.

Section one: policing the capital

Policing in London requires an enormous amount of resources. Whilst the City of London Police are confined to the Corporation of London's 'square mile', the MPS cover a larger area extending beyond the borders of London and into parts of the surrounding counties (Map 6.1). There are also other police forces operating in the capital, such as the British Transport Police, Royal Parks Constabulary, Ministry of Defence Police and various small police units operated by a number of London boroughs.

In 1995, one quarter of the police officers in England and Wales reported for duty in the capital (Church and Holding , 1997). If examined in terms of staffing levels per 100,000 of the population, this means that London had one and a half times the number of officers found elsewhere in England and Wales, and twice the number of civilian staff (Church and Holding, 1997). These higher levels can be partly accounted for by the areas of high deprivation found in Inner London. Here, the combination of intensified social problems and an arguably more vulnerable population require more intensive, proactive methods of policing. However the presence of royalty, Parliament, the central law courts and diplomatic centres of operation also account for a significant percentage of officers and civilian staff. In addition, the National Identification Service (NIS) is located at New Scotland Yard and provides several national services to all police forces, including the Missing Persons Bureau and the management of the National Criminal Record Office and National Fingerprint Collection.

Key findings

In 1995/96, there were a total of 28,213 police officers in the two main London police services, or 378 per 100,000 of the population. This is one and a half times higher than the complement found in England and Wales as a whole, which averaged 242 officers per 100,000 of the population (Church and Holding, 1997).

On the 31st of March 1997, 27,166 police officers were working in the MPS area (MPS, 1997). In 1998, the City of London Police had around 860 officers (City of London Police Press Office, 1998).

MPS structure

There are numerous organisational groups and operational units within the overall MPS structure. As it is not possible to cover all of these, this section outlines those most prominently involved in drug-related enforcement activities.

Home Secretary

Like all police forces in England and Wales, the MPS operate within the broader context of the national law enforcement strategy and are answerable to the Home Secretary (currently Jack Straw). The Home Secretary is responsible for the national policing framework and the development of key objectives and performance indicators. The misuse of drugs and drug-related crime are covered under key objective number three: 'to target and prevent crimes which are a particular problem, including drug-related criminality, in partnership with the public and local agencies' (MPS, 1996). The proposed national key performance indicator for this is the number of arrests and disposals of offences under the *Misuse of*

Box 6.2
Selective overview
of Metropolitan
Police Service
structure

Selective overview of Metropolitan Police Service structure

Government
Home Secretary - responsible for national policing framework and also is the policing authority for London. Assisted in the latter role by the Metropolitan Police Committee.

Senior management
Commissioner
Deputy Commissioner

Five policing areas
The MPS is split into five policing areas. Each of these is headed by an Assistant Commissioner who is responsible for a particular policing activity or 'portfolio'. The head of Area Five is currently responsible for the MPS Drugs Strategy. Each policing area contains a dedicated Drugs Squad and Area Chemist Inspecting Officers. The latter inspect retail chemists supplying controlled drugs (Chapter 3).

63 policing divisions
The five areas are comprised of 63 divisions (a group of one or more stations). Some of these divisions operate their own drug unit.

Specialist units
There are a number of specialist drug-related units in the MPS including: the Organised Crime Group; SO10 (Covert Operations Unit); SO11 (Directorate of Intelligence Branch); Chemical and Pharmaceutical Intelligence Unit; Crimestoppers Unit; and CO54 (Specialist Search Dogs).

External assistance
The National Criminal Intelligence Service (NCIS) Drugs Unit provides strategic and tactical assessments, and acts as a focal point for intelligence relating to drug production.

Map 6.1 Metropolitan Police Service areas and divisions

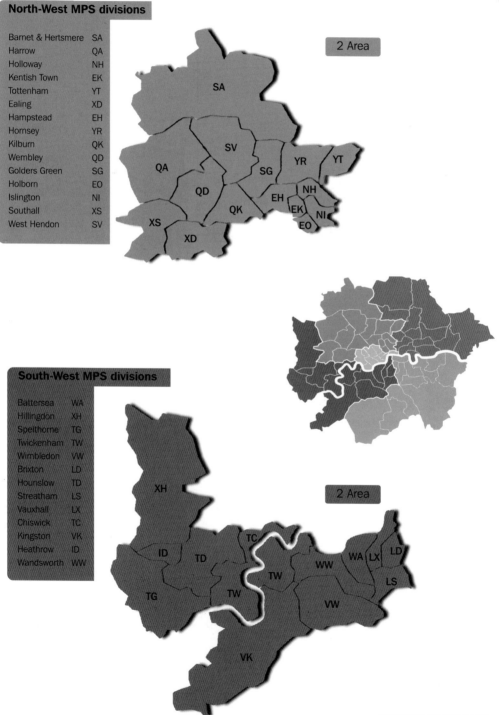

North-West MPS divisions

Barnet & Hertsmere	SA
Harrow	QA
Holloway	NH
Kentish Town	EK
Tottenham	YT
Ealing	XD
Hampstead	EH
Hornsey	YR
Kilburn	QK
Wembley	QD
Golders Green	SG
Holborn	EO
Islington	NI
Southall	XS
West Hendon	SV

South-West MPS divisions

Battersea	WA
Hillingdon	XH
Spelthorne	TG
Twickenham	TW
Wimbledon	VW
Brixton	LD
Hounslow	TD
Streatham	LS
Vauxhall	LX
Chiswick	TC
Kingston	VK
Heathrow	ID
Wandsworth	WW

2 Area

2 Area

Notes: CITY is City of London Police.

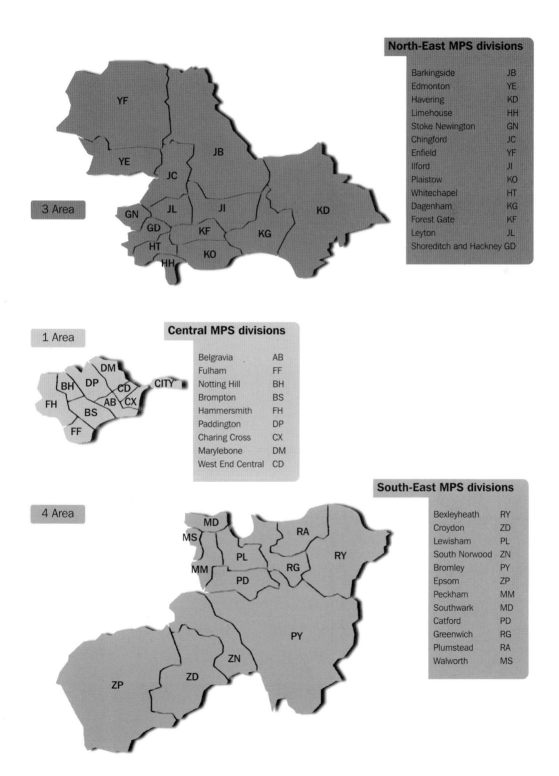

North-East MPS divisions

Barkingside	JB
Edmonton	YE
Havering	KD
Limehouse	HH
Stoke Newington	GN
Chingford	JC
Enfield	YF
Ilford	JI
Plaistow	KO
Whitechapel	HT
Dagenham	KG
Forest Gate	KF
Leyton	JL
Shoreditch and Hackney	GD

3 Area

Central MPS divisions

Belgravia	AB
Fulham	FF
Notting Hill	BH
Brompton	BS
Hammersmith	FH
Paddington	DP
Charing Cross	CX
Marylebone	DM
West End Central	CD

1 Area

4 Area

South-East MPS divisions

Bexleyheath	RY
Croydon	ZD
Lewisham	PL
South Norwood	ZN
Bromley	PY
Epsom	ZP
Peckham	MM
Southwark	MD
Catford	PD
Greenwich	RG
Plumstead	RA
Walworth	MS

Drugs Act 1971 per 1,000 population. However, as in other regional police services in England, this performance indicator has not been adopted by the MPS.

The MPS enjoys a special relationship with the Home Secretary. Unlike police forces outside of the capital, which report to overseeing policing authorities comprised of councillors, magistrates and other independent persons, London's policing authority *is* the Home Secretary. The Home Secretary is assisted by the Metropolitan Police Committee, which is primarily concerned with agreeing MPS objectives and monitoring performance. The policing authority for the City of London Police is a committee of the Corporation of London and includes councillors and magistrates.

Senior management

The Commissioner of the MPS is Sir Paul Condon Q.P.M., M.A. and the Deputy Commissioner is Sir Brian Hayes C.B.E., Q.P.M. B.A. To make the policing of the MPS manageable it has been divided into five geographic areas each of which is commanded by an Assistant Commissioner (AC) with their own port-

Key findings

The annual UK expenditure on tackling drugs through enforcement is not known, but it is estimated that about £209 million is spent on enforcement action by the police and customs, with a further £137 million on the prosecution of drug offenders, prison places, and non-custodial provision (ISDD, 1996).

Policing is financed by central government grants and council tax. In 1997/98, the estimated cost of the MPS came to approximately £1,807 million, or £258 per head of the capital's population (MPS, 1996).

folio of responsibilities (Box 6.3). AC Dennis O'Connor Q.P.M. M.Sc. B.Ed. has overall responsibility for the development and implementation of the *MPS Drugs Strategy*. In addition to the five area Assistant Commissioners, AC David Veness Q.P.M. is Head of Specialist Operations (SO).

Area Drug Squads and Chemist Inspecting Officers (CIOs)

Each of the five policing areas has a dedicated Drugs Squad. Established in 1987, the main aim of the squads is to

**Box 6.3
Metropolitan
Police Service:
areas and
Assistant
Commissioners**

Metropolitan Police Service: areas and Assistant Commissioners

1 Area (Central): AC Tony Speed Q.P.M. Public Order, Vice and Licensing Portfolio.

2 Area (North-West): AC Paul Manning Q.P.M., M.Sc. Head of 24 Hour Response and Traffic Portfolio.

3 Area (North-East): AC Anderson Dunn Q.P.M., LL.B. the Criminal Justice Portfolio.

4 Area (South-East): AC Ian Johnston Q.P.M., B.Sc. Crime Operation Portfolio.

5 Area (South-West): AC Dennis O'Connor Q.P.M., M.Sc., B.Ed. Community Safety and Partnership Portfolio.

target 'middle-tier' drug traffickers. These traffickers are defined as being involved in activities beyond the operational capabilities or resources of individual policing divisions. Each squad is comprised of a Detective Inspector and a number of Sergeants and Constables. In 1997, a total of five Detective Inspectors, 13 Sergeants and 76 Constables were employed by the five MPS Area Drug Squads.

In the MPS, CIOs are police officers specially trained to carry out the inspections of retail chemists. Since 1917, the functions of CIOs have predominantly fallen under five headings: inspection; investigation; intelligence gathering; crime prevention; and liaison. Under the *Misuse of Drugs Act 1971* and associated regulations, CIOs are empowered to examine the stock records of retail chemists to ensure that controlled drugs are only sold or supplied as authorised. The inspection process often leads to the arrest and prosecution of chemists and other professionals.

Key finding

In 1996, CIOs in 3 Area carried out 118 inspections and conducted 32 investigations. This work resulted in 11 arrests and 167 offences were solved.

Divisional drug units

Somewhat against the current trend, a few MPS divisions (a group of one or more stations) run small dedicated drug units (such as the Southwark Division in South East London which is comprised of one Sergeant and four Constables). Given the prevalence of drug misuse and related offending in London, it is not surprising that divisional officers often encounter drug offenders in the course of their duties. At present, however, there is little in the way of systematic operational tactics aimed at 'hard-core'

drug offenders and the majority of arrests at divisional level involve the possession of cannabis. Numerous MPS initiatives have sought to re-address this imbalance and probably the best example of this is Operation Welwyn. This initiative, in the Kings Cross area of London started in January 1992 and aims to suppress an active street-level drug market. Employing tactics such as restricting licenses to fast-food outlets known to be frequented by drug traffickers, and using police officers incognito to purchase drugs for evidential purposes, Operation Welwyn has, so far, resulted in around 376 arrests. Significantly, the majority of these have been for drug trafficking offences involving heroin and crack.

Specialist operations units

The Operational Command Unit (OCU) is the fundamental policing unit in London. It refers either to a division or to a specialist operational unit based centrally or at area level.

Organised Crime Group (OCG)

The aim of the OCG is to investigate specified serious offences (such as blackmail and kidnapping). The OCG has a corporate responsibility to co-operate and liaise with overseas law enforcement agencies to counter international crime. Much of its work is now drug-related and the OCG operational teams, supported by its intelligence units, arrested a number of major heroin and opium drug traffickers in 1997 and early 1998.

SO10 (Covert Operations Unit)

The unit has responsibility for co-ordinating all MPS covert operations and maintains the service's central database of informants. An additional function of the unit is to develop and provide undercover training. In the period April

1997 to October 1997, a total of 322 covert operations were conducted. Many of these operations were drug-related and in 44 cases officers were authorised to buy small amounts of Class A and B drugs from traffickers for evidential purposes.

SO11 (Directorate of Intelligence)

The main purpose of SO11 is to collect information and intelligence on major criminals active in London. The branch comprises a number of units which provide professional support, assistance and advice throughout the MPS. SO11 also provides logistical support and expertise in cases of blackmail and kidnapping. The following SO11 units are engaged in aspects of drug enforcement: Special Intelligence Section (SIS); Chemical and Pharmaceutical Intelligence Unit (CPIU); and the Crimestoppers Unit.

The three teams comprising the SIS (A, B and C) undertake the development of operational intelligence 'packages' against major criminals. They also provide the MPS Commissioner with a pan-London picture of organised crime. Team C (formerly the Drugs Related Violence Intelligence Unit) concentrate on ethnic organised crime groups - primarily Jamaican cocaine traffickers, Turkish heroin traffickers and South-East Asian criminals. The SIS work closely with HM Customs and Excise, NCIS, the South-East Regional Crime Squad and the British Security Services.

The CPIU was set up in July 1995

Key finding

In the period April 1997 to October 1997, SIS officers disseminated intelligence packages resulting in the seizure of 1,417 kilogrammes of cannabis, 134 kilogrammes of heroin and nine kilogrammes of cocaine.

Key findings

Information supplied through the Crimestoppers Unit has resulted, for example, in: four males being arrested in March 1997 for importation of 4.5 kilogrammes of cocaine with a 'street value' of around £350,000; a male arrested in possession of cannabis resin with intent to supply and a handgun in June 1997; and in August 1997 a male arrested in possession of cocaine with intent to supply and a handgun.

As a result of anonymous tip-offs to the Crimestoppers Unit, 385 people have been arrested in London in the last year for crimes, ranging from murder to fraud, of which 235 were drug traffickers (MPS, .5.1./1998).

and acts as a focal point for intelligence on the illicit diversion of pharmaceutical drugs (such as methadone, pethidine and benzodiazapines). It also gathers intelligence on the illicit diversion of chemicals used in the production of controlled drugs. In addition, the unit has responsibility for maintaining the 12,353 records held on the MPS 'addict database'. The database is similar to the Home Office Addicts Index (Chapter 12) in that it collates information on people in the London area who are problematically using one of 14 controlled drugs. This information is identified from reports submitted by Area Chemist Inspecting Officers.

The Crimestoppers Unit collects and disseminates anonymous information relating to criminal activity. The majority of intelligence received by the unit is drug-related. Crimestoppers has provided a powerful stimulus to the 1996 MPS initiative to tackle drug trafficking and related offending, 'Operation Crackdown'.

Specialist search dogs (CO54)

Drugs dogs were first used by the MPS in the East End of London in 1965 (Mahir, 1970). At that time two dogs had been trained to detect cannabis, however, CO54 now has 16 dogs at its disposal specially trained in the detection of controlled drugs. Dogs in the unit are also trained to detect explosives and firearms.

National Criminal Intelligence Service (NCIS)

NCIS provide external strategic assistance and information to MPS activities. Created in 1992, NCIS is responsible for the collection, analysis, research and dissemination of intelligence relating to major criminals involved in serious crime, including drug

trafficking. Its headquarters are located in London and there are five regional offices. NCIS staff are comprised of 274 police posts, 49 Customs and Excise posts and 306 support staff drawn from a variety of places including the Home Office, local authorities and the MPS (NCIS, 1997).

The NCIS Drugs Unit provides strategic and tactical assessments in relation to drugs issues affecting the UK and in the preparation of threat assessments. The unit also acts as a focal point for intelligence in the illicit production of controlled drugs and the purchase of precursor chemicals.

Section two: Tackling Drugs Together and drug-related crime

Prior to the publication of *Tackling Drugs Together* in 1995, the English police service was not required to have an explicit or formal drugs strategy. Although drugs were already an aspect of most operational officers' daily work - with national policing objectives sitting alongside shifting local priorities such as 'drug-related violence' and the 'club scene' phenomenon - *Tackling Drugs Together* attempted to establish a common set of principles which all police services in England could align their work towards. These common principles were not, however, limited to the Police Service and other criminal justice agencies (i.e. HM Customs and Excise, the Prison Service, and Probation Service) were also obliged to adopt them.

The 'Statement of Purpose' outlined in *Tackling Drugs Together* (HMSO, 1995) (Box 6.4 overleaf) focused on three key areas, of which crime was one

(the other two being young people and public health). Significantly, these areas were inter-related, meaning that crime focused initiatives (such as reducing the incidence of drug-related crime) would also have to demonstrate attention had been paid to wider objectives such as protocols for dealing with young offenders involved in drug misuse, or broader public health considerations.

In addition to the overall Statement of Purpose, additional objectives in the area of crime and drugs were also provided. Criminal justice agencies were given the target of translating these objectives into explicit strategies, initiatives and performance indicators. This process began in 1995 and was timetabled to run until the end of 1997. It appears likely that the review of the progress made during this time will inform the successor to *Tackling Drugs Together* (HMSO, 1995).

Box 6.4
Drug-related crime
and Tackling Drugs
Together

Drug-related crime and Tackling Drugs Together

• **The Statement of Purpose**

To take effective action by vigorous law enforcement, accessible treatment and a new emphasis on education and prevention to:

Increase the safety of communities from drug-related crime.

Reduce the acceptability and availability of drugs to young people.

Reduce the health risks and other damage related to drug misuse.

• **Objectives in the area of crime**

See that the law is effectively enforced, especially against those involved in the supply and trafficking of illegal drugs.

Reduce the incidence of drug-related crime.

Reduce the public's fear of drug-related crime.

Reduce the level of drug misuse in prisons.

Source: HMSO (1995).

TDT and the Met

Tackling Drugs Together only provided a framework for criminal justice agencies to work within. Although its underlying principles applied to all agencies, both strategic and operational detail varied across agencies and regions. This variation is present in the *1996 MPS Drugs Strategy* (MPS, 1996) which reflects the unique demands of policing drug-related crime in the capital. Although a revised MPS strategy was released in April 1998 (see later), this has simply specified in more detail most of the areas already outlined in the 1996 strategy.

MPS drugs strategy

The establishment by March 1996 of drugs strategies by all police forces, probation services and prison establishments in England was required by *Tackling Drugs Together* (HMSO, 1995). Driven by a Service Priority 'to reduce the supply of illegal drugs and the demand for them', the *1996 MPS Drugs Strategy* is comprised of six core areas: enforcement; partnership; education; training and raised awareness; publicity; and performance measurement (MPS, 1996). A particular focus of the strategy is on Class A drugs - specifically heroin and crack cocaine - which were identified as causing problems on both individual (health risks) and community (violent and property crime) levels.

Enforcement

The development of work with the Home Office, NCIS and HMCE - particularly in the improvement of performance indicators - is a clear goal of the MPS strategy. However, an equal emphasis on community policing and enforcement is also struck. This involved the production of separate drugs strategies at a divisional and area level, as well as the development of local partnerships to ensure that drug-related police activity is sensitive to local needs and issues. All planned enforcement activity is underpinned by the MPS intelligence system developed by the Directorate of Intelligence.

Partnership

A major thrust of the MPS strategy is to develop partnerships with other agencies. The term partnership may be defined as an association between a number of individuals, groups and agencies to pursue a common goal. Multi-agency partnerships draw together the police with the non-statutory and private sectors, local authorities, schools, parents, health workers, and criminal justice agencies. Partnership strategy groups involve the police and representatives from health, education, probation, housing and social services. These groups provide a joint approach to community problems. In some cases, police personnel are also seconded to work alongside local authority community safety co-ordinators.

The focus for much partnership activity is through local Drug Action Teams (DATs) and Drug Reference Groups (DRGs) (Chapter 1). DATs are multi-agency groups which comprise senior representatives from health, local authorities and criminal justice agencies. Each DAT formulates action plans to tackle local drug problems and ensure that the policies and operations of the different organisations in an area are in line with each other. The MPS believe that its DAT representatives must be in a position to commit resources in order to help shape local policy. The MPS are also represented on DRGs, which consist of local experts from a variety of backgrounds who advise the local DAT.

Education

The MPS aim to support drugs education programmes both in school and non-school settings. Again, this is in accordance with wider objectives stated in *Tackling Drugs Together* (HMSO, 1995). These efforts are undertaken through the MPS Schools Involvement Programme and are co-ordinated by CO20 (Partnership and Community Safety).

In respect of school settings, the MPS offer drug education programmes covering: education initiatives (youth action groups, junior citizens schemes); raising awareness amongst staff and parents; participating in joint training efforts with teachers and other representatives; contributing to Local Education Authority school drug policies and education programmes and helping to manage drug-related incidents (Chapter 5). MPS Schools Involvement Officers may also offer input on local drug trends, drug recognition, and the health and social consequences of drug use.

Contact outside of school settings may orbit around work with DATs and DRGs, raising support and awareness amongst the local business community and media, and encouraging contact with a range of treatment agencies and services.

Training

Internal drug-related training in the MPS is mainly focused around informing officers about the divisional drug policy, the extent and nature of local drug problems, and local partnership activities. Training in general drug recognition and enforcement protocols is also offered.

Publicity

The Directorate of Public Affairs provide media and publicity support to the MPS in three core areas of the strategy: enforcement (where examples of successful police operations are used as a visible deterrent); education (promoting MPS messages through drug campaigns targeting young people); and partnership (mobilising community

Table 6.5 Chronological summary of drugs legislation in the United Kingdom

Date	Act, regulation, by-law etc.	Effect
1783	Medicine Stamp Tax Act	Introduced licensing controls on persons involved in the sale of drugs and medicines. Did not apply to patent medicines.
1810	Sale of Flax Seed and Hemp Seed Act	Regulated the prosecution process in Ireland relating to the sale of poor quality hemp seeds.
1844	Manchester Police Act	Introduced local controls on the sale of arsenic and prussic acid.
1851	Arsenic Act	Introduced national controls on the sale of arsenic.
1854	Bolton Improvement Act	Introduced local controls on the sale of 'virulent poisons'. Term included opium, laudanum etc.
1868	Pharmacy Act	Introduced national controls on the sale of fifteen specifically named poisons. Included opium, opium based products and cocaine.
1908	Poisons and Pharmacy Act	Further regulated the sale of poisons. Police responsible for enforcing some of the provisions.
1909	London County Council by-laws (under section 214 Merchant Shipping Act 1894)	The LCC could suspend or revoke licenses granted to lodging-house keepers if they allowed opium smoking on their premises.
1916	Defence of the Realm Regulations: Reg.40B (under Defence of the Realm Act 1914)	Introduced controls on the unauthorised possession of opium and cocaine.
1920	Dangerous Drugs Act	Regulated the importation, exportation, manufacture, sale and possession of opium, cocaine, morphine etc.
1923	Dangerous Drugs and Poisons (Amendment) Act	Increased penalties and introduced provision whereby police could obtain search warrant.
1925	Dangerous Drugs Act	Extended control to coca leaves, cannabis and cannabis resin.
1932	Dangerous Drugs Act	Extended range of controlled drugs.
1951	Dangerous Drugs Act	Consolidated previous acts.
1964	Dangerous Drugs Act	Introduced new offences in respect of cannabis.

Date	Act, regulation, by-law etc.	Effect
1964	Drugs (Prevention of Misuse) Act	Introduced controls over amphetamines and pemoline.
1965	Dangerous Drugs Act	Consolidated previous acts.
1967	Dangerous Drugs Act	Introduced provisions whereby police could stop and search persons for drug offences.
1968	Medicines Act	Governs the manufacture, supply and sale of medicinal products.
1971	Misuse of Drugs Act	Introduced new offence of possession with intent to supply a controlled drug, increased penalties and extended range of controlled drugs.
1977	Criminal Law Act	Reduced the maximum periods of imprisonment for unlawful possession offences involving Class B and C drugs.
1979	Customs and Excise Management Act	Prohibited the unlawful exportation and importation of controlled drugs and the fraudulent evasion of relevant prohibitions.
1985	Controlled Drugs (Penalties) Act	Increased the maximum periods of imprisonment for trafficking offences involving Class A drugs.
1986	Drug Trafficking Offences Act	Introduced Confiscation Orders and controls on the supply of articles used in the unlawful administration of controlled drugs.
1990	Criminal Justice (International) Co-operation Act	Introduced controls on the manufacture/supply of scheduled substances used in the unlawful production of controlled drugs.
1991	Criminal Justice Act	Amended the Powers of Criminal Courts Act 1973 enabling the courts to link probation orders to treatment for drug or alcohol dependency.
1994	Drug Trafficking Act	Consolidated the 1986 DTOA.
1994	Criminal Justice and Public Order Act	Amended the Prison Act 1952 enabling prison authorities to require prisoners to produce samples of urine for drug testing.
1997	Crime (Sentences) Act	Introduced maximum sentence of 7 years' imprisonment on third conviction for trafficking offence involving Class A drug.

support and action through promoting the success of DATs).

Performance indicators

The development of a series of performance indicators is an objective set in *Tackling Drugs Together* for all criminal justice agencies (HMSO, 1995). In respect of the MPS, only one performance indicator is presently used: to increase the number of detections for the production, supply, and intent to supply controlled drugs. The target for 1996/97 was to increase detections by at least 10 per cent. In the event, the MPS achieved an increase of 26 per cent. However, in conjunction with the Association of Chief Police Officers (ACPO) Drugs Sub-Committee and the Home Office Central Drugs Co-ordination Unit, further work is being undertaken on other indicators. It is expected that partnership indicators will be developed by local DATs. The MPS also commission regular surveys at London-wide and local levels which measure, amongst other things, levels of public concern about drugs and drug-related crime.

Section three: applying the MPS strategy

Notwithstanding the objections of some police officers, it is now clearly recognised that enforcement activity alone is not an adequate response to drug-related offending. Of course it is not suggested that traditional enforcement tactics should be dispensed with - merely that there should be less reluctance to promote more modern approaches. To this end, the MPS is increasingly taking active steps to promote harm reduction initiatives, drug referral schemes and a more structured response in dealing with drug offenders in terms of case disposal.

Policing and harm reduction

Although concerns have always been voiced that drug enforcement is the antithesis of harm reduction, the 1996 and 1998 *MPS Drugs Strategy* explicitly acknowledges the importance of accommodating the principles of harm reduction in the context of policing. In particular, two areas - syringe-exchange and club culture - are singled out as likely to benefit from this approach.

Syringe-exchange

Some commentators propose that harm reduction strategies can often be thwarted by police activity. For example, a passage in the *Release White Paper on Reform of the Drug Laws*, published in 1992, reads:

There is a widespread perception among drug users that it is incriminating to be seen attending a needle-exchange and carrying away large numbers of needles so many injectors run short of clean equipment out of anxiety. [T]he mere carrying of clean or used needles alerts police to the possibility that their owner is probably a drug user; [t]races of drugs in [syringes] may even be used as evidence of illegal drug possession (Release, 1992).

This passage invites a number of reactions. Firstly, aspects of the passage are *technically* correct: section 139 of the *Criminal Justice Act 1988* does create an offence of having an article with a blade or point in a public place without good reason or lawful authority.

However, the Home Office, Crown Prosecution Service (CPS) and the MPS all believe that syringe-exchange schemes will be less effective if the carrying of empty syringes with needles renders problem drug users liable to prosecution. Accordingly, the CPS and MPS have issued internal guidance to this effect. Secondly, prosecutions of unlawful possession offences based on traces of controlled drugs in syringes are now rare: since June 1990 the MPS has prohibited its officers from routinely submitting syringes and needles for forensic examination in drug cases. Furthermore, in the MPD unlawful possession offences involving traces of any class of controlled drug, will now almost invariably be dealt with by means of a formal warning or caution (Chapter 11).

Key finding

Even though it is technically an offence under section 9A of the Misuse of Drugs Act 1971, the CPS and MPS have offered further support to syringe-exchanges by permitting drug workers in some parts of London to distribute sterile water ampoules and medi-swabs to injecting drug users. The Drug and Alcohol Service in Barnet have been involved in such an arrangement since 1990.

Club culture

The Central London area Clubs and Vice Unit (CO14), colloquially known as the 'club squad', is a specialist unit attached to Charing Cross Police Division (Chapter 8). In relation to dance venues, one of the concerns of the unit is the safety of dancers. Consequently, the unit published in 1998 an internal document entitled *Dealing with Drugs in Licensed Premises and at Dance Events: Best Practice Guide*. The document is intended to assist owners, licensees

and security staff in the management of problems arising from drug misuse. The document is supportive of harm reduction initiatives and recommends, for example, that free drinking water is provided at all dance venues.

Developing interventions: drug referral schemes

In 1995, the concept of drug referral schemes (also known as arrest or police referral) was endorsed within *Tackling Drugs Together* as a potentially integral part of any police drug strategy (HMSO, 1995). This followed similar recommendations in the *Task Force to Review Services for Drug Misusers* (Department of Health, 1996) that drug referral schemes (DRS) should be provided at each police station. In response, the MPS strategy promoted DRS as both a worthwhile initiative and a good model of partnership development.

Key findings

The first British DRS was established in 1966 in Birmingham.
The first drug referral scheme in London was piloted in Wandsworth in 1986.

In MPS terminology, a DRS is a partnership initiative which encourages drug users in contact with the criminal justice system to voluntarily participate in confidential programmes of advice and treatment. These partnerships involve the police service, local drug services, and often local general practitioners who prescribe methadone. Under such schemes the police provide detainees with an information card or leaflet detailing local drug services. This is either handed over to all detainees or, in more targeted schemes, to those suspected of being problem drug users. Despite relatively low take-up rates, and difficulties involved in running such schemes, research by Hough has suggested that considerable benefit can be gained from efficient DRS. Furthermore, even schemes involving little more than the routine provision of an information card to all arrestees can often be cost-effective (Hough, 1996). Here, as noted by Hough, the cost is restricted almost entirely to the design and printing of cards - which is unlikely to be in excess of £500 per year (Hough, 1997).

'Hidden' obstacles to DRS

The MPS supports the full range of ways in which DRS can be made more effective: quick access to counselling and prescribing services; improved training for police officers and drugs workers; and defence solicitors acting as important catalysts in the uptake of services by arrestees. There are, however, legal problems obstructing the full development of DRS.

Firstly, the *Police and Criminal Evidence Act 1984* (PACE) imposes statutory limitations on what officers can say and do in regard to detainees. Much of this hinges on the definition of 'interview' contained in the PACE Codes of Practice. Normally any discussion between a suspect or prisoner and a police officer will amount to an interview, regardless of who instigated the conversation. However, the commencement of an interview requires the suspect or detainee to be cautioned, reminded of their entitlement to free legal advice,

with the officer having to ensure that an accurate record of the interview is made. Where then does this leave DRS? As any breach of this code amounts to a disciplinary offence (which furthermore could jeopardise an investigation), it is important that policy makers in the police service and elsewhere are aware of these 'hidden' legal problems.

Secondly, and following on from above, the MPS and any participating drug services must have a clear policy on the legal status of conversations between police officers, problem drug users and agencies offering interventions. The guiding principle of any DRS should be that confidentiality of information will encourage 'voluntary' entry into the schemes. In 1994, the Standing Conference on Drug Abuse published a document on the subject of confidentiality, entitled *Building Confidence* (SCODA, 1994). This provides a starting point for those interested in establishing DRS and similar initiatives.

Case disposal: the MPS side

Case disposal is the decision-making process leading to either the prosecution or diversion of an offender (Box 6.6). This complicated process is important as it is used as the basis for national policing key performance indicators and will feature in the future development of MPS performance indicators.

**Box 6.6
Case disposal
process**

Case disposal process

• Prosecution - summons (for an offence or to answer complaint); charge and/or indictment; or taking an offence into consideration.

• Diversion - no further action; formal warning; formal cautioning; compounding; where the case is not proceeded with; or where another form of disposal is used by some other statutory agency.

Cautioning unravelled

As shown in Chapter 11, diversion in the form of cautioning of drugs offenders has become the predominant way of dealing with minor drug offences. In 1981, the percentage of persons cautioned for offences in the MPS area was less than half a per cent, however, by 1984 this had increased to nine per cent, and by 1995 the average cautioning rate for all drug offenders in the MPS area was 68 per cent (some 12% higher than the UK average). Given that during the last decade the MPS has had consistently higher cautioning rates than the UK average, it is useful to explore the basis and background to its cautioning policy.

Cautioning has long been used as an alternative to prosecution, and although no precise date can be assigned to its origin, its practice dates back to at least the sixteenth century. Moreover, the cautioning of drug offenders has been a recognised form of case disposal for well over one hundred years. Cautioning reflects the exercise of police discretion not to prosecute detected offenders.

Cautioning policy

In July 1990, Home Office Circular 59/1990 provided Chief Officers of Police with guidance on the cautioning of offenders. The purpose of the circular was to establish national standards for cautioning based on consistent general principles in which the courts and police may have full confidence (Box 6.7).

The circular also required each force to produce a policy statement on cautioning. In response, the MPS set up a Cautioning Working Party (CWP) to review its cautioning procedures. Before long, however, the working party realised the scope of the review would need to be widened to include all aspects of case disposal. Accordingly, the Offenders Case Disposal Working Party (OCDWP) was formed in 1991. The OCDWP completed its review in 1993 and made 113 recommendations for change. These recommendations were made after consultation with every statutory criminal justice agency, and a number of London based non-statutory organisations.

A further Home Office circular, published in March 1994 (18/1994), provided additional guidance on the cautioning

Box 6.7
Principles guiding
cautioning

Principles guiding cautioning

The purpose of a formal caution is to deal quickly and simply with less serious offenders, diverting them from unnecessary appearance in the criminal courts whilst reducing the chance of them re-offending.

The national standards for cautioning must be met before a caution can be administered:
- Evidence must exist of the offender's guilt.
- Clear and reliable admission to the offence must be made by the offender; and the offender (or in the case of a juvenile, their parent or guardian) must understand the significance of a caution and give informed consent to the caution being given.
- Significance of the caution is relayed to the offender in that: a central record will be kept; the fact of having a previous caution may influence a decision whether or not to prosecute if they should offend again; and it may be cited in court if they should subsequently be found guilty of an offence.

of offenders and is intended to: discourage the use of cautions in inappropriate cases; seek greater consistency between police force areas; and promote the better recording of cautions. In order to give effect to the OCDWP recommendations and new Home Office guidance, the MPS formed the Case Disposal Policy Implementation Team (CDPIT) in 1994. The CDPIT was tasked with: refining the OCDWP recommendations into policy statements; producing a Case Disposal Manual; and arranging briefings on the new Case Disposal System for MPS staff. A distance learning module on the MPS Case Disposal System was also produced in 1995.

Implementation of these new procedures was effective from January 1st 1995 and all decisions to prosecute or divert offenders from the courts are now based on the guidance and criteria contained in the MPS Case Disposal Manual. From November 1st 1995 all persons cautioned for a recordable offence now have their personal details entered on the Police National Computer. In recordable crime cases the MPS officers are required to complete a crime report on CRIS (Crime Report Information System) which will enable the crime to be considered as solved ('cleared up').

'Formal warnings' and 'not proceeded with'

Two other forms of case disposal deserve explanation - 'formal warning' and 'not proceeded with'. Both these forms of case disposal were introduced by the MPS in 1995 as part of the revised system.

A formal warning is a lesser disposal than a formal caution and equally valid whether the offender is in custody or not. The purposes of a formal warning are the same as those for a formal cautioning. A formal warning is appropriate: for minor offences; in cases where prosecution is not thought appropriate; and where the offender refused a formal caution.

There are also national standards which must be met before a formal warning can be given: the offender must make a clear and reliable admission to the offence; and the offender should consent to being formally warned and asked to sign the relevant form to this effect. However refusal to sign the form does not preclude the warning being given or make the warning invalid. Formal warnings are recorded locally but if the offender resides in another police division, a copy of the form will be sent to that division. MPS officers have been advised not to give formal warnings for drug offences away from the police station unless in exeptional circumstances. Details of formal warnings are not cited in court proceedings, but previous formal warnings can be considered when decisions are being made about how to dispose of future offences. Although not citable in court, details of formal warnings (as well as cautions) are made known to the CPS in the event of any future prosecution.

Previously many offences were classified as 'no further action' when there was clear evidence of the persons' guilt but where, for various reasons, the case did not either proceed to court or result in a caution. In order to accurately reflect work undertaken within the MPS a new category has been introduced - 'not proceeded with' - which will enable such offences to be treated as solved crimes.

At the time of writing, the MPS is also assisting the ACPO Drugs Sub-Committee in the preparation of a document entitled 'Case Disposal Options for Drug Offenders'. It is expected the document will be published in Spring 1998 (Monaghan and White, 1998).

Conclusion: developing and delivering the 1998 MPS drugs strategy

There is much to commend the *1996 MPS Drugs Strategy*. However, where criticism was voiced it was mainly directed at the level of explicit detail and organisational focus contained within the document.

Originally formed in 1991, and reformed in November 1997, the MPS 'drugs strategy group' has sought to respond to such criticisms with the production of the *1998 MPS Drugs Strategy*. Chaired by Dennis O'Connor the group has identified the following operational and strategic focus: reducing the harm associated with drug-related crime. The Deputy to Assistant Commissioner (3 Area) John Townsend Q.P.M. has been tasked with formulating the drugs strategy group objectives, developing performance indicators and devising an operational structure suited to delivering the strategy.

Content of the 1998 MPS strategy

Objective four of the MPS Policing Plan for 1998/99 - which emphasises the importance of developing partnership initiatives - provides a strong indication as to how the *1998 MPS Drugs Strategy* will be developed over the next three years. In recent years many communities in London have experienced an increase in levels of drug trafficking, drug misuse and associated violence. This upsurge has challenged the MPS senior management to find ways of using the limited resources available to contain, and where possible reduce, levels of drug-related offending. Moreover, they must do so while orientating to local community needs and expectations.

In addition, the MPS drugs strategy group have targeted those problem drug users whose use of controlled drugs has caused or contributed to their offending as being of particular importance. An essential component of this approach will be the concentration of enforcement activity in 'hot-spots'. These are locations of 'highest crime density' which are determined by the statistical analysis of reported crimes and reported public disorder incidents. Equally, resources are likely to also be directed towards those offenders engaged in the excessive use of violence as a means of dominating local drug markets.

Delivery

Revisions to the existing drugs strategy will require parallel changes in current organisational arrangements (Figure 6.8 overleaf). However, this will not be easy. As John Townsend has noted drug-related policing spans at least three of the present policing portfolios: crime; partnership and community safety; and criminal justice. Consequently, the difficulties of setting up a centralised unit covering all three of these portfolios in terms of accommodation, management and other personnel issues would be considerable.

Instead, it has been proposed that devolved specialist units co-ordinated by senior management could provide a more feasible alternative to delivering the strategy. On the senior management side, this mainly involves the establishment of a Drugs Directorate. This body will collate input from ACs from 4 and 5 Area, the AC of Specialist Operations, and the views of a larger advisory group to co-ordinate the activities of units such as SO11 and CO20. This would operate with the statistical support of the Performance Information Bureau, whilst information relating to

**Figure 6.8
Organisational
structure for
delivery of future
Metropolitan
Police Service
Drugs Strategy**

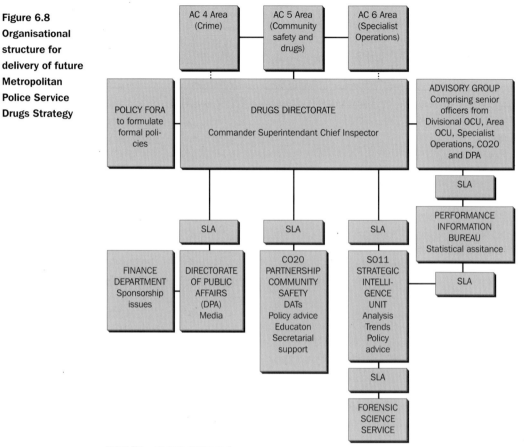

Notes: SLA = service level agreement.

issues such as drug purity would be provided by the Forensic Science Service. In order to secure the effectiveness of each unit, a network of 'service level agreements' (SLAs) will need to be put in place. These are akin to 'formal contracts' which outline the roles and responsibilities of each unit involved in the revised drugs strategy.

Going beyond crime and punishment
The revised MPS drugs strategy and accompanying structural changes are to be put into full effect during 1998.

In summary, the strategy will continue to target drug misuse and drug trafficking, but will also focus on drug-related violence and the emergence

of illicit drug markets. Based on previous experience, additional emphasis will also be given on the establishment of DRS throughout the MPS.

Significantly, the development and the delivery of the *1998 MPS Drugs Strategy* has roughly coincided with the release of two key documents: the revised national drugs strategy; and the *Crime and Disorder Bill* (which stresses the merits of the criminal justice system working in partnership with treatment agencies). Taken together, this trinity of strategic developments will ensure that drug-related policing in London will be unlikely to ever return to being simply a question of crime and punishment again.

Acknowledgements

The author would like to thank the following for their assistance in producing this chapter: Assistant Commissioner Dennis O'Connor; Deputy Assistant Comissioner Alan Fry Q.P.M.; Deputy to the Assistant Commissioner John Townsend; Sylvia Brown (SO11 Typing Manager); and Constable Bob Lowe (Islington Police Station).

References

Church, J. and Holding, A. (eds.) (1997). *Focus on London 97*. London Research Centre, Government Office for London and Office for National Statistics. London: The Stationary Office.

City of London Police Press Office (1998). Personal communication.

Department of Health (1996). The Task Force to Review Services for Drug Misusers. Report of an Independent Review of Drug Treatment Services in England. Wetherby: Department of Health.

HMSO (1995). *Tackling Drugs Together: A Strategy For England 1995-1998*. London: HMSO.

Hough, M. (1996). *Drug Misuse in the Criminal Justice System: A Review of the Literature*. DPI paper 15, Central Drug Prevention Unit. London: Home Office.

Hough, M. (1997). Personal communication.

Institute for the Study of Drug Dependence (1997). *UK National Report 1996 for the European Monitoring Centre for Drugs and Drug Addiction*. London: ISDD.

Mahir, T. (1970). *Police Dogs at Work*. London: J.M. Dent and Sons Ltd.

Metropolitan Police Service (1996). *Drugs Strategy*. London: MPS.

Metropolitan Police Service (5.1./1998) *London Crimestoppers is Ten Years Old* [WWW document]. URL http://www.met.police.uk/police/mps/mps/press/cs0501.htm.

Monaghan, G. and White, A. (1998). *Case Disposal Options for Drug Offenders*. London: ACPO Drugs Sub-Committee (forthcoming).

National Criminal Intelligence Service (1997). *1997 Inspection Report*. Home Office: London.

Release (1992). *A Release White Paper on Reform of the Drug Laws*. London: Release.

Standing Conference on Drug Abuse (1994). *Building Confidence: Advice for Alcohol and Drug Services on Confidentiality Policies*. London: SCODA.

HER MAJESTY'S CUSTOMS AND EXCISE: DRUG TRAFFICKING

John Keep
Her Majesty's Customs & Excise, National Investigation Service

Sections

The role of Her Majesty's Customs and Excise

The role of Her Majesty's Customs and Excise within the Government's original anti-drugs strategy was clearly set out by the Right Honourable David Heathcoat-Amory MP, the former Paymaster General and Minister for Customs at the launch of the *Tackling Drugs Together* Green Paper (HMSO, 1994) on the 19th of October 1994:

'Nationally, Customs will continue to focus on their primary role of detecting and preventing drug smuggling; investigating and prosecuting the organisations and individuals involved; and identifying and confiscating the proceeds of drug trafficking'.

Since April 1996 all major investigations throughout the United Kingdom arising from HMCE's three main business areas (Box 7.1) fall to

Collection Investigation Units, and the Maritime Branch and is under the control of the Chief Investigation Officer. It is regionally based, operating from 14 locations throughout the United Kingdom, and employs around 1,800 officers.

In respect to drug investigations, the NIS works closely with Customs' staff at all ports, airports, land boundaries, inland clearance depots, postal depots, and the Channel Tunnel terminals at Waterloo Station and Cocquelles in France.

HMCE work in close partnership with colleagues in the police, commonly through joint anti-drugs operations. An essential link between these two services was forged in 1992 with the creation of the National Criminal Intelligence Service (NCIS). Although the unit does not undertake any of its

Box 7.1
The statutory responsibilities of Her Majesty's Customs and Excise

The statutory responsibilities of Her Majesty's Customs and Excise

- Collect and manage VAT, Insurance Premium Tax, Landfill Tax, and excise duties, including air passenger tax.
- Fight drug trafficking and enforce other import and export prohibitions and restrictions, including those imposed to prevent the spread of weapons of mass destruction or as sanctions in support of international peacekeeping.
- Collect customs duties and agricultural levies on behalf of the European Union.

Additional responsibilities include compiling trade statistics and giving policy advice to Ministers on these subjects.

the newly created National Investigation Service (NIS). The aim of the NIS is to serve as a centre of expertise for the investigation of customs and excise related criminal offences. The NIS is comprised of the former Investigation Division, the

own operations, it is responsible for the collation, analysis and dissemination of criminal intelligence from home and abroad. The unit covers a range of criminal activities wider than drugs alone and is jointly staffed by the police and HMCE.

Box 7.2
An eclectic history
of smuggling,
trafficking and
customs

An ecelectic history of smuggling, trafficking and customs

91-88 BC

Illegal drug smuggling is reported for the first time. To protect its currency during the Roman Social Wars, Rome imposes a ban upon the importation of the drug 'unguenta exotica'(Frank 1933, quoted in Aune 1990). Whilst the Roman Empire collected customs duties, known as 'portoria', there is no evidence of such a system in Britain.

743 AD

The earliest reference to British customs duties: Aethelbald, King of Mercia grants customs dues to the Abbey of Worcester.

900-1000

Customs levies were being regularly collected in London at Belinsgate (today's Billingsgate), with the following rates applying: '...1/2d on a little ship, 1d on a large ship with sails, a ship full of wood, one piece of wood as tax, Men of Rouen who shall come with wine or large fish give a due of six shillings' (Smith, 1980).

1275

Edward I introduced a levy on wool, thereby establishing a national Customs service, to protect the revenue.

1661

The term 'smuggler' is first used in a proclamation made on 9 August 1661: 'A sort of lewd people called Smuchellers, never heard of before the late disordered times who make it their trade...to steal and defraud His Majesty of His Customs.'.

1683

Today's Excise duties were introduced on a trial basis for the longest ever month in history - 315 years.

1700

HM Customs and Excise's modern powers can be directly attributed to eighteenth century running battles with armed gangs of contraband smugglers. A particularly nasty band were the Ruxley gang from Hastings, who boarded the Dutch vessel the 'Three Sisters' in 1768 and savagely murdered the crew by slashing them from the back of their heads to the base of their spines.

1909

Louis Bleriot became the first man to fly across the English Channel. At the time, however, there was no set customs procedure for aeroplanes, so the plane was treated as a yacht for customs purposes and Bleriot its master. The Dover Collectorate reported the incident to the Board of Customs, with a postscript that this form of transport would not catch on.

1939-1945

Purchase Tax was a war time measure that continued until the 1st of April 1973 and the introduction of Value Added Tax.

1992

National Criminal Intelligence Service formed.

1996

National Investigation Service founded. The largest drug seizure during 1996 was made at a warehouse in Erith where over 15.5 tonnes of herbal cannabis was found concealed in a consignment of wicker furniture from Colombia.

1996

At Heathrow Airport a total of 113 kilogrammes of herbal cannabis was found concealed in the lids of 2,184 pickle jars, whilst another cannabis importation .used home-made fibre glass yams, covered in soil, and moulded around the drug.

HMCE United Kingdom drug seizures in 1996

HMCE seized a record total of over 79.7 tonnes of drugs in the UK during 1996, compared to 55.6 tonnes in 1995. The combined street level value of the drugs seized in 1996 was estimated to be approximately £510.2 million. By conducting follow up investigations and prosecutions HMCE succeeded in seriously disrupting the activities of 96 quality drug smuggling organisations. It is estimated that this had the effect of preventing the smuggling of drugs worth a further £1.5 billion into the country during 1996.

During 1996 record amounts of cannabis were seized, whilst the quantities of cocaine and psychotropics (including amphetamines and ecstasy) were significantly up on 1995. There was a fall in the amount of heroin detected during the year, but seizures still remained above the level during the previous two years.

The number of seizures made during 1996 rose from 7,242 in 1995 to 7,949, an increase of 9.8 per cent, and the number of arrests was also slightly up from 2,323 in 1995 to 2,528. This is a departure from trends over the past few years where the number of seizures and arrests has declined. This can be largely attributed to a decline in the use of internal couriers - colloquially known as 'stuffers and swallowers' - who either use body cavities to conceal small quantities of drugs or swallow them. The average quantity carried by a swallower is 600 grammes, and approximately 500 grammes by a stuffer. In contrast to this decline, the traditional method of single couriers carrying larger quantities of drugs concealed in baggage is again on the increase.

The *Drugs Trafficking Act 1994* (DTA) incorporates the provisions of the former *Drugs Trafficking Offences Act 1986* and the *Criminal Justice International Co-operation Act 1990* (Chapter 6). Under the provisions of section 42 of the DTA an officer can seize money being imported or exported that he or she has reasonable grounds to suspect is connected to drug trafficking. There were 544 notifications of such detections in 1996, involving £22 million (£9.7 million at import and £12.3 million at export). Also during 1996, 60 confiscation orders were issued by the courts at £7.5 million, or a total of five years and 10 months imprisonment in default of payment.

During 1996, HMCE provided information to foreign law enforcement agencies which resulted in these agencies seizing substantial quantities of drugs abroad (Table 7.3).

The total value of the seizures in Table 7.3 was £1.8 billion, based upon UK street level prices. In addition to the UK results, HMCE conducted 124 controlled deliveries. These are where

Table 7.3
Drugs seized abroad following information provided by Her Majesty's Customs and Excise, 1996

Drug type	Quantity of seizures	Number of seizures
Heroin	203 kilogrammes	16
Cocaine	10 tonnes	57
Cannabis	85 tonnes	18

Source: HMCE (1997).

HMCE monitor but do not intercept the delivery of drugs in transit through the United Kingdom to another country, allowing the recipient country to track the case and identify those actually organising the run. As a result of such cases 246 arrests were made abroad in 1996, causing significant disruption to international drug smuggling organisations.

HMCE drug seizures in the London region 1996

As HMCE is charged with collecting the bulk of the nation's indirect tax revenue, this is performed by a network of 14 Collecting Offices located in major cities throughout the United Kingdom.

Each Collection or Executive Unit is responsible for VAT, Customs and Excise within their region. London for the purpose of these analyses relates to three London Collections (Table 7.4). Together these Collections cover the main import and export points within the capital, and provide a picture of the number and quantity of seizures in the Greater London region.

Quantity and street value

Approximately half of all UK drug seizures were made in the London region 3,690 in 1995 and 3,748 in 1996. The estimated street value of these seizures was around £185.3 million. This compares with the £63.7 million and £118.8 million seized during 1994 and 1995 respectively. The 1996 seizures accounted for over 21.2 tonnes of drugs, or over a quarter (27%) of the national total. The increase in the overall weight of drugs seized during 1996 is reflected in the larger quantities of cannabis seized during the year, which, due to bulk volume, tend to arrive in larger single quantities than heroin or cocaine. It also had a direct effect on the number of seizures, most of which would be detected at postal depots. Table 7.6 (overleaf) provides a breakdown of seizures in London by drug type.

Heroin

Nearly all the heroin seized originated from the 'Golden Crescent' of Afghanistan, Pakistan, and Iran (Map 7.5 overleaf). All of the significant seizures were made from commercial and private vehicles, which had been driven overland following the 'Balkan Route'. Since 1968 the 'Balkan Route' has provided the main artery for the transportation of heroin from Turkey to Western Europe. It originally followed the E5 autoroute, but as a result of the

Table 7.4 Her Majesty's Customs and Excise Collections and Sub-offices by location, 1996	Collection	Sub-office
	London Airports	Heathrow, Gatwick, Stansted, Luton, Biggin Hill.
	London Central	City, Westminster, Finchley, Enfield, Notting Hill, Chelsea.
	South London and Thames	Gravesend, Romford, City Airport, Croydon, Waterloo, Mount Pleasant, Tilbury, Parcel Force International Distribution Centre (West Ham), Barking Inland Clearance Depot.

INTERNATIONAL DRUG TRAFFICKING
ROUTES TO LONDON, 1997

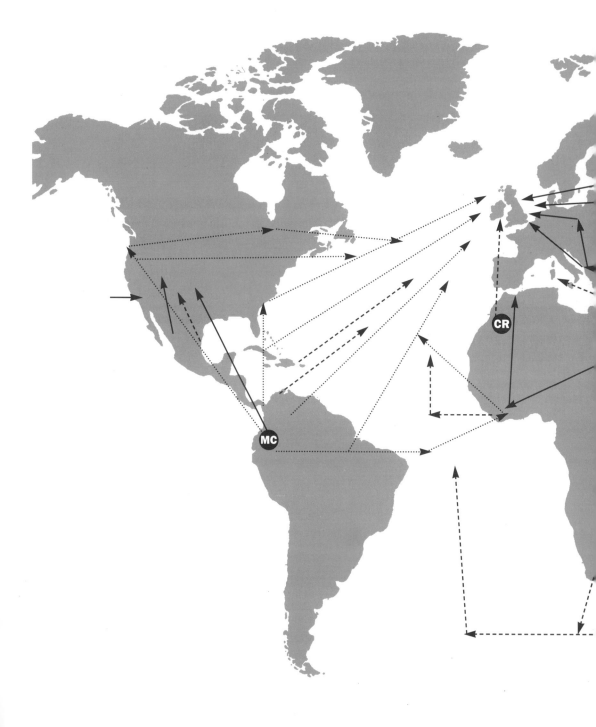

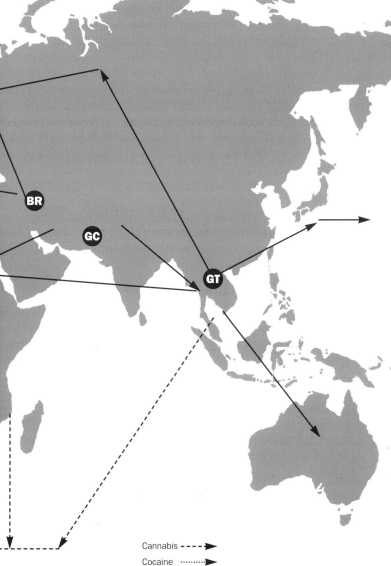

Balkan Route (BR)
Used since 1968 for the trans-
portation of heroin from Turkey to
Western Europe.

Carmen Route (CR)
Cannabis smuggled from Morocco.

Golden Crescent (GC)
Nearly all heroin seized by HMCE
originates from Afghanistan,
Pakistan and Iran.

Golden Triangle (GT)
Heroin supplied from Myanmar,
Laos and Thailand.

Main cocaine route (MC)
The majority of cocaine seized
came from Colombia via the
U.S.A, Venezuela and the
Caribbean. Peru and Bolivia also
operate as sources of cocaine.

Cannabis ----▶
Cocaine ·······▶
Heroin ——▶

Map 7.5

Drug type	Weight seized			Number of seizures		
	1994	1995	1996	1994	1995	1996
Amphetamine	3	1	22	36	55	38
Herbal cannabis	2,179	3,041	19,452	2,382	1,714	1,970
Cannabis oil	2	2	8	25	10	13
Cannabis resin	2,372	893	681	1,134	1,178	951
Cocaine	427	477	960	363	467	488
Heroin	77	487	105	86	86	102
LSD	22,000 tabs	26,518 tabs	50,000 tabs	16	18	7
MDMA	3	8	1	25	32	35
Other	15	11	12	146	130	144
Total	-	-	-	4,213	3,690	3,748

Table 7.6 London drug seizures by drug type, weight and number, 1994-1996

Source: HMCE (1997).

Notes: All weights are in kilogrammes except where otherwise stated.

conflict in the former Yugoslavia more diverse routes have emerged. Besides drug trafficking, the route has also been used in the opposite direction for the smuggling of contraband such as arms and cigarettes.

Over half of the drugs transported along the Balkan Route are overseen by Turkish traffickers. These organisations specialise in sophisticated deep vehicle concealments, which pose a serious problem, due to the heavy volume of inter-continental traffic arriving daily at Customs controls. However, heroin is also supplied from the 'Golden Triangle' area of Myanmar, Laos and Thailand.

Stimulants and psychotropics

The majority of cocaine seized during the year came from Colombia. This is typically sent via the USA, Venezuela, and Caribbean countries through sea and air freight. However, the near continent and Eastern Europe are also used as distribution routes. The Netherlands remains the major source of psychotropic drugs such as amphetamine and MDMA. These mainly arrive in London in vehicles travelling through ferry ports in the south of England.

Cannabis

The weight of herbal cannabis seized rose by almost 800 per cent between 1994 and 1996, even though the actual number of seizures fell by 17 per cent during this time. The majority of

Key findings
During 1996 over two-thirds of all heroin seizures in Western Europe were smuggled along the Balkan Route.
Balkan Route heroin will have passed through as many as seven other countries before reaching London.

cannabis seizures take place at either the Channel ports or at Harwich. Morocco remains the main source for cannabis resin due to its close proximity and easy accessibility. This is smuggled mainly in small craft or driven overland via the 'Carmen Route'. It is also imported from Pakistan and the Netherlands. Herbal cannabis comes from South America, Jamaica and the Netherlands via commercial sea cargo and freight.

Methods of concealment in the London region 1996

Table 7.8 (overleaf) provides a break-down of the methods of concealment encountered by HMCE in respect to seizures occurring in the London region during 1994 to 1996.

Vehicle and freight seizures

The use of vehicles remains the most popular method of concealment in respect of heroin smuggled into the country. There were three notable heroin seizures using vehicles during 1995 directly related to London. A consignment of 187 kilogrammes of heroin was found in London concealed in a shipment of textile goods imported from Turkey. A search in North London of a horsebox and jeep, which had arrived earlier from the Netherlands, produced a total of 90 kilogrammes of heroin. Over 160 kilogrammes of heroin was seized from two private cars in London, and as a direct result of this action a further 50 kilogrammes of heroin was found in transit concealed in a Czechoslovakian registered coach as it was preparing to leave the country at Ramsgate.

Postal seizures

Following a decline in the popularity of South-East Asian heroin from the 'Golden Triangle' in recent years, 1996 saw an increase. In excess of 17.9 kilogrammes of heroin were detected in 30 postal seizures, and over 4.2 kilogrammes was found in unaccompanied baggage at Heathrow (see notes accompanying Table 7.8). The growing trend of cocaine being imported by post throughout the United Kingdom continued during 1996, accounting for 142.2 kilogrammes from 131 seizures compared to 67.4 kilogrammes in 143 seizures the previous year Also there was a marked increase in the amount of cocaine imported via the air courier package services, which provides a similar service to the postal system.

Baggage seizures

Baggage concealment, particularly in suitcases with false bottoms or tops, remains the most popular means of smuggling cocaine and cannabis into London. London's airports are the main entry point for this type of smuggling (Box 7.7). The largest seizure of cocaine during 1996 involved 130 kilogrammes of the drug concealed in the false ceilings of two cargo containers which arrived at Heathrow airport on a scheduled flight from Colombia.

Box 7.7
London airports

London airports

The London area is serviced by three main airports: Heathrow (with its four terminals it is the world's busiest international airport, with a landing or taking off every minute throughout the year); Gatwick; and Stansted Airport. They collectively operate flights to 363 destinations, deal with 720,582 air transport movements a year, and over 85.6 million persons, of whom 75 million are international passengers, with approximately 35 per cent in transit (BAA, 1997). Heathrow is also the UK's largest freight and mail terminal, handling over 1.64 million tonnes of freight valued at approximately £38 billion each year and employing over 1,100 Customs staff.

Over 40 kilogrammes of cocaine was also found during the year at Heathrow concealed in the nose cone section of a Boeing 747 on its arrival from Colombia. The initial detection was made by a drugs dog, who reacted positively to the ventilation system in the first class section of the aircraft. After an extensive search the drug was located in the nose cone section housing the radar sensors. A consignment of avocados from Peru were found to contain 36 kilogrammes of cocaine when examined at Heathrow airport.

Internal seizures

The use of internal couriers - 'stuffers and swallowers' - whilst declining, continues to present a problem in respect to cocaine and heroin. Not only is it one of the most difficult detections for an officer to determine, there is also the possibility that staff may be exposed to conditions such as hepatitis B or HIV.

Method	Weight seized			Number of seizures		
	1994	1995	1996	1994	1995	1996
Vehicle	798	462	125	13	17	2
Baggage	1,196	1,102	1,230	515	829	402
On person	340	115	118	548	308	348
Internal	63	24	2	144	92	64
Freight/cargo	1,869	94	16,028	16	23	69
Aircraft	6	0	60	4	0	15
Post	192	282	1,043	2,560	2,046	2,180
Vessel	177	1,467	0	34	13	1
Air courier	112	3	2	31	1	24
Other	332	1,254	2,633	345	361	643
Total	5,085	4,803	21,241	4,213	3,690	3,748

Table 7.8 Methods of concealment encountered in Her Majesty's Customs and Excise seizures, 1994-1996

Source: HMCE (1997).

Notes: All weights are in kilogrammes. Weights have been rounded to the nearest kilogramme. LSD seizures are excluded from this table. The number of postal seizures shown here does not correlate with the number of postal seizures described in Chapter 11. This is due to both the 'live' nature of the Customs database (which is constantly updated with new data) and the different dates that the data used in Table 7.7 and Chapter 11 were compiled on.

The changing role of Customs

HMCE does not operate in a vacuum. Domestically, its long established practices which were straightforward and predictable are giving way to a rapidly changing environment. Significant recent developments include: the reorganisation of HMCE during the early 1970s; the demise of Purchase Tax; the introduction of Value Added Tax; the expansion of the European Union (EU) with the UK acceding as a full member; the introduction of Landfill Tax, Insurance Premium Tax, and Airport Tax; and a recent Fundamental Expenditure Review of HMCE.

Internationally there have also been radical changes to the environment in which HMCE operates. These changes include: the cohesion of the European Union; the fragmentation of Eastern European countries with the collapse of communism, and their chaotic move towards a market economy; the re-unification of Germany; a democratic South Africa; an increase in the volume of individuals emigrating to Western Europe and North America; the impact of rapid technological and communication advances, together with global banking transfers; and Hong Kong's reversal to Chinese rule.

All of these developments are contributing to a new world order. However none of these changes can compare with the dramatic global increase in the magnitude of drug trafficking, and its wide ranging ramifications.

Acknowledgement

Thanks go to Brenda Mooney for her assistance with the laborious task of number crunching.

Hotline

The public can assist HMCE further by using the Customs Drugs Hotline which they can telephone in confidence to report their suspicions. Any person with information leading to an arrest will be eligible for a cash reward. The number to ring is:
CUSTOMS DRUG HOTLINE - 0800 59 5000.

References

Aune, B.R. (1990). *Maritime Drug Trafficking: An Underrated Problem*. Bulletin on Narcotics, 42, 63-72.

B.A.A. (1997). *Traffic Summary*. London: B.A.A.

HMCE (1995). *86th Report of the Commissioners of Her Majesty's Customs and Excise*. London: HMSO.

HMCE (1997). Personal communication.

HMSO (1994). *Tackling Drugs Together: A Consultation Document on a Strategy for England 1995-1998*. London: HMSO.

Letters Patent (1671).

Smith, G. (1980). *Something to Declare: 1000 Years of Customs & Excise*. London: George G. Harrap & Co.

DANCE CULTURE AND DRUG USE

Jenni Ward and Chris Fitch
The Centre for Research on Drugs and Health Behaviour

With additional contributions from: Dr Kellie Sherlock, Faculty of Health, University of Central Lancashire and Mr Bob Dog, Megadog.

Sections

Dancing and drug use

Rightly or wrongly, dancing has become synonymous during the past decade with drug use. Although drugs have always been associated with music and young people - from the jazz cocaine tribute, 'wacky dust', to the amphetamine fuelled 1960s Mod culture and beyond (Shapiro, 1997) - the sheer scale and visibility of those involved in house, acid house, trance, garage, hardcore, euro, jungle and other dance scenes passing through the capital, have brought the genre special (and sometimes unwanted and undeserved) attention.

There are around 760 clubs in the London area (Church and Fielding, 1997). However, the 200 or so licensed dance events held each week are concentrated in a core of 80 clubs (Swindels, 1997). Charging an entrance fee between three to 15 pounds, these clubs will usually accommodate one to five-hundred people until at least 3 or 4 am and often much later (around 7 to 10 am). A number of daytime clubs also operate in the capital, picking up on those crowds who want to keep dancing after normal club hours.

Licensed events, however, are only part of the overall picture - an unknown number of unadvertised, unlicensed or one-off events, clubs and parties (pay and sometimes free) also take place. Information about these events will often be distributed through word of mouth, flyers in a number of London's 300 plus record shops and 4,860 pubs and bars (EYP, n.d./1997; Church and Fielding, 1997), and through the capital's network of 34 pirate dance radio stations (0171, n.d./1998).

Estimates of the numbers who could be involved in the dance scene range widely. The few UK calculations produced to date have ranged from a modest 30,000 (Keene, 1997), to the impressive 250,000 people each week (London Drug Policy Forum, 1996), with an estimated one million ecstacy pills being consumed a week (Henley Forecasting Centre, 1990). However, it would appear that equivalent London calculations have yet to be produced. Similarly, the proportion of people attending dance events in the capital who have ever taken drugs, or currently use drugs in a dance-related environment, are also surprisingly under-researched. The handful of surveys completed to date suggest that between 50 to 97 per cent of London club-goers have taken drugs at some time (Harris Research Centre, 1997; Release, 1997; Branigan et al, 1997; Sherlock, 1998), with 90 per cent reporting the use of at least one drug during a club night (Release, 1997).

This chapter takes another look at dance and drug culture in the capital: its roots and London's contribution towards the scene; the people involved, the drugs they've taken, and their experiences of dance and drug culture; as well as examining the legal and intervention frameworks within which this has taken place.

One history of dance culture

People often mistakenly identify the 'Ibiza story' - British youth visit the Spanish Island in the late 80s, discover a combination of ecstasy and house, come back with more than a suntan and proceed to start 'rave' culture proper - as *the* history of dance and club culture. Although Ibiza undoubtedly played an important role in the lives of many clubbers and DJs (Danny Rampling's creation of the influential London club Shoom soon after returning from Ibiza being the most obvious example) this was only part of a larger story involving a range of other characters, stages and soundtracks. As in other UK cities, the London dance scene was both influential in this process (spawning collectives such as the Mutoid Waste Company and Club Dog), whilst also being influenced by wider events such as the 1992 Castlemorton free festival and reactive government legislation.

Psychedelics, politics and parties: 1986-1989

Before Ibiza, 'Balaeric Beat' (the musical genre emanating from the island) and ecstasy gripped the nation's minds and spines, an alternative 'dance culture' in and around London was dominated by sound systems like the Mutoid Waste Company and drugs such as LSD, mushrooms and cannabis. Here, a combination of both the ideals and drugs of psychedelic culture (with its emphasis on outdoor events at spiritual sites) with a small but growing political counter culture (partly in reaction to the events of the 1984 Miners' strike) led to a number of parties taking place in and around the capital. These were organised by politically aware people who - clued up on squatting laws, warehouse occupation, and how to generally 'get round' the police - opportunistically used vacant areas of land and empty properties to stage dance events. Although the music at these free festivals and illegal parties didn't much resemble the dance music of today, or even a few years later, this organisational

foundation and political knowledge was to be adopted later by more dance orientated sound systems and collectives.

Two become one

Just as London club nights such as Delirium began to cater for a mainly Ibiza educated crowd, the end of 1987 and early part of 1988 also saw some of the more adventurous members of the London Ibiza set and other 'rave-heads' beginning to turn up at free festivals such as the Treworgy Tree Fair in Cornwall. Traditionally, such events had been dominated by live bands such as Hawkwind and were mainly attended by hippies and crusties (crusties are associated with the adoption of a resourceful traveller lifestyle, but are perhaps more widely known today for their involvement in direct political action often in support of ecological causes). However, the Treworgy Tree Fair and other festivals like it, began to witness ravers, hippies, and crusties alike dancing together to the embryonic forms of soon-to-be influential dance sound systems such as Conspiracy, Bedlam and Spiral Tribe. Although a now unavoidably romantic image, this stark marriage of very different scenes and drugs was a clear indication of the mass popularity that dance culture would later gain.

At the time, there were a number of responses to this situation. Some, such as Club Dog in London, acted to avoid the common situation of a party not coming off - either due to bad organisation, promoters getting arrested, or equipment failure or confiscation - and took dance culture away from the empty warehouse and field and into the regular environment of the pub and club. Others, however, saw that dance culture could be hugely profitable and began to organise even larger outdoor events. Consequently, throughout

1988/89 huge events equipped with lasers, light shows, and additional attractions such as bouncy castles took place under names such as Fantazia and Sunrise. Regardless of the context in which these events took place, the growing public profile and interest in dance culture inevitably led to increasing governmental and police interest.

Ecstasy culture and beyond: the 1990s

By the early 1990s, ecstasy had become firmly established as *the* dance drug in both London and the rest of the UK. The growing profile of dance culture and the drug itself did not pass unnoticed, however, and the shadow of governmental legislation soon loomed over dance culture. Two types of event were key in this process: the 'orbital' raves taking place in and around London at the end of the 1980s; and the legal and social consequences of over 30,000 people attending the 1992 Castlemorton free festival in Worcestershire. As Collins notes, although such events undoubtedly often did breach health and safety regulations, the governmental response was received by many involved in dance culture as primarily an attempt to reduce the large scale supply and demand for drugs (Collins, 1997).

Orbital

Between 1987 and 1990, the M25 motorway and its numerous service stations staked their place in dance history. The 'orbital' raves (so-called because of their geographical proximity to London's M25 motorway) were characterised by individuals gathering at service stations to swap information about illegal dance events taking place

in and around London and the M25. As these events were highly visible - attracting up to 11,000 people and often supporting a noticeable drugs culture - the Government finally introduced in July 1990, what was arguably the first piece of 'dance legislation': the *Entertainments (Increased Penalties) Act.*

The Act, however, did not introduce any *new* drug legislation. Instead, it served to raise the maximum level of fines available for contravening the law in relation to the 'licensing of premises or places used for dancing, music or other entertainment'. Consequently, this rose from £2,000 to £20,000 (or imprisonment for a term not exceeding six months).

Castlemorton

The 1992 Castlemorton event was attended by all the main faces on the London dance scene - including Club Dog - and, for many, signalled the end of spontaneous 'rave' events and the beginning of a wider and more sophisticated 'club culture'. Here, the May Bank Holiday weekend allowed up to 25,000 people to enjoy over 100 hours of non-stop music in the surroundings of the Malvern Hills near Worcestershire.

Previously, the police had tried to restrict such events by invoking minor legislation such as the *1986 Public Order Act.* However, the sheer scale of Castlemorton played a large part in the introduction of a newer, tougher measure: the *Criminal Justice and Public Order Act 1994.* Within this Act, police powers in relation to dance events were increased substantially with the police now allowed 'to remove persons attending or preparing for a rave'. Here, a rave was defined as any gathering of 100 or more people in the open air

Box 8.1
Overview of dance
and drug culture

Overview of dance and drug culture

1912

MDMA synthesised for the first time by German pharmecutical company Merck.

1914

Merck patent MDMA.

1943

Albert Hofmann has the first ever LSD trip.

1965

Alexander Shulgin 'rediscovers' MDMA and fails to keep it a secret.

1970s

MDA reported as sporadically available in London's gay clubs and Soho media scene.

1977

Ecstasy and MDMA derivatives made illegal by revision to Misuse of Drugs Act (1971).

1980s

Ecstasy from the USA becomes available in London at £25 a tablet.

1988

Britain's first ecstasy death is also recorded. Media discover rave culture and the round, yellow face of 'Mr Smiley' appears on News at Ten.

1989

Unlicensed mass outdoor raves peak and Government declares war on rave culture.

1989

The 'Pay Party Unit' - primarily set-up by the Government to police unlicensed dance events such as the 'orbital' raves - releases its first publication.

1990

The *Entertainments (Increased Penalties) Act* is introduced.

1991

Just as the Pay Party Unit is shut down, Club Dog becomes Megadog.

1992

Castlemorton free festival attracts over 30,000 revellers. John Henry publishes 'E and the Dance of Death' one of the first medical papers on the consequences of ecstasy use (Henry, 1992).

1993

The UK Dance Scene is officially big business: the Henley Forecasting Centre estimates it to be worth 1.8 billion pounds (Collins, 1997).

1994

The *Criminal Justice and Public Order Act (1994)* becomes law.

1995

Safer Dancing Conference takes place in Manchester.
Leah Betts dies.

1996

London Drug Policy Forum launch safer dancing guidelines, *Dance till Dawn Safely*. Lifeline publish a new version of the seminal *It's Too Damn Hot* with further guidance from Peanut Pete on drug use and water consumption.

1997

Public Entertainments Licences (Drug Misuse) Act 1997 is heard for the first time in Parliament.

1998

UK's latest ecstasy death is recorded.

where amplified music was played. '[This] [m]usic', the Act advised unaware police officers, '[was] wholly or predominantly characterised by the emission of a succession of repetitive beats'. The introduction of the *Criminal Justice and Public Order Act 1994* made it extremely difficult, although not impossible, for sound systems and collectives to organise and put on ad-hoc or unlicensed outdoor events.

The growing legislation encircling outdoor dance events was initially met with resistance, but ultimately broke down with a large number of dance events becoming licensed and club based affairs. In the capital, spontaneous parties and dance events were witnessed on a less frequent basis, whilst the establishment of hugely successful commercial exercises such as the Ministry of Sound (who were among one of the first dedicated dance music venues in the country) became the goal of many promoters.

London today

Dance culture in London today is no different, and perhaps marginally less important, than in places such as Bristol, Manchester, Sheffield, and Brighton. Although the psychedelic and 'crusty' roots of the culture still resonate in events such as the Hackney Homeless Festival and the Deptford Free Festival, London has gained an insiders' reputation of often being a cynical and fickle town to work in, and a sometimes sullen place to go clubbing. Although the balance is somewhat addressed by the wide range of dance scenes taking place in the capital and the success of a handful of 'superclubs' (such as the now world famous Ministry of Sound which recently launched its own 'dance and club culture' magazine), London appears to be waiting for something new to happen - just as it did so explosively in the mid to late 1980s.

London: putting drugs into context

Although surveys have been completed in London which shed some light on the general prevalence of drug use among young people (Chapter 10), data relating to the context in which drug use actually takes place are scarce. Consequently, data in various forms and from numerous sources have to be pieced together to gain a wider picture.

Three main studies examining drug use connected to, or taking place within, London dance environments were undertaken between 1992 and 1997: a poll of 136 young adults in queues for three clubs in London and the South-East conducted in 1992 (Harris Research Centre, 1997); 268 people interviewed in 20 different dance venues as part of the 1997 London Dance Safety Campaign

(LDSC) (Branigan et al, 1997); and an interview study with 520 individuals in 18 different clubs in London and the South-East (Release, 1997). To complement these studies, this chapter also includes data on ecstasy use collected from 462 London-based readers, and 4,042 readers from the UK as a whole, of the UK dance and club magazine Mixmag (Sherlock, 1998).

Who goes clubbing in London?

Those attending dance events in London tend to be white, male, under thirty years of age and in employment (Release, 1997; Branigan et al, 1997). Given the musical diversification of the capital's dance scene, this absence of a similar degree of *social* diversification may be somewhat surprising. However, the over-representation of certain groups could be partly explained by the narrow selection of venues and club nights at which data collection was conducted.

In the three surveys conducted at dance events, between 85 and 98 per cent of respondents were aged under 30 (Table 8.2). In both the Release, Mixmag and LDSC studies there was also a larger number of 20 to 24 year olds than any other age group.

results of surveys conducted outside of the capital in Sheffield (Christophorou et al, 1997).

Attendance

The Release and LDSC studies both provide data on the frequency of attendance at London clubs. Almost fifty per cent of the LDSC sample classed themselves as 'regular' club goers, whilst two-thirds of the Release study attended dance events either one or more times a week (31%) or every fortnight (36%) (Release, 1997). Men attended

Table 8.2 Respondents attending, or indicating attendance at, dance events in the London area by age, 1992-1997

%	1992 Harris	1996 Release	1996 Mixmag	1997 LDSC
Under 20	59	30	17	17
20-24	41	35	47	52
25-29	-	20	25	29
30 or more	-	15	11	2

Source: Harris Research Centre (1997), Release (1997), Sherlock (1998), Branigan et al (1997).

Notes: Here and elsewhere, 1992 Harris and 1996 Release data refer to London and the South-East.

Different age bands were used in the various surveys, and for convenience they have been grouped together as accurately as possible. Anomalies are as follows: the 'under 20' category refers to respondents aged 16 to 20 in the Harris survey, 15 to 19 year olds in the Release survey, 16 to 19 year olds in the Mixmag survey, and respondents under 20 in the LDSC survey; the '20-24' category refers to respondents aged 21 to 25 in the Harris survey, and 20 to 25 year olds in the LDSC survey; the '25-29' category refers to 26 to 30 year olds in the LDSC survey; and the '30 or more' category refers to respondents aged 31 and over in the LDSC survey.

The overall ratio of men to women attending dance events in London was found to be around 60:40 for all surveys. Employment status and ethnicity data were only collected as part of the Release study. The majority of respondents were working (45% full-time and 13% part-time), with the remainder mainly comprising of the unemployed and students (19% each) (Release, 1997). The vast majority of those interviewed were white (90%), with black and Asian ethnic groups only comprising three per cent each of the total sample. These socio-demographic characteristics correspond to the

dance clubs on a more frequent basis than women (Release, 1997).

Do clubbers take more drugs than non-clubbers?

Table 8.3 shows that, predictably, in surveys undertaken among those attending London dance events, the majority of reports of lifetime drug use for all types of drugs were higher than both London and England figures reported by respondents to the 1994 British Crime Survey (BCS) and the 1995 Health Education Authority's (HEA) National Drugs Campaign Survey (Chapter 10).

Table 8.3		Dance			General population			
Dance and general		1992	1996	1997	1994		1995	
population survey		Harris	Release	LDSC	BCS		HEA	
respondents' life-	%	(16-25)	(16-29)	(<20->30)	(16-34)		(16-34)	
time use of drugs					London	E&W	London	England
by drug type and	Cannabis	47	91	80	41	30	50	43
location,	Ecstasy	25	81	63	10	5	13	9
1992-1997	Amphetamine	-	81	58	16	12	20	18
	Cocaine	-	57	57	8	3	9	5
	LSD	-	74	41	9	7	10	11
	Magic mushrooms	-	60	45	9	9	10	11
	Amyl nitrite	-	61	38	12	11	14	17
	Tranquillisers	-	29	-	4	3	10	7
	Heroin	3	15	13	1	1	1	1
	Crack	-	17	-	1	*	1	1
	Ketamine	-	28	-	-	-	-	-
	Methadone	-	9	-	*	*	*	1

Source: Harris Research Centre (1994), Release (1997), Branigan et al (1997), Percy (1997), HEA/BMRB International (1997).

Notes: Here and elsewhere E&W refers to England and Wales.

Apart from cannabis, ecstasy was the most popular drug reported on a lifetime basis in all of the dance surveys. Between 25 and 81 per cent reported lifetime use of ecstasy, which, depending on the figures used, is between nearly two to six times higher than reports made by their counterparts in the HEA London data set. However, ecstasy was only the fourth most popular drug reported by London respondents, and the sixth most commonly reported on a national level, in both the BCS and HEA studies.

Key findings
21 per cent of respondents had at some time purchased drugs in a pub, club or rave (Time Out, 1994; Harris Research Centre, 1994). 50 per cent of respondents obtained drugs from a friend who did not regularly sell or deal drugs (Release, 1997).

Stimulants such as amphetamines were clearly the third most popular drug amongst dance participants, with cocaine also featuring strongly in both the Release and LDSC reports.

Interestingly, lifetime use of amyl nitrite - a drug often strongly associated with the dance scene - had a higher rating of popularity among BCS and HEA responders than responders to the dance surveys. Lifetime heroin use was reported to be between three to 15 times higher amongst dance participants than in the general population. This would appear to give some support to recent anecdotal evidence of the use of 'chasing' (heroin smoking) amongst dance participants.

'That night' drug use
'Lifetime', 'last year' and 'last month' are all familiar time periods used in surveys concerning drug use (Chapter 10). However, interviews in the Release study were conducted during actual club nights, giving birth to a new surveillance category: 'that night' use (Table 8.4).

Eighty-seven per cent of respondents reported 'that night' use, and were either planning to take, or had already taken, at least one drug that evening (Release, 1997). Although the drugs listed as being taken that night did not

Table 8.4
Respondents
attending dance
events who have
ever taken a drug,
who plan to take,
or had already
taken, a drug 'that
night', 1996

%	Planned to take, or had already taken, that night	Lifetime use
Cannabis	59	91
Ecstasy	53	81
Amphetamines	39	81
Cocaine	8	57
LSD	16	74
Magic mushrooms	4	60
Amyl nitrite	8	61
Tranquillisers	2	29
Heroin	1	15
Crack	2	17
Ketamine	4	28
Methadone	1	9
None	10	-

Source: Release (1997).

differ greatly from those reported as ever being used, the proportion of respondents using that night was much lower. Nearly 60 per cent reported 'that night' cannabis use, 53 per cent ecstasy use, 39 per cent amphetamine use and 16 per cent LSD (Table 8.4). Therefore, unlike 'lifetime' use, which may be indicative of one-off drug taking some time ago, 'that night' use (like 'last year' and 'last month' use) may provide a more suggestive marker of regular drug use.

Club versus post-club drugs

Data on the drugs that people take according to their context, or for a context-related purpose, are depicted in Table 8.5. These data are only available from the 1996 Release study.

Table 8.5
Respondents'
choice of drug by
context and drug
type, 1996

%	Dance events	Chill out	Generally
Cannabis	38	95	64
Ecstasy	68	12	28
Amphetamines	35	3	15
Cocaine	13	7	8
LSD	21	8	14
Magic mushrooms	9	6	8
Amyl nitrite	6	1	2
Tranquillisers	1	11	1
Heroin	1	2	2
Crack	2	1	1
Ketamine	3	3	2
Methadone	*	1	*
None	5	-	4

Source: Release (1997).

Notes: A '*' in a cell, here and elsewhere, represents a percentage less than 0.5, similarly, a '-' indicates categories where data were not collected.

Predictably, ecstasy (68%) was the drug of choice at dance events, but was also commonly reported as being used for winding down after a hard night's session (12%), as well as for general use (28%). Three-fifths of individuals interviewed had taken ecstasy outside of dance events (61%), with a third of these (20%) claiming to do so regularly (Release, 1997). The 'dance drug' status of amphetamines (35%), LSD (21%), and cocaine (13%) was also confirmed, with twice as many respondents reporting a preference for amphetamine use in a dance environment than in a general context.

Key finding

Drug taking was ranked as only the fifth most pleasurable experience at a dance event, coming after music, socialising, atmosphere and dancing (Release, 1997).

Unsurprisingly, stimulants did not feature heavily amongst those wishing to chill out (although 7% and 3% reported the respective use of cocaine and amphetamines). Cannabis was the clear favourite in this category (95%), with 11 per cent also voicing a preference for tranquillisers. Hallucinogens such as LSD (8%) and magic mushrooms (6%) were also mentioned.

Ecstasy reconsidered

As Tables 8.3 to 8.5 have shown, with the exception of cannabis, ecstasy is the most popular of all the 'dance drugs'. However, until recently, few data were available which detailed patterns of the consumption and use of the

Key finding

Underground testing of ecstasy tablets in London suggest that 10% of tablets are likely to be fakes, with no effect at all. A further 5% will contain amphetamine or caffeine (Fox and Thompson, 1997).

drug. The UK dance and club culture magazine Mixmag, in conjunction with Lifeline Manchester, attempted to address this problem by including a two page questionnaire on ecstasy use in their April 1996 edition (Mixmag, 1996). The only criterion for inclusion in this study was that respondents should have used ecstasy at least once.

Overall, 97 per cent of London respondents were 'current clubbers', with 82 per cent reporting the current use of ecstasy (Sherlock, 1998). This was similar to the rest of the wider UK sample (97%, and 81% respectively) (Petridis and Sherlock, 1996).

Thirty percent of London respondents to the Mixmag survey reported taking ecstasy once a week, 31 per cent once ever two weeks, and 27 per cent on a monthly basis (Table 8.6). Only 12 per cent took the drug less regularly. Almost 10 per cent less Londoners took the drug on a weekly basis compared to their UK counterparts.

Table 8.6 Frequency of ecstasy use by location, 1996

%	Weekly	Fortnightly	Monthly	Less often
London	30	31	27	12
UK	39	27	22	12

Source: Petridis and Sherlock (1996), Sherlock (1998).

Notes: UK figures exclude London.

Table 8.7 Total number of ecstacy tablets ever taken by respondents by location, 1996	Tablets	London %	UK %
	1-2	2	3
	3-10	8	10
	11-20	11	10
	20-50	21	21
	50-75	17	13
	75-100	14	15
	150-200	7	9
	200+	19	19

Source: Sherlock (1998), Saunders (n.d./1998).

Notes: UK figures include London.

reported the use of one to two ecstasy tablets per session (Sherlock, 1998). On either side of this figure were the 25 per cent of the London sample taking one or less tablets, and the 29 per cent consuming between two to five tablets per session. Very few respondents, in either the UK or London sample reported taking five or more pills in a single session.

Although the most common total number of tablets taken by respondents (London and UK) was between 20 to 50 doses (21%), over half of both samples had taken more (Table 8.7). Collectively, the 462 London respondents took over 33,000 ecstasy tablets between them, with 87 people being responsible for almost half of this consumption (17,400 tablets).

As Table 8.8 indicates, almost half of respondents (46% London; 44% UK)

Table 8.8 Number of tablets taken by respondents per session by location, 1996	London %	UK %
Less than half	5	5
half to 1	20	22
1-2	46	44
2-3	19	17
3-4	7	6
4-5	3	3
5-6	*	1
6-7	-	0.5
7-8	-	*
8 and over	*	0.5

Source: Sherlock (1998), Saunders (n.d./1998).

Notes:UK figures include London.

Safer dancing and safer dancers

As already described, studies considering the context in which Londoners dance and take drugs have been few and far between. Until recently, this has also applied to public health initiatives, with little regard being given to either the link between the health of clubbers and their immediate environment, or the urgent need for 'behavioural change' amongst those promoting and organising events in the capital. This section collates those examples of good practice - policy, service and information provision - occurring in the London area.

Safer dancing

The Safer Dancing conference held in March 1995 in Manchester (a city that has always led the field in club and clubber safety) helped re-focus attention on the health and safety responsibilities of dance event organisers towards the people paying their wages: clubbers. Anecdotal evidence given at the conference of cold water supplies being disconnected in toilets and heating being turned on to boost bar sales of bottled water, poor crowd control and door staff attitude, and the lack of medically trained and drug aware staff, lead to a consensus that quality standards for clubs had to be introduced quickly.

A number of dance health and safety guidelines followed the conference including Lifeline's *Too Damn Hot* (Lifeline, 1996) and the Home Office's draft circular *Drugs Misuse: Health and Safety of Young People at Dance Events* (Home Office, 1996). However, unlike other documents, the capital's guidelines - *Dance till Dawn Safely* (London Drug Policy Forum, 1996) - were produced by the London Drug Policy Forum. Significantly, this was produced in collaboration with the Association of London Government (who represent the interests and activities of London's local authorities), resulting in all 33 local authorities in the capital signing up to a document which required licensees to prevent overcrowding, to provide adequate ventilation, medical and first aid, and information and advice about drugs within clubs.

> **Key findings**
>
> It costs club promoters, on average, £9 an hour to hire a trained paramedic, (Dog, 1998).
>
> A bottle of water in a London club costs between £1.50 and £2.50.

However, the situation remains far from perfect and 28 per cent of London club goers still feel that safety at venues could be improved (Branigan et al, 1997). Other improvements such as water availability and on-site medical staff have also been identified (Table 8.9).

Door staff: vetting and training

Recent surveys have identified the activities of door staff as of particular concern (Release, 1997; Branigan et al, 1997). In response to concerns such as this, the 'Doorman Certification Scheme' - originally set up in Wales as a reaction to the level of violence and anecdotal reports of drug dealing among door security staff and the public - was adopted by the London borough of Westminster during 1991/92. On application for employment as a door person, each club undertakes a vetting procedure whereby applicants are investigated as to whether they have a history of violence or drug dealing. To date, the majority of London boroughs have either adopted it, or intend to do so shortly.

In addition to undertaking research on drug use in dance-related contexts, the 1997 *London Dance Safety Campaign* also provided training to club personnel including club management, door supervisors, door security staff, and those drug agencies working in clubs

Table 8.9 Clubbers' suggested areas for improvement in London dance venues, 1996/97	Areas to be improved	1996 Release	1997 LDSC
		% of respondents	
	Availability of cold water	44	18
	Chill-out area	17	8
	Controlled temperature/good ventilation	16	-
	Crowd control	4	21
	Door staff	9	34
	Drug/ecstasy testing	28	-
	Medical staff	20	12

Source: LDSC (1996), Release (1997).

(Branigan et al, 1997). This training covered issues ranging from drug recognition and awareness, to responding to first aid and emergency situations.

Bobbies on the beat (per minute)

Public health initiatives are not the exclusive territory of drugs services and agencies. The 'Eight Area, Clubs and Vice Unit', colloquially known as the 'club squad', is a police unit specifically created to enforce licensing regulations in the 260 or so clubs in the central London area. Part of the work undertaken by the 80 police officers and 100 civilian staff at the unit involves the regular inspection of around 60 dance venues in central London. However, the unit has a responsibility for providing policy advice and officer assistance to the whole of the Metropolitan Police Service (MPS).

> **Key finding**
> In 1996 the 'club squad' carried out 4 raids and made approximately 15 arrests related to the supply of drugs in clubs.

The unit has a range of responsibilities other than licensing laws, the most significant of which has been the recent development of an internal MPS 'drugs in clubs' package. This package is intended as a good working practice document for the policing of dance and club events, and indicates the steps that should be taken by club managers to avoid closure, for example by offering assistance to the club to tackle drug dealing.

Safer dancers

Arguably, 'dance drug' use has created a need for a different type of health intervention. Until recently, a continuing problem for service providers has been the lack of attendance at drug agencies by young drug users, making them a group about which little is known. This is partly due to two factors: the fact that drug services have traditionally been designed to attract and cater to the needs of 'problem' users (typically heroin users); and dance drug users tend to perceive their drug use as fairly unproblematic. Things in London, however, are changing and a number of bodies - such as the Junction Project, Newham Drugs Advice Project, Release, Project LSD and the Dance Information Network (DIN) - have developed services and interventions aimed specifically at young dance drug users. Some of these are outlined below.

Outreach

One of the most effective ways found to get information across has been to establish 'outreach' services (Chapter 2) in pre-club bars, clubs and other dance venues . Such programmes have been set up in and around London by Newham Youth Awareness Project, Project LSD, Release and the Caravan Project. Individuals with specialist knowledge of the 'dance' scene are present at these venues to provide information to clubbers, and to deal with any complications associated with the use of dance drugs (ranging from paranoia to heat-stroke). Since 1994, Project LSD have provided an outreach service in London clubs and bars, specifically targeting gay, lesbian and bi-sexual drug users. Much of their work focuses on sexual safety and drug use.

> **Key finding**
> The 1996 'Tribal Gathering' in Luton was one of the first outdoor dance events to operate a needle-exchange (Millar, 1997).

Information

When compared to cities such as Manchester and Edinburgh, London's record in organising effective, pan-city health interventions around dancing and drug use is poor. In an attempt to address this balance, Release and a group of individuals active in London dance culture, created the *Dance Information Network* (DIN) in February 1996. Although the venture was perhaps often fuelled more by its strong beliefs than organisational prowess, DIN played a significant part in drawing attention on a pan-London basis to the health and safety of those attending dance venues. This is evident in its mission statement:

'The Dance Information Network is a forum of organisations and individuals whose aim is to promote the health, welfare and safety of young people attending raves, dance clubs and dance events in and around London'. (Dance Information Network, 1996)

Although the network has now ceased to operate, it's advocacy and fund-raising efforts did leave an indirect legacy: the ultimate creation of the *London Dance Safety Campaign* which was launched in January 1997.

In addition to undertaking research on drug use in dance related contexts, the *London Dance Safety Campaign* continued the work of DIN in promoting the health and safety of people going to London dance events. An important part of this process was the provision of health information posters aimed at dance drug users in the capital. Around 2,500 posters providing harm reduction information on and the phone numbers of help services were displayed in London Underground stations, on tube trains, and London buses throughout the capital (Lloyd-Hayward, 1997). Each of these posters gave information on a single drug such as ecstasy, amphetamines, LSD or cannabis. The campaign received £145,000 funding from the Drugs Challenge Fund and £90,000 worth of free advertising space on London Transport.

Furthermore, the *London Dance Safety Campaign* also employed an idea used by drug agencies since the early 1990s, with a credit card size drug information booklet (the VIP - Vital Information Pack) being distributed to people at dance events. This was mainly achieved through a series of London Dance Safety promotion nights held in 20 London dance clubs during the course of the campaign.

Clubbing in the capital: what next?

Dance and club culture in London and the rest of the UK is now both a respectable pastime and a hugely profitable business. House music, once the preserve of the underground, has been dubbed the 'disco music of the nineties' (Chipchase and Buckle, 1997). Dance music and club culture have become billion pound industries (Henley Forecasting Centre, 1993). Indeed dance culture has become a part of daily life to the extent that, somewhat ironically, current Governmental interest in the scene is not wholly preoccupied with issues of legislation, repression and punishment as it once was. Today, the UK dance music scene is lauded by the Government (with the rest of the UK's cultural achievements) under the glib soundbite of 'Cool Britannia' - a far throw from the days and ideology of the Mutoid Waste Company and Spiral Tribe.

Barry Legg

That legislation which has reached the statute books of Parliament, has been the legacy of the previous Conservative government. The *Public Entertainments Licences (Drug Misuse) Act 1997* was introduced by the previous MP for Milton Keynes, Barry Legg. The Act (which is still to be fully implemented) enables local authorities, on receipt of a police report, to withdraw licences from venues where drug use or drug dealing have been identified as taking place. Prior to the Act, the process of closing a club down could take as long as two years due to the time required to be granted a court hearing and various appeal procedures. However, under the new Act the process can now be completed within two weeks.

Initially, the Act was met with horror from club promoters and clubbers alike. Projections were made that the new legislation could potentially be the end of clubbing, or give rise to more illegal events being organised in unlicensed venues. Other critics noted that those clubs who adopted a visible harm reduction policy towards drug use (i.e. not disconnecting cold water supplies, providing trained staff to deal with medical emergencies, offering information and leaflets on drug use) could be shut down on the grounds that such measures implied that drug use was taking place inside the club (Chipchase and Buckle, n.d. 1998). However, given that the powers granted under the Act have not been extensively used at the time of writing by the police, the consequences of the Act for dance and club culture have yet to be realised.

Pils not pills?

Alcohol and club culture have had a long association. Until recently, however, this has been mainly a one-way relationship, with ideas and icons from club culture feeding into the design and promotion of alcoholic drinks. Perhaps the best example of this, have been the 'alco-pops' genre of alcoholic beverages with their catching designs specifically targeting a youth market.

However, reflecting the 'respectability' and widespread appeal of dance and club culture has been the return of drinking. The dance scene in London has both spawned and been influenced by the growth of pre-club bars. These provide a regular club type ambience with DJs and sound systems with the additional attraction of alcohol (The Dog Star in Brixton, for example, is well known amongst London clubbers for providing a range of flavoured vodkas). Although by no means replacing clubs, such locations provide useful meeting places or 'club type' atmospheres for those not wanting the full club experience.

The next counter-culture

Dance and club culture as we know it today has arguably been spawned from counter-culture. The ideology of psychedelic culture, the political reawakening in the UK after the 1984 Miners' strike, and even the hedonistic urge to escape the drudgery of a nine-to-five job to the Spanish island of Ibiza are all examples of this. Although London now plays host to the respectable face of dance and club culture, it is this respectability and the wider political, economic, and social changes taking place across London which will arguably provide the very basis for the capital's transient, youthful and aware population to react against. The next counter-culture then - and the drugs, music and behaviours emanating from this - is already taking shape.

Acknowledgements

The authors would like to thank Mixmag and Lifeline Manchester.

References

0171 (n.d./1998). *Pirate Radio Guide*. Pirate Guide to London [WWW document]. URL http://www.0171.com/theradio/pirateradio/pirateradio.html.

Branigan, P., Kuper, H., Wellings, K. (1997) *Posterspotting. The Evaluation of the London Dance Safety Campaign*. London: London School of Hygiene and Tropical Medicine.

Chipchase, J. and Buckle, K. (n.d./1998). *1997 Public Entertainments Licences (Drug Misuse) Act* [WWW document]. URL http://www.obsolete.com/ecstasy.

Christophorou, A., Scorthornie, J. and McGauley, A. (1996) *Results of a Major Survey Into Safer Dancing*. Sheffield: SHED.

Church, J. and Holding, A. (eds.) (1997). *Focus on London 97*. London Research Centre, Government Office for London and Office for National Statistics. London: The Stationary Office.

Collins, M (1997). *Altered State*. London: Serpents Tail.

Dance Information Network (1996). Personal communication.

Dog, R. (1998). Personal communication.

Electronic Yellow Pages (n.d./1998). *London record shops* [database]. URL http://www.eyp.co.uk.

Fox, K. and Thompson, T. (1997). London clubbers benefit from 'E' tests. *Time Out* (Dec 17-31).

Harris Research Centre (1997). Personal communication.

Health Education Authority/BMRB International (1997). *Drug Realities National Drugs Campaign Survey*. Summary of Key Findings. London: HEA.

Henley Centre for Forecasting (1990). *Time Use*. Leisure Futures Series.

Henry, J.A. (1992). Ecstasy and the dance of death. *British Medical Journal*, 305, 5-6.

Home Office Draft Circular (1996). *Drugs Misuse: Health and Safety of Young People at Dance Events*. London: Home Office.

Keene, J. (1997). *Drug Misuse Prevention, Harm Minimisation and Treatment*. London: Chapman & Hall.

Lifeline (1996). *Too Damn Hot*. Manchester: Lifeline.

Lloyd-Hayward, S. (1997). Personal communication.

London Drug Policy Forum (1996). *Dance Till Dawn Safely*. London: London Drug Policy Forum.

Millar, R. (1997). Personal communication.

Percy, A. (1997). Personal communication.

Petridis, A. and Sherlock, K. (1996). How much ecstasy do the British really take? *Mixmag*, July.

Release (1997). *Release Drugs and Dance Survey: An Insight Into The Culture*. London: Release.

Saunders, N. (n.d./1998). *Ecstasy Use Survey* [WWW document]. URL http://www.obsolete.com/ecstasy/mixmag.html.

Shapiro, H. (1997). Personal communication.

Sherlock, K. (1998). *Psychosocial Determinants of Ecstasy Use*. Unpublished PhD Thesis. School of Psychology, University of Leeds.

Swindles, D. (1997). Personal communication.

Time Out (1994). *Readers Survey*. Time Out (18-25 March).

LONDON AT A GLANCE

Doreen Kenny
London Research Centre

Sections

Why London at a glance?

We cannot appreciate drug use and its related responses without an understanding of the wider context in which these take place. However, when the context covers 1,578 km² of land and is populated by over seven million people this can be difficult. Furthermore, that information about London which is available is often collated by a wide range of different research agencies and for a multitude of purposes. For the uninitiated, such data are consequently often hard to both obtain and unravel.

This chapter recognises the problems in obtaining key indicators - demographic, economic and social - which are reflective of life in contemporary London, and attempts to answer key questions about the capital that a reader may have.

Who lives in London?

With a population of just over seven million people, London is six times the size of Birmingham, ten times bigger than Glasgow, and eleven times larger than Manchester. Indeed, one in six of the entire population of England and Wales live in London.

London is also one of the largest cities in the Western World. In comparison to other European capitals, London's population is twice that of Rome, nearly four times the size of Lisbon, and six times larger than Amsterdam. Furthermore, only Paris and Brussels are more densely populated, with London having an average 4,365 people per square kilometre.

Two and a half million people presently reside in Inner London boroughs, with the remaining four million or so living in the capital's outer districts (Table 9.1). This situation has been the result of a gradual shift in movement since Inner London's population peak of five million in 1911. The present population of Inner London is now the same as it was in the 1850s, whilst Outer London's population has increased three-fold since 1901.

As can also be seen in Table 9.1 (opposite), Croydon is the largest of all the London boroughs (with a population of around 331,00), followed by Barnet (312,000) and Bromley (just under 294,000). The largest Inner London borough is Wandsworth with around 265,000 residents. Excluding the City of London, Kingston upon Thames has the lowest borough population at just over 140,000 people.

How old are they?

London has a comparatively younger age structure than other parts of the country (Table 9.2). Almost one in four of the capital's population are currently aged between 15 to 29 (23%), two in five are between 20 to 44 (41%), whilst in Inner London close to one in every two persons are aged 20 to 44 (45%). This is compared to the 20 per cent in the remainder of England and Wales aged between 15 to 29 and 35 per cent aged 20 to 44. There are proportionately fewer residents aged over 45 in London than in the rest of the country.

This younger age structure is determined partly by London's key 'pull' factors: education, employment and entertainment. In 1995, the only age group in which London gained numbers from migration within the UK were

**Table 9.1
Mid-year
population
estimates by
London health
authority and
borough, 1995**

London health authority	Population	London borough	Population
Barking and Havering	385,800	(o) Barking and Dagenham	154,800
		(o) Havering	231,000
Brent & Harrow	455,300	(o) Brent	245,300
		(o) Harrow	210,000
Ealing, Hammersmith & Hounslow	652,000	(o) Ealing	292,000
		(i) Hammersmith	156,000
		(o) Hounslow	204,000
Kingston & Richmond	315,700	(o) Kingston upon Thames	140,000
		(o) Richmond upon Thames	175,700
Barnet	312,400	(o) Barnet	312,400
Merton, Sutton and Wandsworth	618,600	(o) Merton	179,200
		(o) Sutton	174,400
		(i) Wandsworth	265,000
Kensington & Chelsea and Westminster	349,200	(i) Kensington and Chelsea	153,900
		(i) City of Westminster	195,300
Camden & Islington	359,400	(i) Camden	184,900
		(i) Islington	174,500
Enfield & Haringey	474,600	(o) Enfield	261,300
		(i) Haringey	213,300
Lambeth, Southwark & Lewisham	733,400	(i) Lambeth	261,700
		(i) Southwark	232,000
		(i) Lewisham	239,700
East London and The City	600,600	(i) City of London	5,200
		(i) Hackney	194,200
		(i) Tower Hamlets	172,800
		(i) Newham	228,400
Croydon	330,900	(o) Croydon	330,900
Redbridge & Waltham Forest	448,400	(o) Redbridge	227,300
		(o) Waltham Forest	221,100
Bexley and Greenwich	431,700	(o) Bexley	220,300
		(o) Greenwich	211,400
Bromley	293,400	(o) Bromley	293,400
Hillingdon	245,300	(o) Hillingdon	245,300
		Inner London	2,677,000
		Outer London	4,330,000
		All London	7,007,000

Source: Office for National Statistics (1997).

Notes: Population estimates have been rounded to the nearest hundred. Totals for Inner, Outer and All London have been rounded to the nearest thousand. Category 'o' denotes Outer London boroughs, 'i' denotes Inner London boroughs. Population figures given cover ages 0-85+ and differ from those given in Chapter 13.

those aged 16 to 24. This trend was repeated in international migration figures, with the largest net increase again being amongst the 16 to 24 age group.

Sex

London, as in England and Wales, has a higher number of women than men in its population (Table 9.3). However, unlike

Table 9.2		Outer London	Inner London	All London	England and Wales
Mid-year					
population	Less than 15	841,900	514,000	1,355,900	8,645,400
estimates by age	15-19	254,200	149,600	403,800	2,622,300
and location, 1995	20-24	294,900	207,400	502,300	2,992,200
	25-29	384,900	301,100	686,000	3,408,400
	30-34	398,700	315,500	714,200	3,520,400
	35-39	326,900	219,400	546,300	3,108,200
	40-44	284,000	160,800	444,800	2,903,300
	45-49	295,300	149,800	445,200	3,213,300
	50-54	231,000	121,400	352,400	2,600,700
	55-59	210,800	115,000	325,800	2,334,800
	60-64	188,700	100,700	289,400	2,169,500
	65 & over	620,000	322,200	942,200	7,294,500
	Total	**4,331,000**	**2,677,000**	**7,007,000**	**44,813,000**

Source: Office for National Statistics (1997).

Notes: Population estimates have been rounded to the nearest hundred. Totals for Inner, Outer and All London have been rounded to the nearest thousand. Estimates for England and Wales exclude London.

the national average, London has slightly more women than men aged between 20 to 29 and also above the age of 40. In the rest of England and Wales, women outnumber men only at age 55 and above.

Ethnicity

Close to one in two of Britain's ethnic minority population currently live in London (45%). Of the approximately three million people in Britain who belong to an ethnic minority group, 1.35

Table 9.3		Males		Females	
Mid-year		London	E&W	London	E&W
population	Less than 15	693,400	4,436,600	662,400	4,208,800
estimates by sex	15-19	206,000	1,351,000	197,700	1,271,300
and location, 1995	20-24	250,400	1,540,700	251,900	1,451,500
	25-29	342,700	1,749,700	343,300	1,658,600
	30-34	366,800	1,793,200	347,400	1,727,200
	35-39	276,400	1,567,500	269,900	1,540,700
	40-44	222,000	1,457,000	222,800	1,446,400
	45-49	219,100	1,611,200	226,000	1,602,200
	50-54	172,300	1,301,900	180,000	1,298,800
	55-59	161,100	1,160,500	164,700	1,174,400
	60-64	143,300	1,060,600	145,000	1,108,900
	65 & over	378,000	2,971,400	564,200	4,323,000
	Total	**3,432,000**	**22,001,000**	**3,575,000**	**22,812,000**

Source: Office for National Statistics (1997).

Notes: Population estimates have been rounded to the nearest hundred. Totals for London and England and Wales have been rounded to the nearest thousand. Estimates for England and Wales exclude London.

million of these live in the capital and form 20 per cent of the total resident London population.

Of course, the overall proportions vary greatly between boroughs as do the distributions of different ethnic minority groups. However, the largest groups in London are comprised of Black Caribbean residents and those from an Indian origin (Table 9.4). Inner London boroughs such as Lambeth (13%), Hackney (11%), and Lewisham (10%) have a higher concentration of Black Caribbean residents. Meanwhile, Londoners classing themselves of Indian origin are more likely to reside in Outer London boroughs such as Brent (17%), Ealing (16%) and Harrow (16%). The age structure of ethnic minority groups tends to be younger than white populations, so there are larger numbers amongst the younger age groups.

Table 9.4
Population by
ethnic group and
location, 1991

%	Inner London	Outer London	All London	Britain
White	74.4	83.1	79.8	94.5
Black Caribbean	7.1	2.7	4.4	0.9
Black African	4.4	1.3	2.4	0.4
Black other	2.0	0.7	1.2	0.3
Indian	3.0	6.5	5.2	0.9
Pakistani	1.2	1.4	1.3	0.9
Bangladeshi	2.8	0.4	1.3	0.3
Chinese	1.1	0.7	0.8	0.3
Other Asian	1.8	1.6	1.7	0.4
Other	2.2	1.5	1.8	0.5
All persons (thousands)	2,504	4,175	6,680	54,889

Notes: Figures are based on 1993 mid-year population estimates. Percentages are not inclusive and may not total to 100%.

Source: OPCS (1993).

Who are London's 'haves' and 'have nots'?

Every city has it's 'haves' and 'have nots'. These are the people who either manage to obtain access to the financial and material resources that can make life easier - such as a paid job or decent housing - or those who have to live on low levels of income, perhaps in poor or temporary accommodation and possibly with the attendant chance of ill-health. Although we should be aware that a large proportion of the population are now unlikely to experience serious levels of poverty or deprivation, financial and material resources are more polarised in London than anywhere else in the UK.

Employment

Employment in London increased as the economy grew in the late 1980s, reaching a peak of 2.9 million in 1990, but London suffered more severely from the recession of the early 1990s than the country as a whole, with employment falling to 2.5 million in 1994, and

%	Employees	Self-employed	Others in employment	ILO unemployed	Total labour force (thousands)
Males					
London					
1987	72.2	16.3	1.0	10.5	1,984
1997	73.2	15.9	0.9	10.0	1,969
UK					
1987	72.5	14.3	2.0	11.2	16,117
1997	75.3	15.4	1.1	8.1	16,023
Females					
London					
1987	84.5	6.7	0.7	8.1	1,510
1997	83.5	7.4	1.0	8.0	1,570
UK					
1987	81.8	6.4	1.6	10.2	11,826
1997	86.1	6.8	1.3	5.8	12,692

**Table 9.5
Components of the labour force by sex and location, 1987 and 1997**

Source: Labour Force Survey (1997), Office for National Statistics (1997).

Notes: The Labour Force Survey measures labour force composition at Spring of each year. 'Others in employment' category covers government-supported employment and training schemes, unpaid family workers (1997 only) and those not stating employment status. The category 'ILO unemployed' is based on a recommended measure by the International Labour Organisation (ILO). This counts as unemployed those aged 16 and over who are without a job, are available to start work in the next two weeks and who have been seeking a job in the last four weeks, or are waiting to start a job already obtained. The measurement is used in the Labour Force Survey and refers to figures for Spring 1997.

recovering slightly to 2.7 million in Spring 1997.

As Table 9.5 demonstrates, the male labour force (all those people eligible to work) in both London and the UK fell by one per cent over the period 1987 to 1997. However, London's female labour force increased by four per cent, with the wider female national figure growing by seven per cent.

Major changes have also occurred in the age structure of London's labour force since 1987. There has been a rise of around five per cent in the number of workers aged between 25 and 34 (3% in the UK), whilst the proportion of those aged under 25 fell by nine per cent (7% in the UK).

Unemployment

Historically, London has always had a lower unemployment rate than the rest of the UK. However, due to changes outside of the capital, this situation has been reversed (Table 9.5). Based on a sample of 60,000 private households in the UK, the Labour Force Survey indicates that around nine per cent of the London work force (males and females) were ILO unemployed in Spring 1997, compared to seven per cent in the rest of the UK. In terms of actual numbers, London had 322,000 ILO unemployed in 1997, with just over two million unemployed in the UK.

Key findings

There are almost as many people unemployed in London than the whole of Scotland and Wales' unemployment figures combined (Labour Force Survey, 1997). Three-quarters of all unemployed black people in Britain live in London.

Table 9.6
Distribution of gross household income by location, 1996/97

% households in each weekly income group	London	UK
Under £100	16.1	13.7
£100 but under £150	9.8	11.1
£150 but under £250	13.0	17.0
£250 but under £350	12.5	13.1
£350 but under £450	9.5	11.7
£450 but under 600	13.8	13.3
£600 but under £750	10.9	8.4
£750 or over	14.4	11.8
Average gross weekly household income (£)	454.5	369.9

Source: Family Expenditure Survey (1996/97), ONS (1997).

Notes: The Family Expenditure Survey is a continuous, random sample survey of over 7,000 private households in the United Kingdom and collects information about incomes as well as detailed information on expenditure. In 1996/97, the number of private households taking part was 6,415. Of these, 632 were located in London.

The Office for National Statistics provide another measure of unemployment and this indicates that 247,000 people were claiming unemployment-related benefits in London in October 1997. Around 90,000 of these people had been unemployed for a year or more. Women accounted for under a quarter of this total, with the over 50 age group (men and women) forming a seventh. The under 25 age group also comprised a quarter of the total, with a fifth of all male clients and a third of all female clients coming from this age group.

Long-term unemployment is a considerable problem in London. Only Northern Ireland and Merseyside having higher proportions of people out of work for more than a year. The over 50 age group comprised nearly half of this category, with the under 25 age groups forming a fifth. Men were generally more likely to be long-term unemployed than women.

Unemployment rates are also higher among ethnic minority groups. This is reflected in the 40, 30 and 12 per cent of the unemployed in Inner London, Outer London and Great Britain respectively, who came from minority groups.

Income

In 1996/97, 25 per cent of households in London had an income of more than £600 per week, compared with 20 per cent in the UK as a whole (Table 9.6). In contrast, around 16 per cent of London households were on incomes of less than £100 per week, compared with nearly 14 per cent in the UK.

Welfare and deprivation

As Table 9.7 (overleaf) demonstrates, about twice as many households in Inner London received the main means tested benefits (Income Support, Family Credit, Housing Benefit and Council Tax Benefit) in 1995 as those in Outer London. However, a larger proportion of people in Outer London received non-means tested support such as Retirement Pensions and Child Benefit. Otherwise, the proportion of households receiving benefits is very similar to other metropolitan regions such as Greater Manchester or Tyne and Wear.

Key finding

London contains 14 out of the 20 most deprived districts in the country, according to the Department of the Environment's Index of Deprivation. The London boroughs of Newham, Southwark, Hackney and Islington are the four most deprived (Map 9.9).

Housing

In 1996, there were three million dwellings in London, of which 57 per cent were owner occupied - a lower percentage than in Britain as a whole - 67

Table 9.7 Households in receipt of social security benefits by location, 1995/96

%	Inner London	Outer London	All London	Metropolitan county areas	Britain
Family Credit or Income Support	34	19	25	28	21
Housing Benefit	37	17	26	26	20
Council Tax Benefit	38	22	29	34	25
Unemployment Benefit	1	2	2	1	1
Retirement Pension	23	28	26	31	30
Incapacity or Disablement Benefits	12	12	12	20	15
Child Benefit/One Parent Benefit	29	33	31	33	32
Any benefit	71	72	72	80	75

Source: Family Resources Survey (1995/96), Department of Social Security (1997).

Notes: 1995/96 figures refer to households in which at least one member is currently in receipt of benefit. 'Metropolitan county areas' category excludes London. 'Incapacity or Disablement Benefits' category includes: Incapacity Benefit; Disability Living Allowance (Care and Mobility components); Severe Disablement Allowance; Industrial Injuries Disabilities Benefit; War Disablement Benefit; and Attendance Allowance.

per cent. In common with the rest of the country, this proportion increased over the 1980s, but stabilised in the 1990s.

Key finding
Around eight per cent of London's housing stock - 230,000 dwellings - is statutorily 'unfit for human habitation'. This is primarily in the private sector.

The proportion of accommodation rented from a local authority has remained stable, but is still higher than in the country as a whole - 22 per cent in London, compared with 19 per cent in Great Britain. The proportion rented privately is also higher - 15 per cent in London and 10 per cent in Britain.

Rents in all tenures have increased considerably since the late 1980s. Local authority and housing association rents have more than doubled on average since 1988, while private sector rents have increased by over 75 per cent.

Homelessness

There are various estimates of the numbers of homeless people and households in London. In December 1996, there were around 29,000 households accepted as homeless by London boroughs and placed in temporary accommodation. This number had fallen from 42,000 in 1992, but is still double the number of homeless in 1986.

Key finding
Around four per cent of the housing stock in London is currently vacant. This amounts to approximately 120,000 empty dwellings. The majority of these are privately owned.

Data on single homelessness has also been collated by Health Action for Homeless People. In 1996, they estimate that there were nearly 84,000 homeless people in London. According to this classification, health authorities such as East London and The City and Enfield & Haringey have the largest number of homeless people. A London Research Centre estimate placed the 1995 homeless figure at around 109 thousand, including people in hostels, bed and breakfast hotels and short life accommodation and sleeping rough, as well as the 'hidden homeless' - those staying with family or friends who would wish to live separately.

London at a glance: health authorities

Map 9.8

1 Barking and Havering
2 Barnet
3 Bexley and Greenwich
4 Brent & Harrow
5 Bromley
6 Camden & Islington
7 Croydon
8 Ealing, Hammersmith & Hounslow
9 East London and The City
10 Enfield & Haringey
11 Hillingdon
12 Kensington & Chelsea and Westminster
13 Kingston & Richmond
14 Lambeth, Southwark & Lewisham
15 Merton, Sutton and Wandsworth
16 Redbridge & Waltham Forest

London has:

- Sixteen health authorities. These are agencies within the National Health Service responsible for identifying and meeting the health needs of local populations. Since April 1996, health authorities have taken over the role of District Health Authorities and family health service authorities (FHSAs).
- Two regional offices of the NHS executive (North Thames and South Thames). These replaced the monitoring role of health care in the capital previously undertaken by the old Regional Health Authorities (RHAs) in March 1996.
- Sixty-nine NHS trusts providing health services under contract to health authorities and general practitioner (GP) fund holders. Nearly all hospitals and other health providers in London are formed into NHS Trusts, and these cover a variety of functions: some are general hospitals, some are specialist hospitals (such as Moorfields Eye Hospital), whilst others provide community and mental health services.
- Nearly four thousand GPs providing treatment and health services to Londoners, of whom 1,728 are currently organised into 703 fundholding practices with budgets to buy a range of hospital and community services for their patients.
- Thirty community health councils (CHCs), independent statutory bodies representing local peoples' interests to the NHS.

Source: National Health Service Executive (1997).

London at a glance: local authorities, deprivation and unemployment

Inner London

Outer London

Map 9.9

Borough	[1]Jarman UPA score	[2]Department of the Environment Index of deprivation ranking	[3]Total ILO unemployed	Borough	Jarman UPA score	Department of the Environment Index of deprivation ranking	Total ILO unemployed
1 Barking & Dagenham	32.2	18	4.3	18 Hounslow	22.1	99	4.9
2 Barnet	6.8	139	7.2	19 Islington	49.3	4	10.7
3 Bexley	-3.6	181	4.7	20 Kensington & Chelsea	27.7	19	4.8
4 Brent	28.1	29	11.7	21 Kingston upon Thames	-2.4	169	2.2
5 Bromley	-10.8	208	5.3	22 Lambeth	47.6	8	15.5
6 Camden	40.4	15	9.0	23 Lewisham	35.4	11	11.9
7 City of London	-12.3	90	0.1	24 Merton	14.0	104	4.2
8 Croydon	6.8	125	9.4	25 Newham	55.5	1	11.2
9 Ealing	25.5	38	8.5	26 Redbridge	5.4	120	6.2
10 Enfield	13.4	96	8.3	27 Richmond upon Thames	-3.1	173	2.7
11 Greenwich	36.6	14	9.4	28 Southwark	56.1	2	12.8
12 Hackney	62.4	3	14.1	29 Sutton	0.7	183	2.8
13 Hammersmith & Fulham	35.3	16	7.1	30 Tower Hamlets	72.7	7	9.7
14 Haringey	36.9	10	12.9	31 Waltham Forest	30.4	20	8.6
15 Harrow	1.8	207	4.1	32 Wandsworth	25.1	21	9.2
16 Havering	-12.3	158	3.7	33 Westminster, City of	41.2	26	8.2
17 Hillingdon	7.3	156	4.1				
				London			247.3

Source: Jarman (1997), Department of the Environment, Transport and the Regions (1991), Labour Force Survey (1997).

Notes: [1]The Jarman UPA (under privileged area) score ranks areas in order of deprivation. An area with a larger score is more deprived than one with a smaller score. Further details are given in Table 12.2 in Chapter 12.

[2]Department of the Environment (1991) deprivation index measures relative levels of deprivation across the 366 local authority districts of England. The index gives weight to 13 indicators: levels of unemployment and proportion of long-term unemployed within it; proportions of adults receiving Income support and of children in low-earning households or unsuitable accommodation; proportion of households without a car; standardised mortality rate; low educational (GCSE) achievement and educational participation of 17 year-olds; house contents insurance premiums (as a proxy for crime); proportion of housing which is overcrowded or lacks basic amenities amount of derelict land. A score of zero is taken as the norm for England. A positive score shows above average levels of deprivation, a negative score indicates lower than average levels.

[3]The total unemployment figure is taken from the Labour Force Survey. This is described in more detail in Table 9.5.

Acknowledgements

The majority of the information, tables and figures contained in this chapter are from Focus on London 97 and Focus on London 1998. These are annual, joint London Research Centre, Government Office for London, and Office for National Statistics publications. Aimed at both the general and specialist reader, they bring together key statistical information from a wide variety of sources to examine trends and changes over recent years in London.

NATIONAL SURVEYS OF DRUG USE

Ali Judd and Chris Fitch
The Centre for Research on Drugs and Health
Behaviour

Sections

National surveys of drug use

At present, large scale population surveys provide the best estimates of the level of drug use in Britain today. These types of survey have been given much attention in recent years. The Government's 1995 White Paper, *Tackling Drugs Together*, designates them as one of three key performance indicators with which to measure the progress of the objective of 'helping young people to resist drugs' (HMSO, 1995).

These surveys commonly employ stratified sampling techniques - methods which attempt to recruit samples of respondents that are representative of the population as a whole. Respondents' questionnaires are often anonymous, to ensure confidentiality and to encourage truthful reporting.

This chapter draws on the results of two such large scale surveys - the 1994 British Crime Survey (BCS), organised by the Home Office, and the 1995 National Drugs Campaign Survey, co-ordinated by the Health Education Authority (HEA). The BCS is now conducted on a bi-annual basis, and is predominantly concerned with people's experiences and perceptions of crime.

It also asks respondents if they have used various drugs. In 1994 nearly 10,000 people aged between 16 and 59 in England and Wales answered the drugs component of this survey (Ramsay and Percy, 1996).

The HEA survey aims to 'assess the level of knowledge of the risks associated with drug use, attitudes and other characteristics of drug users, and the context in which people use drugs' (HEA/BMRB International, 1996). In 1995 just under 5,000 young people aged 11 to 35 in England answered questions concerning their lifetime use of drugs.

In addition, data are available from the School Health Education Unit's Health Related Behaviour Surveys (SHEU). The SHEU's work for health authorities includes asking school children between the ages of 11 to 16 (in years 7 to 11 at school), several questions about drugs (Balding, 1996).

At the heart of the drug use components of all these surveys are questions concerning 'ever/lifetime', 'last year' and 'last month' use of drugs.

How many adults have taken drugs?

Figure 10.1 (overleaf) depicts the percentage of respondents reporting lifetime use of illicit drugs in the 1994 BCS and 1995 HEA surveys. Generally, more respondents in 1995 reported lifetime drug use than their 1994 counterparts. This could in part be due to the inclusion of respondents living in Wales in the 1994 BCS survey, who may be reporting very low levels of lifetime drug use. It could also reflect the different years that the surveys took place, with the possibility that drug use

has become even more prevalent in 1995 than 1994. It could also be related to the different sampling techniques used in the 1994 BCS and 1995 HEA survey.

In each year, the proportion of the London sub-sample of respondents reporting lifetime use of drugs was consistently higher than that of the complete sample as a whole - London respondents are probably pushing up overall prevalences.

**Figure 10.1
Adult lifetime use
of illicit drugs,
solvents and
steroids by age
and location, 1994
and 1995**

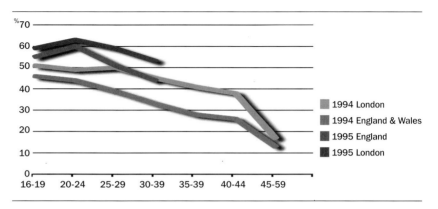

Source: Percy (1997), HEA/BMRB International (1997).

How many young adults take drugs?

As Parker and colleagues note, 'the twin issues of young people and drug use have received an unprecedented amount of public concern and debate during the 1990s' (Parker et al, 1995).

Data for lifetime, last year and last month drug use of young people are depicted in Table 10.2. Although the London figures provide the best estimates of drug use among young people in London, they are based on relatively small sample sizes (684 respondents in 1994, and 512 in 1995) - this may in part account for the considerable variation in the figures over the two years.

These data show that around half of all 16 to 34 year olds in London in 1994 had used drugs at some time, rising to sixty per cent in 1995. Similarly, two of every five 16 to 34 year olds in England and Wales had taken drugs, increasing to about fifty per cent for England in 1995. Within each age band and year,

**Table 10.2
Young adults'
lifetime, last year
and last month
use of illicit drugs,
solvents and
steroids by age
and location, 1994
and 1995**

	Lifetime					Last year			
	1994		1995			1994		1995	
%	London	E&W	London	England	%	London	E&W	London	England
16-19	51	46	59	55	16-19	45	34	36	35
20-24	49	44	63	60	20-24	32	25	39	30
25-29	50	39	59	51	25-29	25	15	34	21
30-34	45	33	53	44	30-34	12	8	20	12
Total 16-34	48	39	58	52	Total 16-34	25	18	29	23

	Last month			
	1994		1995	
%	London	E&W	London	England
16-19	21	20	24	21
20-24	27	15	19	18
25-29	17	9	22	13
30-34	8	4	8	6
Total 16-34	17	11	17	13

Source: Percy (1997), HEA/BMRB International (1997).

Notes: Here and elsewhere E&W refers to England and Wales.

London respondents report higher drug use than respondents from England and Wales as a whole.

Moving on to drug use in the last year, in both years in London, and England and Wales, the 16 to 24 year old age group were more likely to report using drugs than other age groups. Some of these young respondents, and indeed older respondents, may have taken drugs for the first time in the last year, and their responses therefore contribute to both lifetime and last year estimates.

Drug use in the last month probably causes most concern. Lifetime use may be indicative of one-off drug taking some time ago, while last month use is possibly a marker for more regular drug use (Parker et al, 1995). Again, last month drug use is higher amongst 16 to 24 year olds, with over a quarter of London 20 to 24 year olds reporting recent drug use in 1994.

Key findings

Three in five young adults in London have taken drugs at some time.

One in two young adults in England have taken drugs at some time.

Around 315,000 20 to 24 year olds in London in 1995 may have used drugs at some time.

Nearly two million 20 to 24 year olds in England in 1995 may have used drugs at some time.

Notes: These estimates have been calculated by multipling the data by 1995 mid-year population estimates provided by the Office for National Statistics. These figures should be treated with caution as they are based on statistical assumptions which may not translate readily to the real world.

Injecting

The 1994 BCS and 1995 HEA survey did not ask respondents for information on the route by which they took their drugs. However, a recent analysis of the 1990 National Survey of Sexual Attitudes and Lifestyles provides estimates of the prevalence of injecting drug use in London, and England and Wales (Wadsworth et al, 1996). Around one in twenty males aged between 16 and 59 in Inner London, compared to one in three-hundred in Outer London, and one in a hundred in England and Wales, are thought to have injected drugs at some point in their lives. Similarly, around one in a hundred females in Inner London, compared to one in two-hundred in Outer London and England and Wales, are thought to have injected drugs at some time.

How often do older people take drugs?

Estimates of prevalence of drug use among 35 to 59 year olds are only available from the 1994 BCS. Data concerning the drug habits of people aged 60 and above are not currently collected in the UK, mainly for reasons of cost-effectiveness, as drug use is assumed to be rare among this age group, and there is generally less policy interest in it (Ramsay and Percy, 1996).

Table 10.3 (opposite) shows the percentage of older respondents reporting lifetime, last year and last month drug use. Again, London respondents generally report drug use with greater frequency than all respondents in England and Wales. London respondents report fairly high levels of lifetime drug use - 41 per cent of 35 to 39 year olds have taken drugs at some time, decreasing to 17 per cent among 45 to 59 year olds (similarly 28 per cent and 13 per cent for England and Wales).

Twice as many Londoners aged 35 to 44 have taken drugs in the last year and last month, as compared to all respondents aged 35 to 44.

Table 10.3
Older adults'
lifetime, last year
and last month use
of illicit drugs,
solvents and
steroids by age
and location, 1994

%	Lifetime		Last year		Last month	
	London	E&W	London	E&W	London	E&W
35-39	41	28	11	5	5	3
40-44	38	26	7	4	6	2
45-59	17	13	2	2	1	1
Total 35-59	27	20	5	3	3	1

Source: Percy (1997).

However, Londoners and all respondents aged 45 to 59 report the same levels of drug use in the last year and month.

Do males report higher levels of drug use?

Age and sex breakdowns for lifetime and last month use of any drug are shown in Table 10.4. In virtually every age band, more males than females report drug use. The only exception is the 45 to 59 age group, where males and females report the same relatively low levels of drug use in the past month.

Lifetime use of drugs is highest among males aged 16 to 29, and again amongst respondents to the 1995 HEA survey. Similarly high numbers of males aged 16

Key finding

Drug use by older respondents is higher in London than England and Wales as a whole.

Table 10.4
Adults' lifetime
and last month use
of illicit drugs,
solvents and
steroids by age,
sex and location,
1994 and 1995

%	Lifetime				Last month			
	1994		1995		1994		1995	
	London	E&W	London	England	London	E&W	London	England
Males								
16-19	63	48	63	61	28	25	28	27
20-24	60	51	67	65	35	19	20	22
25-29	59	51	62	60	20	12	29	18
30-34	46	40	58	52	14	5	11	7
35-39	46	32	-	-	7	3	-	-
40-44	43	31	-	-	7	2	-	-
45-59	21	15	-	-	1	1	-	-
Total 16-34	55	47	62	59	22	14	21	17
Total 16-59	42	33	-	-	12	7	-	-
Females								
16-19	42	45	55	49	17	16	21	14
20-24	43	38	58	55	23	12	19	14
25-29	43	28	54	41	15	6	14	8
30-34	44	27	47	37	3	3	5	4
35-39	36	25	-	-	3	2	-	-
40-44	33	23	-	-	5	1	-	-
45-59	13	12	-	-	1	1	-	-
Total 16-34	43	33	53	45	13	8	14	9
Total 16-59	34	25	-	-	8	4	-	-

Source: Percy (1997), HEA/BMRB International (1997).

to 29 in the HEA survey report lifetime use of drugs, whether living in London or England. Conversely, 1994 BCS male respondents living in London report higher lifetime drug use than respondents in England and Wales. Whatever the case, for both years males aged 16 to 29 living in London report strikingly high, and similar, levels of lifetime drug use. It will be interesting to see how this 'cohort' of males changes the survey results of such studies over time, when they contribute to older age bands in future years.

Joe Public

Applying the figures of Table 10.4 to the 'average' person on the street, it is very unlikely that a fifty year old man

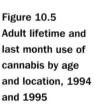

Key findings
Two in three young men in London have used drugs at some time.
One in two young women in London have used drugs at some time.

has taken an illicit drug in the last month, although there is a one in five chance that he has taken a drug sometime in his life if he lives in London. There is a fifty-fifty chance that a twenty-five year old woman living in London has used drugs at some time, reducing to 15 per cent in the last month. An 18 year old man, living anywhere in the country, probably has taken drugs, and there are one in four chances that he has also taken them in the last month.

Drug use amongst adults

Unsurprisingly, cannabis is the most frequently reported drug of use. Figure 10.5 and Table 10.6 show that within each survey, London respondents report lifetime and last month cannabis use with greater frequency than all respondents. Trends in the use of cannabis are similar to those for any drug - use is highest among young people living in London, and decreases with age.

Figure 10.5
Adult lifetime and last month use of cannabis by age and location, 1994 and 1995

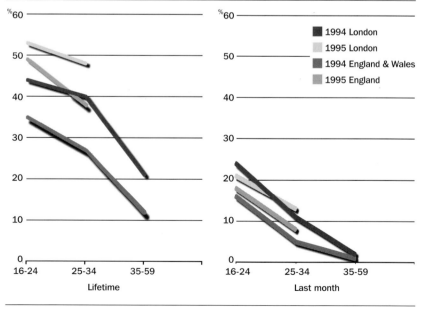

Source: Percy (1997), HEA/BMRB International (1996).

Lifetime use of cannabis is reported by more respondents in London than in the rest of England, with one in two respondents aged 16 to 34 in the capital, and 50 per cent of 16 to 24 year olds in England, using the drug at some time. A quarter of 16 to 24 year olds in London, as opposed to one-fifth of the 16 to 24 age group in England, report cannabis use within the last month.

Stimulants and hallucinogens

Table 10.7 (overleaf) depicts the percentage of adult respondents reporting lifetime and last month use of amphetamines, amyl nitrite, magic mushrooms, LSD and ecstasy, by location and survey year. A fairly consistent trend of declining use with increasing age, and higher use in 1995, is evident.

Amphetamine is clearly the most popular drug in this group. At least one in five respondents aged 16 to 34 in 1995 reported lifetime use of amphetamine, declining to one in fifty respondents reporting last month use. Around 15 to 20 per cent of 16 to 24 year olds reported lifetime use of amyl nitrite in both the survey years, with 16 to 24 year olds in England as a whole reporting higher use than their London counterparts in 1995. Lifetime use declined steadily with age, and use in the last month was low.

One in ten respondents aged 16 to 34 reported lifetime use of magic mushrooms, and very few respondents among all the age categories reported last month use. However, this low reporting of last month use could be influenced by the timing of the BCS and HEA surveys, which were both conducted several months after the

Table 10.6
Adult lifetime and last month use of cannabis by age and location, 1994 and 1995

%.	Lifetime				Last month			
	1994		1995		1994		1995	
	London	E&W	London	England	London	E&W	London	England
Cannabis								
16-24	44	35	53	49	24	16	21	18
25-34	40	27	48	38	11	5	13	8
35-59	21	12	-	-	2	1	-	-
Total 16-34	41	30	50	43	16	9	16	12
Total 16-59	31	20	-	-	9	5	-	-
Smoke unknown								
16-24	8	8	15	14	*	1	0	1
25-34	3	4	16	12	*	*	*	*
35-59	4	2	-	-	*	*	-	-
Total 16-34	5	6	16	13	*	*	*	1
Total 16-59	4	4	-	-	*	*	-	-

Source: Percy (1997), HEA/BMRB International (1997).

Notes: A '*' in a cell, here and elsewhere, represents a percentage less than 0.5, whilst a '0' represents 0%, indicating no affirmative responses. Similarly, a '-' indicates age bands where data were not collected in 1995, and summary percentages that are incalculable as a result. 'Smoke unknown' is a category used by the BCS, meaning that the respondent 'smoked something, excluding tobacco, which [the respondent] didn't know what it was' (Ramsay and Percy, 1996). Both national and London data show that this is reported more commonly on a lifetime rather than last month basis, implying occasional use.

'mushroom season' had finished. Lifetime and last month use of both LSD and ecstasy was highest among the youngest age group. The small proportion of 35 to 59 year olds reporting lifetime ecstasy use probably reflects its relatively recent introduction onto the drugs market.

Key findings

One in five 16 to 34 year olds in England has used amphetamine at some time.

One in six 16 to 24 year olds in London has used ecstasy at some time.

Last month use of amphetamine and ecstasy is most common in the 16 to 24 age group.

Table 10.7
Adult lifetime and last month use of stimulants and hallucinogens by age and location, 1994 and 1995

%	Lifetime 1994 London	Lifetime 1994 E&W	Lifetime 1995 London	Lifetime 1995 England	Last month 1994 London	Last month 1994 E&W	Last month 1995 London	Last month 1995 England
Amphetamine								
16-24	18	15	20	23	5	4	1	4
25-34	15	10	20	15	1	1	2	1
35-59	7	5	-	-	*	*	-	-
Total 16-34	16	12	20	18	3	2	2	2
Total 16-59	12	8	-	-	2	1	-	-
Amyl nitrite								
16-24	16	16	15	22	1	2	*	1
25-34	9	7	14	13	*	*	*	*
35-59	3	1	-	-	*	*	-	-
Total 16-34	12	11	14	17	*	1	*	1
Total 16-59	7	5	-	-	*	*	-	-
Magic mushrooms								
16-24	9	11	8	11	0	*	0	*
25-34	9	8	12	12	*	*	0	*
35-59	3	2	-	-	0	*	-	-
Total 16-34	9	9	10	11	*	*	0	*
Total 16-59	6	5	-	-	*	*	-	-
LSD								
16-24	12	11	12	15	1	2	1	1
25-34	7	4	8	8	*	*	0	*
35-59	3	2	-	-	*	*	-	-
Total 16-34	9	7	10	11	1	1	*	*
Total 16-59	6	4	-	-	*	*	-	-
Ecstasy								
16-24	17	8	16	12	4	2	4	3
25-34	6	2	11	6	1	*	1	1
35-59	1	1	-	-	*	*	-	-
Total 16-34	10	5	13	9	2	1	2	2
Total 16-59	5	2	-	-	1	*	-	-

Source: Percy (1997), HEA/BMRB International (1997).

Opiates and cocaine

Lifetime and last month use of cocaine, crack, heroin and methadone is depicted in Table 10.8. The low levels of consumption of all of these drugs is reflected in the many ones, zeros, and asterisks in the table.

Lifetime and last month cocaine use was higher both among London respondents, and among the 25 to 34 age group. Lifetime and last month use of crack, heroin and methadone was very low among all respondents.

Key findings

Around one in a hundred 16 to 24 year olds in London and England and Wales have used crack, heroin or methadone at some time. Ten per cent of Londoners aged 25 to 34 have used cocaine in the past, although only one to two per cent have used the drug in the last month.

Table 10.8
Adult lifetime and last month use of opiates and cocaine by age and location, 1994 and 1995

%	Lifetime				Last month			
	1994		1995		1994		1995	
	London	E&W	London	England	London	E&W	London	England
Cocaine								
16-24	6	3	7	4	1	*	1	1
25-34	9	3	10	5	1	*	2	*
35-59	4	1	-	-	*	*	-	-
Total 16-34	8	3	9	5	1	*	2	*
Total 16-59	6	2	-	-	1	*	-	-
Crack								
16-24	1	1	1	1	0	0	0	0
25-34	*	*	1	1	0	*	0	0
35-59	*	*	-	-	*	*	-	-
Total 16-34	1	*	1	1	0	*	0	0
Total 16-59	1	*	-	-	*	*	-	-
Heroin								
16-24	2	1	1	1	0	*	*	*
25-34	*	1	1	1	0	0	0	0
35-59	1	*	-	-	*	*	-	-
Total 16-34	1	1	1	1	0	*	*	*
Total 16-59	1	1	-	-	*	*	-	-
Methadone								
16-24	1	1	*	1	1	*	0	*
25-34	*	*	*	*	0	*	0	0
35-59	*	*	-	-	0	*	-	-
Total 16-34	*	*	*	1	*	*	0	*
Total 16-59	*	*	-	-	*	*	-	-

Source: Percy (1997), HEA/BMRB International (1997).

Notes: 1994 BCS methadone figures refer to non-prescribed methadone. 1995 HEA figures refer to both prescribed and non-prescribed methadone.

'Other' drug use

'Other' drugs comprise a range of substances that can be considered illegal in certain circumstances, such as tranquillisers, glues and solvents, and anabolic steroids.

On first glance at Table 10.9 it appears that many more people report lifetime use of tranquillisers in 1995 than 1994. However, the 1994 BCS figures refer to only illicit, or non-prescribed, tranquillisers, while the 1995 HEA figures also include medical prescriptions of tranquillisers.

One in seven Londoners aged 25 to 34 reported lifetime use of both prescribed and non-prescribed tranquillisers in 1995. However, one per cent or less of all respondents reported use of tranquillisers in the last month in both surveys.

Five to ten per cent of young people report lifetime use of glues and solvents, although use in the last month

Table 10.9
Adult lifetime and last month use of 'other' drugs by age and location, 1994 and 1995

%	Lifetime				Last month			
	1994		1995		1994		1995	
	London	E&W	London	England	London	E&W	London	England
Tranquillisers								
16-24	2	3	3	5	1	1	0	1
25-34	5	3	14	8	1	*	1	*
35-59	5	4	-	-	1	*	-	-
Total 16-34	4	3	10	7	1	*	1	1
Total 16-59	4	3	-	-	1	*	-	-
Glues and solvents								
16-24	5	7	9	7	0	*	0	*
25-34	2	2	2	5	0	0	0	0
35-59	1	*	-	-	*	*	-	-
Total 16-34	3	4	5	6	0	*	0	*
Total 16-59	2	2	-	-	*	*	-	-
Pills/powders unknown								
16-24	2	3	4	3	0	*	*	*
25-34	2	1	2	2	0	*	0	*
35-59	2	1	-	-	*	*	-	-
Total 16-34	2	2	3	3	0	*	*	*
Total 16-59	2	1	-	-	*	*	-	-
Steroids								
16-24	1	1	2	1	0	*	0	*
25-34	1	1	1	1	0	*	0	*
35-59	*	1	-	-	*	*	-	-
Total 16-34	1	1	1	1	0	*	0	*
Total 16-59	1	1	-	-	*	*	-	-

Source: Percy (1997), HEA/BMRB International (1997).

Notes: 1994 BCS tranquilliser figures refer to non-prescribed tranquillisers. 1995 HEA figures refer to both prescribed and non-prescribed tranquillisers.

drops to zero for this age group. Very low lifetime, and almost non-existent last month, use of steroids and unidentified pills and powders was reported among all respondents in both years.

Key finding

Last month use of all 'other' drugs is very low or zero among all age groups and locations.

Are there regional variations in drug use?

Regional variations within England and Wales, from the 1994 BCS and the more recent 1996 BCS, are compared in Table 10.10.

London maintains its league position in 1996 as having the highest proportion of 16 to 29 year olds that have taken any drug in the last year, even though this proportion has declined since 1994. In contrast, in the North the proportion of respondents reporting any drug use in the last year increased from around one in five in 1994 to one in four respondents in 1996.

Stimulant and hallucinogen use in London similarly declines from 13 per cent in 1994 to nine per cent in 1996, and again, the largest increase is in the North, where reported use increases from 11 per cent in 1994 to 14 per cent in 1996.

**Table 10.10
16 to 29 year olds'
last year use of
any drug, and
stimulants and
hallucinogens, by
location, 1994 and
1996**

%		Any drug		Stimulants and hallucinogens	
		1994	1996	1994	1996
North		22	26	11	14
Midlands		16	19	9	11
East Anglia		22	22	9	8
Wales		27	15	9	10
South		25	26	10	10
London		32	29	13	9

Source: Ramsay and Spiller (1997).

Notes: 'Stimulants and hallucinogens' include amphetamines, amyl nitrite, magic mushrooms, LSD and ecstasy. North = North + Yorkshire/Humberside + North-West; Midlands = East + West Midlands; South = South-East + South-West (excluding London).

How many children have taken or been offered drugs?

Data on the drug habits of 11 to 16 year olds are available from the School Health Education Unit's Health Related Behaviour Surveys (SHEU) of school-children attending secondary schools in London, and England and Scotland. Although 11 to 16 year olds were also interviewed as part of the HEA's 1995

Figure 10.11 Percentage of 11 to 16 year olds that have ever been offered and used any drug by age and location, 1994/95

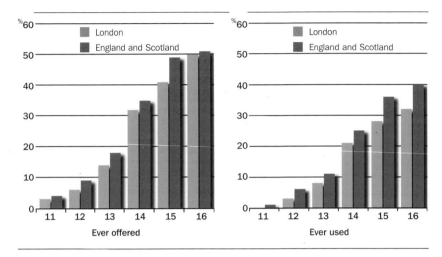

Source: Balding and Regis (1996), Congdon (1996).

survey, the results for this age group are not reported here as only a small number of children were surveyed in the London area, consequently making London estimates unreliable.

Recently, the SHEU sampled schoolchildren in two Greater London health authorities: Lambeth, Southwark and Lewisham in 1994; and Barking and Havering in 1995. The combined results of these two surveys, and results from all schools sampled in 1995 in England and Scotland, are compared here. The London results do not give a representative picture, but do provide a useful

indicator, of drug use among this age group in London.

Figure 10.11 and Table 10.12 depict the percentage of 11 to 16 year olds that have been offered and used drugs at any time. As can be seen, there is a steady increase in the chances of a child being offered all types of drugs by age. Eleven to 16 year olds in London are slightly less likely to have been offered drugs than 11 to 16 year olds in England and Scotland. Males in the 11 to 16 age group are more likely to have been offered and used drugs than their female counterparts.

Table 10.12 Percentage of 11 to 16 years olds that have ever been offered or used any drug by age, sex and location, 1994/95

| % | Ever offered | | | | | | Ever used | | | | | |
| | London | | | England and Scotland | | | London | | | England and Scotland | | |
	M	F	All	M	F	All	M	F	All	M	F	All
11	4	2	3	5	2	4	1	0	*	1	1	1
12	6	5	6	10	8	9	2	3	3	6	5	6
13	15	13	14	18	17	18	9	7	8	12	10	11
14	36	28	32	37	33	35	23	19	21	27	22	25
15	43	39	41	50	47	49	33	24	28	38	33	36
16	55¥	44¥	50	54	48	51	38¥	25¥	32	43	38	40
Total	22	19	21	28	25	27	15	11	13	20	17	19

Source: Balding and Regis (1996), Congdon (1996).

Notes: ¥ these percentages should be treated with caution as they are based on sample sizes less than 50.

15 and 16 year olds

Table 10.13 shows the percentage of 15 and 16 year old schoolchildren that have been offered or used a drug by drug type. This age group were more likely to have been offered, and used, cannabis 'leaf', or grass, followed by cannabis resin, than any other drug.

One in ten 15 and 16 year olds had used amphetamine, falling to one in 25 for ecstasy, and one in 100 for heroin. Around two-thirds of all 15 and 16 year olds had not used drugs.

Children who know a drug user

The SHEU survey asks schoolchildren if they know anyone that takes any of the drugs listed in the questionnaire. 'Know another drug user' means that the respondent is 'sure' or 'fairly sure' they know a drug user. This is an indicator of how close a pupil may be to a source of drugs, and possibly how easily a pupil could therefore obtain drugs. The percentage of young people

Table 10.13
Percentage of 15 to 16 year olds who have ever been offered or used a drug by drug type and location, 1994/95

%	Ever offered		Ever used	
	London	England and Scotland	London	England and Scotland
Cannabis resin	21	23	15	19
Cannabis leaf	34	41	25	31
Amphetamine	16	19	9	10
Magic mushrooms[1]	5	12	1	7
LSD[2]	10	16	6	10
Ecstasy	10	12	3	4
Cocaine	4	3	2	1
Crack	4	3	2	1
Heroin	1	2	1	1
Glues and solvents	8	11	3	7
Tranquillisers	1	4	0	2
Barbiturates	2	2	1	2
Other	0	*	0	*
None of the above[3]	77	51	71	64

Source: Balding and Regis (1996), Congdon (1996).

Notes: [1] Includes any natural hallucinogen. [2] Includes any synthetic hallucinogen. [3] Includes missing data.

that are certain or fairly certain that they know a drug user is depicted in Table 10.14.

Schoolchildren in England and Scotland are more likely to know a drug user than the London subset, and this likelihood increases with age - three-quarters of 15 and 16 year olds in England and Scotland know a drug user.

Table 10.14
Percentage of 11 to 16 year olds that know another drug user by age and location, 1994/95

%	Age 11	Age 12	Age 13	Age 14	Age 15	Age 16	All
London	12	24	39	57	69	63	43
England and Scotland	14	28	41	63	75	79	51

Source: Balding and Regis (1996), Congdon (1996).

How much do drugs cost?

Table 10.15 shows drug prices for various UK towns and cities, based on data from Customs and Excise, and the Institute for the Study of Drug Dependence.

According to these figures, prices of drugs in London are quite similar to the UK average. Cannabis resin is the cheapest in Cardiff, and amphetamine and cocaine the most expensive in Leeds. The price of LSD is fairly constant in the UK at around £3 per unit, as is ecstasy, at around £10 to £13 per unit, and crack, at around £20. The price of heroin varies markedly, being the cheapest in Manchester, Sheffield and Liverpool, and by far the most expensive in Belfast.

Table 10.15
UK drug prices,
£ sterling, 1996

	Cannabis resin (£/oz)	Amphetamine (£/gm)	LSD (£/unit)	Ecstasy (£/unit)	Cocaine (£/gm)	Crack (£/0.2gm)	Heroin (£/gm)
Belfast	100-110	5-7	3-5	6-12	70-80	-	250
Birmingham	10 (£/gm)	10-12	2-3	10-15	80	25	80
Brighton	75-110	5-15	1.5-5	8-20	35-100	-	45-100
Bristol	80-100	10	3-5	12	80-100	20	100
Cardiff	60	8-15	3	5-25	80-100	-	80-120
Edinburgh	120	10	3-5	8-15	60-65	-	60
Exeter	80	10	2-5	10-15	60-80	-	80
Glasgow	80-120	10-15	5	10-20	50-80	-	80-100
Leicester	100	10-12	2-3	10	100	20	100
Leeds	110	20	2-5	10-13	160	20	80-120
Liverpool	90	5-8	3-5	8-18	40-60	20	40-60
London	70-120	10-12	3-4	10-15	50-65	20-25	60-80
Manchester	90	10-15	2-3	10-20	70	20	45
Newcastle	120	10	2.5-5	10	45	-	100-120
Sheffield	100	10	3-5	10-15	50	20	40-60
UK average	94	11	3.5	12.5	65	22	70

Source: HM Customs and Excise, and ISDD, quoted in ISDD (1997).

Conclusions

Surveys indicate that large proportions of individuals in all age groups in Britain have tried illegal drugs at some time in their lives. Furthermore, 50 to 60 per cent of young adults in London, and England and Wales, have taken drugs. Indeed, it is now more common for young people to have taken drugs than to not have taken drugs. Thirty to forty per cent of young adults have taken drugs in the last year, and twenty to twenty-five per cent have taken drugs in the last month. Males of all ages generally take more drugs than females, both in London and elsewhere.

Canabis and amphetamines

Cannabis is the most commonly used drug, with one in two young people having taken it at some time in their lives. Cannabis also accounts for much of the drug use reported in the last month. Amphetamine is the second most popular drug, with around one in five young adults having taken it at some point, although relatively few in the last month.

Other drugs

The use of cocaine, and hallucinogens, such as LSD and ecstasy, is reported by around ten per cent of young people on a lifetime basis, and between one to four per cent on a last month basis. Around one per cent of young people, and fewer older people, report lifetime use of heroin, methadone and crack, while very few people report use of these drugs on a last month basis.

Geography

Regional variations within England and Wales suggest that the proportions of young people taking drugs in the last year is falling in London, and increasing in the North. Whether these are true trends, or the result of sampling variation, remains to be seen.

Age

As they get older, 11 to 16 year olds are steadily at increased risk of having been offered and having used drugs. They are most likely to have been offered, or used, cannabis, followed by amphetamine and LSD. Two-thirds of 15 year olds in London, and three-quarters in England and Scotland, know another drug user.

In adults, the proportion of people using drugs is usually higher among London respondents, as compared to respondents in England and Wales as a whole. Conversely, more 11 to 16 year olds in England and Scotland have used drugs than their London counterparts. It is unclear why this should be the case. Scottish schoolchildren could be pushing up prevalences, or maybe more young drug users around the country migrate to London at school-leaving age than non-drug users. The SHEU London sample might be very unrepresentative of all schoolchildren in London (schools are not selected on a random or representative basis, and the data presented here are based on the survey results of only two district health authorities), although it is the best data currently available for this group.

References

Balding, J. (1996). *Young People and Illegal Drugs in 1996*. Exeter: University of Exeter.

Balding, J. and Regis, D. (1996). Personal communication.

Congdon, P. (1996). Personal communication.

Health Education Authority (1996). Unpublished data.

Health Education Authority/BMRB International (1996). *Drug Realities National Drugs Campaign Survey. Summary of Key Findings*. London: HEA.

HMSO (1995). *Tackling Drugs Together: A Strategy For England 1995-1998*. London: HMSO.

Institute for the Study of Drug Dependence (n.d./1997). *UK Trends and Updates* [WWW document]. URL http://www.isdd.co.uk.

Office for National Statistics (1997). Personal comunication.

Parker, H., Measham, F. and Aldridge, J. (1995). *Drug Futures - Changing Patterns of Drug Use Amongst English Youth*. London: ISDD.

Percy, A. (1997). Personal communication.

Ramsay, M. and Percy, A. (1996). *Drug Misuse Declared: Results of the 1994 British Crime Survey*. London: Home Office.

Ramsay, M. and Spiller, J. (1997). *Drug Misuse Declared in 1996: Latest Results from the British Crime Survey*. London: Home Office.

Wadsworth, J., Hickman, M., Johnson, A.M. et al (1996). Geographical variation in sexual behaviour in Britain: implications for sexually transmitted disease epidemiology and sexual health promotion. *AIDS*, 10, 193-199.

SEIZURES, CONVICTIONS AND PRISONS

Ali Judd, Chris Fitch and Paul Turnbull
The Centre for Research on Drugs and Health
Behaviour

Sections

Seizures, convictions and prisons

This chapter deals with various aspects of drugs and the criminal justice system. It covers police and customs seizures of drugs, drug purities, convictions for drug offences including cautioning, and other aspects of sentencing. It also considers

drug-related imprisonment, drug use whilst imprisoned, and mandatory and voluntary drug testing in prison.

The statistics on seizures and offenders relate to drugs controlled under the *Misuse of Drugs Act 1971*.

Seizures

Seizure statistics cover those seizures made during the year by police and officials of HM Customs and Excise and other bodies such as the British Transport Police. All seizures of controlled drugs are included, whether or not there is an offender, and whether the case results in court proceedings, the administration of

in terms of numbers are conducted by the police, in terms of weight the majority are seized by Customs and Excise (Home Office Statistical Bulletin 1996b).

Police seizures of drugs

In total, 27,511 seizures were made by the Metropolitan Police Service (MPS) and the City of London Police Service combined in 1995, and similarly 88,628 for England and 107,695 for the UK police as a whole (the latter two figures include British Transport Police seizures). A further 6,844 UK seizures were made by Customs and Excise.

As shown in Table 11.1, MPS seizures for cocaine and crack were especially high when compared to the UK, and accounted for two-thirds of all UK seizures. Conversely, there were lower seizures of LSD and amphetamines in the London area than in the UK as a whole.

> **Key finding**
> The Metropolitan Police accounted for one -third of the number of police seizures in England, and a quarter of the total number of police seizures in the UK in 1995.

a caution or compounding action, or no further action (compounding is a Customs and Excise procedure where a case is dealt with by the payment of a fine in lieu of prosecution). Seizures are measured both by the number of seizures completed and also by the respective weights or doses of drugs seized. Although the majority of seizures

Table 11.1
Seizures of drugs by the Metropolitan Police Service and other authorities by drug type, 1995

		Cocaine	Crack	Heroin	LSD	MDMA	Meth	Cannabis	Amph
	MPS	1,071	963	1,628	216	1,519	374	21,366	2,544
	UK police	1,771	1,442	6,330	1,126	5,459	936	85,276	15,299
	MPS as % UK	60	67	26	19	28	40	25	17

Source: Home Office Statistical Bulletin (1996b).

Notes: As a seizure can involve more than one drug, figures for individual drugs cannot be added together to produce totals. MPS figures include seizures made by City of London Police. Seizures from joint operations involving HM Customs and Excise and the police are generally recorded against HM Customs; HM Customs seizures are not included here. UK figures include seizures made by British Transport Police. Meth = Methadone. Amph = Amphetamines.

Table 11.2
Rates of seizures
of drugs by the
Metropolitan Police
Service by drug
type per million
population, 1995

	Cocaine	Crack	Heroin	LSD	MDMA	Meth	Cannabis	Amph
MPS	271	128	217	29	203	50	2,851	339
UK	55	25	108	19	93	16	1,455	261

Source: Home Office Statistical Bulletin (1996c), Office for National Statistics (1997).

Notes: Rates are calculated by relating the number of seizures made by each police force to the 1995 mid-year population estimates provided by the Office for National Statistics for each area; seizures made by HM Customs and Excise and other authorities are not included. As a seizure can involve more than one drug, figures for individual drugs cannot be added together to produce totals. Mid-year population estimates should be treated with caution as they are based on statistical assumptions which may not translate readily to the real world. Meth = Methadone. Amph = Amphetamines. MPS figures include seizures made by City of London Police.

The seizure rate for London during 1995 was 3,670 seizures per million population, for all drug types, as compared to 1,838 for the UK as a whole. Seizure rates for specific drugs are depicted in Table 11.2.

Key findings

Seizure rates in London per million population for all drugs combined were twice the UK average in 1995.

Cannabis was by far the most commonly seized drug both for the Metropolitan Police Service and for the UK.

Cocaine and crack seizure rates in London were five times the UK average per million population in 1995.

Size of Police seizures

Table 11.3 shows the quantities of police seizures in 1995 by drug type. The vast majority of doses of LSD, and

kilogrammes of crack, were seized by the MPS. Conversely, few cannabis plants and kilogrammes of amphetamines were seized by the MPS in 1995 compared to England and Wales.

Customs postal seizures

HM Customs and Excise made 2,993 postal seizures of drugs in the London area during 1995 and 1996. Data in Table 11.4 (overleaf) refer to seizures over one gramme in weight. Figures for the total number of seizures made between 1994 and 1996 by Customs and Excise can be found in Chapter 7.

Most herbal cannabis packages seized in the London area originated either in Africa (45% in 1995 and 56% in 1996) or the Caribbean (40% and 31% respectively). Conversely, cannabis resin postal seizures were more likely to originate in Western Europe (63% in

Table 11.3
Quantities of
Metropolitan Police
Service seizures by
type, 1995 esti-
mates

	All drugs	Cocaine & crack	Crack	LSD (doses)	Heroin	MDMA (doses)	Cannabis (herbal)	Cannabis (plants)	Cannabis (resin)	Amph
MPS	2,694	46	6	382,520	174	130,750	628	9,430	1,741	79
E&W	6,101	69	8	407,140	276	360,910	1,167	93,810	4,029	483
MPS as % E&W	44	66	75	94	63	36	54	10	43	16

Source: Based on data from the Home Office database on 7th February 1996.

Notes: Quantities are in kilogrammes except where otherwise stated. Numbers of doses and numbers of plants rounded to the nearest 10. 'All drugs' excludes cannabis plants, LSD and MDMA. Amph = Amphetamines. MPS figures include seizures made by City of London Police. Here and elsewhere E&W refers to England and Wales.

Table 11.4 Number of Her Majesty's Customs and Excise postal seizures made in London by drug type, 1995 and 1996

	Cocaine	Heroin	Cannabis (herbal)	Cannabis (resin)	Amphet-amine	Other	All
1995	64	52	853	431	9	24	1,433
1996	76	12	1,059	398	3	12	1,560
Total	140	64	1,912	829	12	36	2,993

Source: HMCE (1996).

1995 and 70% in 1996) or Asia (32% and 23% respectively). As might be expected, cocaine detected in the postal system mainly originated in South America (55% in 1995 and 42% in 1996). Of the 52 postal seizures containing over one gramme of heroin in 1995, and 12 in 1996, 73 per cent and 50 per cent respectively originated from Asia.

The intended destinations of postal seizures confiscated in London varied considerably. Approximately 49 per cent in 1995 and 57 per cent in 1996 were thought to have reached their final destination (London), albeit the wrong recipient. A considerable proportion of seizures were intended to reach people elsewhere in England (35% in 1995 and 30% in 1996). Other destinations included Scotland, Ireland, Wales and Western Europe, and such far away places as Canada and the Middle East.

Drug couriers stopped by Customs

Of the 2,949 couriers that were stopped in their tracks in 1995 and 1996 in the London area, 49 per cent were British, and 77 per cent were male (Table 11.5). On average, four couriers a day were intercepted in the London area.

Customs stations in London

A total of 3,588 seizures were made at Customs stations in and around London in 1995, and similarly 3,716 in 1996. Customs stations in this area are located at airports, postal depots, central investigation units, freight terminals, and ports. Of the London airports (Gatwick, Heathrow, London City, Luton and Stansted), most seizures were made at Heathrow (56% in 1995 and 53% in 1996), followed by Gatwick (32% in

Table 11.5 Number of couriers stopped by Her Majesty's Customs and Excise in London by drug type and sex, 1995 and 1996

		Cocaine	Heroin	LSD	MDMA	Cannabis (herbal)	Cannabis (resin)	Amphet-amine	Other	All
1995										
	Male	221	96	9	14	428	349	16	32	1,165
	Female	131	18	2	8	95	92	7	13	366
	All	352	114	11	22	523	441	23	45	1,531
1996										
	Male	240	15	3	15	519	276	8	21	1,097
	Female	140	7	2	0	124	39	4	5	321
	All	380	22	5	15	643	315	12	26	1,418
	Total	732	136	16	37	1,166	756	35	71	2,949

Source: HMCE (1996).

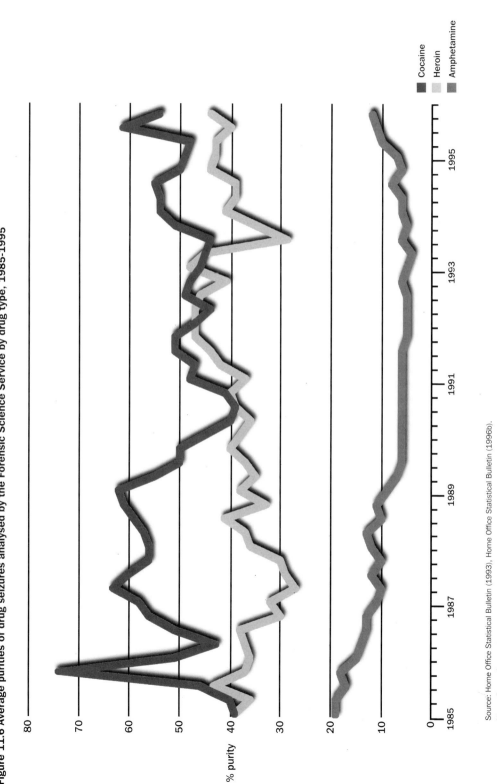

Figure 11.6 Average purities of drug seizures analysed by the Forensic Science Service by drug type, 1985-1995

Cocaine
Heroin
Amphetamine

Source: Home Office Statistical Bulletin (1993); Home Office Statistical Bulletin (1996b).

Notes: Data refer to seizures made by the police only. Includes the Metropolitan Police Forensic Science Laboratory, police laboratories in Scotland and the Northern Ireland Forensic Science Laboratory.

1995 and 34% in 1996). A stunning 91 per cent and 96 per cent of drugs seized at postal depots in 1995 and 1996 respectively occurred at Mount Pleasant Post Office, presumably because this post office is the central sorting point for international mail in London. The main London investigation unit was responsible for 190 seizures in 1995 and 264 seizures in 1996. Similarly 29 and 35 seizures in 1995 and 1996 respectively occurred at the customs stations in two container base terminals in the London area. Lastly, the customs stations at two ports made 16 seizures in total in 1995, and 19 in 1996.

Drug purities

Information on average drug purities is provided by the Drugs Intelligence Laboratory of the Forensic Science Service whose laboratories analyse seizures made by police forces. The information includes the results of the Metropolitan Police Forensic Science Laboratory and other laboratories. Not all seizures are sent for analysis, particularly where the offender pleads guilty to possession of a small amount of cannabis for personal use. Figures on the purity of heroin and amphetamines refer to seizures weighing more than one gramme.

Figure 11.6 (previous page) depicts average purities of heroin, cocaine and amphetamines seized by police in the UK for the period 1985 to 1995 by year quarter. Between 1989 and 1993 amphetamines maintained a relatively stable average purity level of five to six per cent, before beginning to rise. In this eleven year period, average heroin purity has never been below 27 per cent or above 48 per cent. Cocaine shows a wider variation in average purity, ranging from 39 to 73 per cent.

Table 11.7 shows that both amphetamines and heroin purities were lowest in Scotland and highest in London and the South-East in 1995. A similar trend was also found in 1993 (King, 1997). This is probably a reflection of the fact that most drugs are imported into Southern England from abroad, and that the further drugs are carried once within the UK, the more opportunities there are for dilution before final sale.

> **Key finding**
> Average purities in the UK for heroin are around 40 per cent, for cocaine about 60 per cent, and amphetamines about 5 per cent.

Table 11.7 Geographical variation in the mean purity of amphetamines and heroin, 1995	% purity	Amphetamines	Sample size	Heroin	Sample size
	London	14	186	44	145
	South-East	12	115	55	35
	Scotland	4	148	31	29
	All UK	10	1,075	42	688

Source: King (1997).

People found guilty or cautioned for drug offences

Table 11.8 shows the number of persons per year that have been cautioned or found guilty of drug offences by the MPS, and for the UK as a whole, as a result of the powers conferred by the *Misuse of Drugs Act 1971*. The number of persons being cautioned or found guilty in London has shown a threefold rise during the decade, from 8,500 to 24,000.

Key finding

Around three people every hour in London received a caution or were found guilty for drug offences in 1995.

The 24,198 people cautioned or found guilty by the Metropolitan Police Service in 1995 was by far the highest for any individual UK police force

authority (the second highest was 5,097 by the Greater Manchester Police). However, the proportion of UK offenders that have been cautioned or found guilty in London has been decreasing since 1988. Each year an additional 1,500 to 2,500 people in the UK are found guilty or cautioned as a result of Customs and Excise activities. These are not included in the table.

Key finding

Of those found guilty or cautioned for drug offences in the UK in 1995, around a quarter occurred in London.

The last two columns of Table 11.8, and Figure 11.9 (overleaf), show the rate of persons found guilty or cautioned

		Actual Number		Rates per million population	
Year	MPS	UK	MPS as % of UK	MPS	UK
1985	8,567	25,237	34	1,259	446
1986	7,972	22,410	36	1,172	395
1987	8,456	24,506	35	1,251	428
1988	11,860	28,710	41	1,761	500
1989	14,392	35,902	40	2,130	627
1990	16,017	42,473	38	2,357	740
1991	14,631	45,485	32	2,153	792
1992	13,345	46,915	28	1,998	823
1993	16,555	66,538	25	2,230	1,165
1994	22,970	83,809	27	3,078	1,435
1995	24,198	92,136	26	3,228	1,572

**Table 11.8
Persons, and rates of persons, found guilty or cautioned for drug offences by Metropolitan Police Service area or other authority, 1985-1995**

Source: Home Office Statistical Bulletin (1996c), Office for National Statistics (1997).

Notes: These rates are calculated by relating the number of persons found guilty or cautioned for each police force to the 1995 mid-year population estimates provided by the Office for National Statistics for each year; persons dealt with by HM Customs and Excise and other authorities are not included. Offenders dealt with following joint operations involving HM Customs and Excise and the police are generally recorded against HM Customs and Excise. UK figures include offenders dealt with by British Transport Police. Mid-year population estimates should be treated with caution as they are based on statistical assumptions which may not translate readily to the real world. MPS figures include City of London Police.

**Figure 11.9
Rates of persons
per million
population found
guilty or cautioned
for drug offences
by Metropolitan
Police Service
area or other
authority, 1985-
1995**

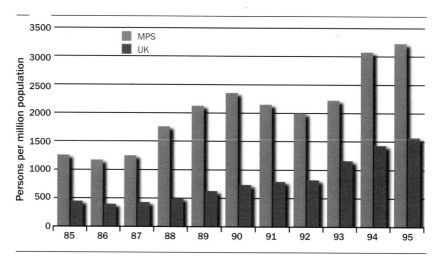

Source: Home Office Statistical Bulletin (1996c).

Notes: See Table 11.8.

Key findings

In 1995 three out of every thousand people living in London were found guilty or cautioned for drug offences.
London has double the rate of individuals being found guilty or cautioned for drug offences, as compared to the UK as a whole (per million population).

when controlling for different population sizes. The offending rate of persons found guilty or cautioned in London is at least double the average UK rate for each year.

Types of offence

As can be seen in Table 11.10, the vast majority of those found guilty or cautioned were charged with unlawful possession, both in London, and UK wide. Only a small proportion of UK offences involving the unlawful use of premises occurred in London. Conversely, around 12 per cent of UK trafficking offences, and 27 per cent of UK unlawful possession offences, occurred in the London area.

**Table 11.10
Persons found
guilty or cautioned
for drug offences
by Metropolitan
Police Service
area or other
authority, 1995**

Offence Type	MPS	UK Total	MPS as % of UK total
Trafficking offences	2,357	19,336	12
Unlawful possession	22,618	82,796	27
Permit premises to be used unlawfully	36	669	5
Other Misuse of Drugs Act offences	215	755	28
Other offences involving controlled drugs	1	4	25
All drug offences	24,198	92,136	26

Source:Home Office Statistical Bulletin (1996c).

Notes: As a person may be found guilty or cautioned for more than one type of offence, rows cannot be added together to produce sub-totals or totals. Offenders dealt with following joint operations involving HM Customs and Excise and the police are generally recorded against HM Customs and Excise; offenders dealt with by HM Customs and Excise are not included here. Trafficking offences include unlawful import or export, unlawful production, unlawful supply, possession with intent to supply unlawfully, production of cannabis. MPS figures include City of London Police.

Table 11.11
Percentage of persons found guilty or cautioned for drug offences by Metropolitan Police Service area or other authority and type of drug, 1995

%	Cocaine	Crack	Heroin	LSD	MDMA	Amphetamines	Cannabis
London	3	1	4	1	4	6	85
UK	2	1	5	1	4	11	82

Source: Home Office Statistical Bulletin (1996c).

Notes: Figures do not add up to 100% as an offence can involve more than one drug type. Offenders dealt with following joint operations involving HM Customs and Excise and the police are generally recorded against HM Customs and Excise; offenders dealt with by HM Customs and Excise are not included here. MPS figures include seizures made by City of London Police.

Drugs involved in drug offences

The percentage of drug offences involving MDMA, LSD, crack and cannabis were quite similar for those found guilty or cautioned in London and the UK (Table 11.11). However, a lower proportion in London were found guilty or cautioned for offences involving amphetamines.

Trends in the use of cautioning

From Table 11.12 and Figure 11.13 (overleaf) we can see similar Metropolitan Police Service and UK trends in the use of cautioning for drug offences, although the latter at a lower rate. For both the Metropolitan Police Service and UK police authorities as a whole, cautioning as a percentage of those found guilty or cautioned rose in successive years from 1985. London rates have continued to increase in the last couple of years, albeit at a slower pace, and UK rates have started to level off.

> **Key finding**
> Cannabis was involved in the offences of nearly nine out of ten persons in London that were found guilty or cautioned.

Although the Metropolitan Police Service gave more cautions to drug offenders than the UK average, they were not the most liberal authority in the country - police in Warwickshire

Table 11.12
Cautioning rates for drug offences by Metropolitan Police Service area or other authority, 1984-1995 (percentage of offenders dealt with)

%	MPS	UK	Year	MPS	UK
1984	9	9	1990	60	40
1985	22	14	1991	63	46
1986	33	20	1992	66	53
1987	47	25	1993	65	54
1988	51	31	1994	63	57
1989	54	34	1995	68	56

Source: Home Office Statistical Bulletin (1996c).

Notes: Persons cautioned as a percentage of those found guilty or cautioned. Offenders dealt with following joint operations involving HM Customs and Excise and the police are generally recorded against HM Customs and Excise; offenders dealt with by HM Customs and Excise are not included here. Scotland's cautioning figures are omitted here as a caution offence is defined differently in Scotland. UK figure includes offenders dealt with by British Transport Police, British Airports Authority and Port of London Authority (England). MPS figures include City of London Police.

Figure 11.13 Cautioning rates for drug offences by Metropolitan Police Service area or other authority, 1984- 1995

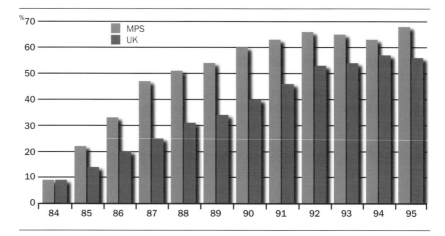

Source: Home Office Statistical Bulletin (1996c).

Notes: See Table 11.12.

Key finding

In 1995 around two-thirds of drug offenders in London received a caution, compared to about half for the UK.

gave 77 per cent of offenders a caution in 1994, followed by Cleveland at 72 per cent. Drug users in Northern Ireland certainly had the hardest time of all, with no offenders receiving cautions.

Sentence or orders given to drug offenders

Figure 11.14 depicts the proportions of offenders receiving different types of sentence or order, in London and the UK.

Sixty-eight per cent of drug offenders received cautions in London in 1995. Seventeen per cent were fined,

Figure 11.14 Percentage of different types of order given to those found guilty or cautioned by Metropolitan Police Service area or other authority, 1995

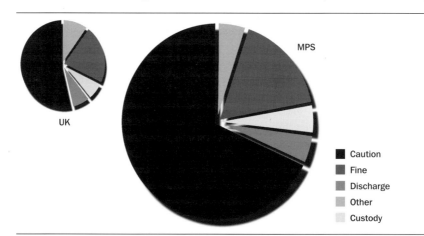

Source: Home Office Statistical Bulletin (1996c).

Notes: Where a person is found guilty of two or more drug offences at the same court appearance the sentence or order shown in this figure is the most severe penalty. UK figures derived from Figure 11.4 relating to the percentage of drug offenders receiving a caution will be lower than those presented in Table 11.2. This is due to Figure 11.4 including the number of persons in Scotland committing any offence in the denominator, none of which were in the numerator due to differences in the definition of cautioning in Scotland. MPS figures include City of London Police.

five per cent received an absolute or conditional discharge and five per cent were imprisoned. Smaller numbers received probation or supervision orders, community service orders, combination orders, and suspended imprisonment sentences.

Similarly in the UK, 53 per cent of drug offenders received cautions, 22 per cent were fined, seven per cent received absolute or conditional discharges and seven per cent were imprisoned. Again, small numbers received probation or supervision orders, community service orders, combination orders, and suspended imprisonment sentences.

Stops and searches

Table 11.15 depicts the number of searches of individuals or vehicles, and Table 11.16 (overleaf) the resultant arrests of individuals, made by the police under the *Police and Criminal Evidence Act 1984* (PACE), and other legislation. The powers of the police to stop and search individuals and vehicles for drugs under PACE added to the previous powers of the police to conduct drug searches under the *Misuse of Drugs Act 1971*. Other legislation relates to searches made

Key finding

London drug searches account for three-fifths of all drug searches made in England and Wales under PACE.

by means of other police powers, such as those conferred by the Prevention of Terrorism Act 1989, or the Aviation

Security Act 1982 (Home Office Statistical Bulletin 1996a).

Key finding

London drug arrests account for just under half of all drug arrests made in England and Wales under PACE.

The number of searches in both London, and England and Wales, increased between 1993 and 1995. The proportion of drug searches as a percentage of all searches remained stable in London and England and Wales for the years 1993 and 1994, and rose in 1995.

Similarly, the number of arrests made in London and England and Wales, under PACE legislation, shows an increasing trend between 1993 and 1995 (Table 11.16). However, the proportion of searches resulting in an

Table 11.15 Searches of persons or vehicles under Police and Criminal Evidence Act 1984, and other legislation, by reason for search and location, 1993-1995		London			England and Wales			London drug
	Year	Drug searches	All searches	Drug searches as % of all searches	Drug searches	All searches	Drug searches as % all searches	searches as % of all E&W drug searches
	1993	82,400	228,300	36	135,700	442,800	31	61
	1994	106,300	292,000	36	179,100	576,000	31	59
	1995	134,300	320,400	42	231,900	690,300	34	58

Source: Home Office Statistical Bulletin (1996a), du Parq (1997).

Notes: Numbers of searches are rounded to the nearest 100.

Table 11.16

Arrests of persons under Police and Criminal Evidence Act 1984, and other legislation, and the proportion of searches resulting in arrest in parentheses, by reason for arrest and location, 1993-1995

	London			England and Wales			London
Year	Drug arrests	All arrests	Drug arrests as % of all arrests	Drug arrests	All arrests	Drug arrests as % of all arrests	drug arrests as % of all E&W drug arrests
1993	8,600 (10%)	25,400 (11%)	34	19,400 (14%)	55,900 (13%)	35	44
1994	11,800 (11%)	33,300 (11%)	35	25,400(14%)	70,300 (12%)	36	46
1995	13,600 (10%)	35,200 (11%)	39	30,700 (13%)	81,000 (12%)	38	44

Source: Home Office Statistical Bulletin (1996a), du Parq (1997).

Notes: Numbers of arrests are rounded to the nearest 100.

arrest has remained remarkably stable over this period. In England and Wales, around 14 per cent of drug searches lead to an arrest, compared to 10 per cent for London.

Prisons in Greater London

In the London area there are eight prisons: a male young offender institution (Feltham); a female prisoner institution (Holloway); five adult male institutions (Belmarsh, Brixton, Pentonville, Wandsworth and Wormwood Scrubs); and a male closed training prison (Latchmere House). They all hold sentenced (convicted of an offence), tried and unsentenced, and remand (awaiting trial) prisoners, except Latchmere House, which only holds those that have been sentenced. In the rest of England and Wales there are a total of 121 prison establishments.

were a total of 28,015 receptions into prison service establishments in London, accounting for 18 per cent of all receptions to prisons in England and Wales (Table 11.18 overleaf). A reception is when an individual prisoner is first received into prison as an untried, tried and unsentenced, or sentenced, prisoner. Therefore, individuals can be included in reception figures as many as three times, as they may progress from untried, to tried and unsentenced, and finally to sentenced prisoner classification.

Key finding

London had a higher proportion of sentenced drug offenders received into custody in 1995 than in the rest of England and Wales.

Prisoners in London prisons

On the 30th of June 1995, London establishments held a total of 5,384 prisoners (Table 11.17 overleaf), comprising 11 per cent of the prison population of England and Wales.

During the whole of 1995, there

Drug offenders in London prisons

Nine per cent of the sentenced population received into custody in London prisons in 1995 were prisoners

Table 11.17
Prison population
of England and
Wales by area,
30th June 1995

Establishment	Remand	Sentenced	Total	Non-criminal
Belmarsh	309	304	613	13
Brixton	310	292	602	4
Feltham	406	394	800	-
Holloway	237	307	544	19
Latchmere House	-	136	136	-
Pentonville	413	422	835	12
Wandsworth	248	802	1,050	12
Wormwood Scrubs	275	529	804	26
Total London	2,198	3,186	5,384	86
Other E&W establishments	8,858	36,193	45,700	563
Total England and Wales	11,056	39,379	51,084	649

Source: Home Office Offenders and Corrections Unit (1997).

Notes: Non-criminal offences fall under two main categories: the default of a payment or fine; and charges brought under
the Immigration Act 1971.

sentenced for drug offences, and similarly six per cent for England and Wales excluding London (Table 11.18 overleaf).

There were 1,154 receptions to London prison establishments for drug offences in 1995, constituting nearly a quarter (24%) of all receptions for drug offences to prison establishments in England and Wales. However, on June 30th 1995, only 334 individuals were held under sentence for drug offences in London prisons (Table 11.19 overleaf). It is unclear whether these figures give us an impression of the lengths of custodial sentence ordered, the numbers of repeated drug re-offenders, or movements of prisoners from London to establishments in other parts of the country after initial reception.

The most common offences amongst the 334 individuals sentenced for drug offences and held in London prisons on June 30th 1995 were possession with intent to supply (34%), unlawful supply (29%) and unlawful import or export (29%) (Table 11.19 overleaf).

Drug users in London prisons

Imprisonment is not uncommon amongst problematic drug users. Roughly half to three-quarters of injecting drug users have been in prison at some time (Dolan et al, 1990; Donoghoe et al, 1992; Covell et al, 1993; Turnbull and Stimson, 1994). In a survey of injecting drug users in London in 1993, 77 per cent reported being imprisoned at sometime (Turnbull and Stimson, 1994). Prison establishments will contain a substantial number of former and current drug users. However, the actual numbers of prisoners with a history of problematic drug use is not known.

Key finding

Little data are available on the numbers of drug users held in prisons in London.

Information concerning the drug using status of prisoners is not routinely collected by prison authorities. Therefore, to make an assessment of the numbers of

Table 11.18
Number of
receptions into
Prison Service
establishments,
England and Wales,
by area and
sentence, January
to December 1995

Establishment	Untried	Convicted unsentenced	Sentenced	Total	Sentenced drug offenders
Belmarsh	1,505	787	1,651	3,943	201
Brixton	1,477	826	1,853	4,156	119
Feltham	419	1,197	2,068	3,684	63
Holloway	1,269	780	1,554	3,603	237
Pentonville	2,003	1,094	2,223	5,320	209
Wandsworth	1,429	949	1,720	4,098	152
Wormwood Scrubs	1,182	510	1,519	3,211	173
Total London	9,284	6,143	12,588	28,015	1,154
Other E&W Establishments	46,003	25,896	56,428	128,327	3,575
Total England and Wales	55,287	32,039	69,016	156,342	4,729

Source: Home Office Offenders and Corrections Unit (1997).

Notes: These figures are for receptions and are not for individuals. It excludes persons committed in default of payment of a fine.
Data are not available for Latchmere House

drug using prisoners, data have to be pieced together, resulting in a patchy picture. For example, although data on offence type gives an indication of the numbers of drug users in prison, it has a number of limitations. For example, some of those imprisoned for drug offences may not use drugs, and many drug users will have been imprisoned for acquisitive crimes associated with their drug use, or for other crimes.

The most extensive study of the English prison population and drug using behaviour prior to imprisonment was conducted in 1988 (Maden et al, 1990a,b). Eleven per cent of men and 23 per cent of women in the sentenced population (non-remand prisoners) were considered to be drug dependent in the six months prior to imprisonment. In the same time period, seven per cent of men and 15 per cent of women reported having taken drugs by injection. On the basis of these data, it has been previously estimated that approximately 3,400 prisoners, or seven per cent, of the average prison population at any one time, and 15,000 of prisoner receptions in any one year, will have injected within the six months prior to imprisonment (Turnbull et al, 1992). Extrapolated to the London sentenced population on the 30th of June 1995, this would suggest that 317 out of the 2,879 sentenced male prisoners in London were dependent before imprisonment and 202 had injected before imprisonment.

Table 11.19
Population in
Prison Service
establishments in
England and Wales
under sentence for
drug offences on
30th June 1995

Establishment	Drug production	Drug supply	Possession with intent	Possession	Unlawful import/export	Other	Total
London	2	96	113	22	98	3	334
Other England and Wales	48	1,054	1,187	378	1,352	47	4,066
Total England and Wales	50	1,150	1,300	400	1,450	50	4,400

Source: Home Office Offenders and Corrections Unit (1997).

Notes: Excludes persons committed to prison in default of payment of a fine.

Two other sources of information give an indication of the number of problems drug users in London prisons. Ten per cent of all first notifications of drug users by any source in London in 1995 to the Home Office Addicts Index were from Prison Medical Officers (PMOs), some 811 individuals (Home Office Research and Statistics Directorate, 1996). First notifications in 1995 by PMOs in London accounted for 16 per cent of all notifications by PMOs in the UK.

North Thames Drugs Misuse Database (NTDMD) figures for the

Key finding

The data available suggest that problem drug users make up a significant group within prisons.

Thames region in 1995/96 show that 926 individual reports were made by three North London prisons, HMP Holloway, HMP Pentonville and HMP Wormwood Scrubs (NTDMD, 1997). However, for the 1995 calendar year, only 619 drug offenders were sentenced to imprisonment in these establishments. Data are not available from prisons in the South Thames region in 1995/96.

Female prisoners constituted three-fifths, and prisoners aged between 20 and 30 three-fifths (59%), of all those reported from prisons to NTDMD. The main drug reported to have been used was heroin (68%), followed by methadone (15%), cocaine (6%) and crack (5%). The majority of reported prisoners had previously or were currently injecting drugs (76% and 59% respectively) (NTDMD, 1997).

It is hard to square the results from the different sources of information. The Maden et al survey was conducted seven to eight years before the RDMD data. The Maden et al survey, the

Addicts Index, and the RDMD use different definitions, and with the last two coverage, compliance and the population denominator are unknown or unclear. What is certain is that the number of identified *problem drug users* is much lower than the number of drug users identified within prison by Mandatory Drug Testing.

The extent and nature of drug taking in London prisons

Only a few sources of data give an indication of the extent and nature of drug use in prison. Firstly, Mandatory Drug Testing (MDT) is now conducted in all prison establishments in Britain. It has three objectives: to establish the level of drug use in prison; to gauge where to invest in treatment; and to send a clear message that drug use in prison will not be tolerated (Wilson, 1997). Initially, random urine testing of prisoners was introduced on a pilot basis in eight prisons in England and Wales. Between February 1995 and January 1996, 3,785 pilot tests were carried out, with an average of two in five prisoners testing positive over the 12 months. Of the total 'positives', 81 per cent were for cannabis and nine per cent for opiates (Lee, 1996).

The programme of mandatory and voluntary drug testing was expanded in 1996, and between March and September 1996 a total of 47,425 tests were carried out in prisons in England and Wales. Just under a quarter of these samples tested positive for cannabis, and eight per cent tested positive for opiates. For the whole of the financial year 1996/97 around a quarter of random MDT tests were positive, the vast majority for cannabis. Thirty-five per cent of tests at Pentonville were positive, and similarly 25 per cent at Wormwood

Scrubs, 21 per cent at Feltham, 20 per cent at Holloway, 12 per cent at Brixton, eight per cent at Wandsworth and 6 per cent at Latchmere House (Wilson, 1997). MDT data broken down for Belmarsh Prison are not currently available. MDT costs £45.32 per test, and the total cost of introducing MDT to the Prison Service was £940,840 (House of Commons, 1996).

Secondly, surveys of drug users in the community, once released from prison, provide another source of infor-mation on the extent and nature of drug use in prison. In a 1993 survey of injecting drug users in London, of those who had been in prison at some time, three-quarters reported using at least one drug whilst imprisoned. Twenty eight per cent of those that had been in prison reported injecting in prison, and two-thirds of these reported sharing the needles they had injected with (Turnbull and Stimson, 1994).

The Probation Service

The Probation Service in England and Wales consists of 54 probation 'areas'. Five such areas have a remit to provide services in Greater London: Inner London; North-East London; South-East London; South-West London; and Middlesex. A few of the main responsibilities of the Probation Service are to: provide courts with advice on offenders to assist in sentencing decisions; implement and enforce community sentences passed by courts; assist offenders, before and after their release, to lead law-abiding lives; and work in partnership with other services in order to utilise the most constructive methods of dealing with offenders and defendants (Home Office, 1996).

Table 11.20 shows supervision order commencements by type of offence and area. Supervision orders include court orders, such as parole, and combination orders (a mixture of probation supervision and community

Table 11.20 Supervision order commencements by type of offence and area, 1995	Number of orders	Drugs indictable	Summary drugs	All other offences
	Inner London	1,024	8	9,530
	NE London	233	0	2,686
	SE London	156	0	2,155
	SW London	116	0	1,136
	Middlesex	438	7	4,942
	Total London	1,967	15	20,449
	TOTAL E&W	9,575	76	143,524
	London as % of E&W	21	20	14

Source: Home Office Research and Statistics Directorate (1997).

Notes: Individual London areas should not, strictly speaking, be added to produce overall London totals. Similarly totals from London and other areas should not be added to produce totals for England and Wales. This is because, in theory, an individual could commence, or complete and commence, two supervision orders, each in a different area, in the same year. However, it is thought that in practise the numbers of individuals doing so are small.

service, lasting from 12 months to three years). Indictable offences are generally serious breaches of the criminal law triable only at Crown Court. Summary offences are triable only at magistrates courts and are dominated by motoring offences.

In each year, more supervision orders commenced in Inner London than any other part of London. Around one in five supervision orders commencing in England and Wales in 1995 for drugs offences (indictable and summary) were commenced in London. This compares with a figure of 14 per cent for all other types of offences.

Probation orders with additional requirements

Individuals commencing probation orders in 1995, with additional requirements stipulating drug or alcohol treatment, are depicted in Table 11.21. Offenders aged 16 and over may be sentenced with their consent to a probation order, which is a criminal penalty lasting for six months to three years (Barclay 1995). Each offender is supervised by a probation officer. Courts have additional powers to include other requirements to the probation order as

Key finding
A higher proportion of supervision orders relating to drug offences, as compared to all other offences, occur in London.

appropriate, such as treatment for drug or alcohol dependency.

Around a third of all additional requirements to probation orders relating to drug and alcohol treatment in England and Wales occurred in London. Inner London had the highest number of additional requirements relating to drug and alcohol treatment imposed by the courts in 1995.

Combination orders with additional requirements

Table 11.22 (overleaf) depicts the number of individuals commencing combination orders stipulating additional requirement of treatment for drug or alcohol dependency. It should be noted that a combination order combines elements of probation supervision and community service, and can last from 12 months to three years.

Approximately a third of all additional drug and alcohol treatment requirements relating to combination orders in England and Wales were ordered in

Table 11.21 Persons commencing probation orders by type of additional requirement and area, 1995	Number of persons	Residential drugs/alcohol treatment	Non-residential drugs/alcohol treatment	Drugs/alcohol treatment by qualified medical person
	Inner London	98	169	97
	NE London	17	8	27
	SE London	2	10	6
	SW London	6	8	10
	Middlesex	20	56	33
	Total London	143	251	173
	TOTAL E&W	370	760	555
	London as % of E&W	39	33	31

Source: Home Office Research and Statistics Directorate (1997).

Notes: See Table 11.20.

	Number of persons	Residential drugs/alcohol treatment	Non-residential drugs/alcohol treatment	Drugs/alcohol treatment by qualified medical person
Table 11.22 **Persons** **commencing** **combination orders** **by type of addition-** **al requirement and** **area, 1995**	Inner London	2	17	9
	NE London	0	0	1
	SE London	0	0	0
	SW London	0	0	1
	Middlesex	0	11	7
	Total London	2	28	18
	Total E&W	6	108	61
	London as % of E&W	33	26	30

Source: Home Office Research and Statistics Directorate (1997).

Notes: See Table 11.20.

London in 1995. Only six additional requirements of residential treatment for drug or alcohol dependence were attached to combination orders in England and Wales in 1995.

Acknowledgements

The authors would like to thank Sylvia Mazabel for her assistance in compiling the Customs and Excise data presented in this chapter.

References

Barclay, G.C. (1995). *The Criminal Justice System in England and Wales 1995*. London: Home Office.

Covell, R.G., Frischer, M., Taylor, A. et al (1993). Prison experience of injecting drug users in Glasgow. *Drug and Alcohol Dependence*, 32, 9-14.

Dolan, K.A., Donoghoe, M.C. and Stimson, G.V. (1990). Drug injecting and sharing in custody and the community: an exploratory survey of HIV risk behaviour. *The Howard Journal of Criminal Justice*, 29, 177-186.

Donoghoe, M.C., Stimson, G.V. and Dolan, K.A. (1992). *Syringe Exchange in England: An Overview*. London: Tufnell Press.

du Parq, R. (1997). Personal communication.

HMCE (1996). Unpublished data.

Home Office (1996). *Probation Statistics England and Wales 1995*. London: Government

Statistical Service.

Home Office Offenders and Corrections Unit (1997). *Personal communication*.

Home Office Research and Statistics Directorate (1996). *Personal communication*.

Home Office Research and Statistics Directorate (1997). *Personal communication*.

Home Office Statistical Bulletin (1993). *Issue 30/93 Statistics of Drug Seizures and Offenders Dealt With, United Kingdom, 1992*. London: Government Statistical Service.

Home Office Statistical Bulletin (1996a). *Issue 12/96 Operation of Certain Police Powers Under PACE*. London: Government Statistical Service.

Home Office Statistical Bulletin (1996b). *Issue 25/96 Statistics of Drugs Seizures and Offenders Dealt With, United Kingdom, 1995*. London: Government Statistical Service.

Home Office Statistical Bulletin (1996c). *Area Tables. Issue 25/96 Statistics of Drug Seizures and Offenders Dealt With, United Kingdom, 1995*. London: Government Statistical Service.

House of Commons (1996). *Hansard Written Answers for 5 November 1996*. London: House of Commons.

King, L.A. (1997). Drug content of powders and other illicit preparations in the UK. *Forensic Science International*, 85, 135-147.

Lee, M. (1996). Proof positive. *Druglink*, May/June, 4.

Maden, A., Swinton, M., and Gunn, J. (1990a). Drug dependence in prison. *British Medical Journal*, 302, 880.

Maden, A., Swinton, M. and Gunn, J. (1990b). Women in prison and the use of illicit drugs before. *British Medical Journal*, 301, 1133.

North Thames Drugs Misuse Database (1997). *Unpublished data*.

Office for National Statistics (1997). Personal communication.

Turnbull, P.J., Stimson, G.V. and Dolan, K.A. (1992). Prevalence of HIV infection among ex-prisoners in England. *British Medical Journal*, 304, 90-91.

Turnbull, P.J. and Stimson, G.V. (1994). Drug use in prison. *British Medical Journal*, 308, 1716.

Wilson, P. (1997). *Drugs in Prison*. London Drugs Policy Forum Conference, Guildhall, London.

DRUG USERS ATTENDING TREATMENT SERVICES

Arun Sondhi
The Centre for Research on Drugs and Health
Behaviour

Sections

Treatment services in London

There are estimated to be approximately 150 services providing treatment or care to problem drug users in London (Box 12.1). Adequate information about individuals attending such treatment services is useful in: assessing the overall extent of the drug 'problem' within and across different areas, and also over time; examining the nature of problem drug use (whether, for example, individuals prefer to inject or smoke drugs); and to help improve the provision of services for those populations with the greatest health needs.

This chapter attempts to answer key questions about individuals currently in treatment in London, whilst highlighting some of the difficulties and problems encountered in doing this. After outlining data relating to the number of problem drug users seeking treatment, the chapter considers the characteristics of these individuals, and the drugs they are taking. The chapter also briefly reflects on the likely future of treatment demand and its surveillance in the capital.

Box 12.1
Drug services in
London, 1997/98

Drug services in London, 1997/98

London has:

- Over sixty-five community-based services providing health care to those individuals in the local population affected by problem drug use.
- Thirteen drug dependency units (DDUs) offering a range of usually out-patient services with a focus on prescribing substitute drugs and providing health care.
- Twelve structured day programmes (SDPs) offering community-based support through a fixed weekly programme of activities.
- Eighteen residential rehabilitation units providing intensive support to those individuals unable to address their drug problems in a domestic setting.
- Fifty-three needle-exchange schemes providing services through dedicated outlets, community-based services and outreach schemes.
- Twenty one pharmacy-based needle-exchange schemes.
- A number of specialist residential 'crisis intervention' care services for those individuals who have experienced a medical or drug-related emergency.
- Nearly four thousand general practitioners (GPs).

Reporting systems

Drug users in contact with treatment services in London and the UK are monitored by two main reporting systems: the Home Office Addicts Index (HOAI) and the Regional Drug Misuse Databases (RDMD).

Home Office Addicts Index (1968-1997)

The Home Office has collected information since 1934 on those problem drug users treated by general and private practitioners in the UK. However, until 1968, the system was based upon informal information provided to the Home Office Drugs Branch, whose primary concern was to prevent problem drug users receiving prescribed drugs from more than one doctor ('dual scripting').

Following the recommendations of the 1965 Brain Committee, a more formal notification system was established in 1968. This was one of a series of measures introduced around the same time, reflecting increasing governmental concern about the now national drug problem (Chapter 3).

The new 'Home Office Addicts Index' served three functions: firstly, it continued to provide information to doctors on patients involved in dual scripting; secondly, it facilitated collation of a national record of those doctors prescribing and their prescribing regimes; and thirdly it introduced a measure of the national drug problem.

Drugs

With the introduction of the *Misuse of Drugs Act 1971*, all medical practitioners were legally required to notify the HOAI of any patient considered to be 'addicted' to one of 14 controlled drugs ('new' notifications). These were Class A drugs - covering heroin, other named opiates, and cocaine. Doctors were also obliged under the regulations to re-notify long-term patients to the Index once every 12 months ('re-notifications').

Details provided by doctors to the HOAI included the full name of the patient, their date of birth, home address and NHS number. In addition, information on the range of drugs being used, whether or not the patient was injecting, and the doctor's prescribing plan were also given.

Problems

The HOAI suffered from several problems. The major difficulty was that notifications to the Index represented only a small proportion of those actually receiving treatment. This was for a number of reasons. Firstly, only medical practitioners were able to notify the Index, excluding non-statutory agencies or services without medical staff. Secondly, only a small range of drugs were recorded (notable exclusions being amphetamines and benzodiazepines). Thirdly, compliance with the system was reported to be poor - it has since been estimated that only one-quarter of the problem drug users seen by a medical practitioner at a surgery, general or psychiatric hospital were actually notified to the HOAI (Strang and Shah, 1985).

Following the introduction of the Regional Drug Misuse Databases in 1989, the use of the Addicts Index as an epidemiological tool was questioned even further. Ironically, the rationale for establishing the Index - to allow doctors to check that patients were not receiving a prescription elsewhere - was identified as particularly problematic due to the low levels of compliance. In consideration of this, and in light of the substantial cost of maintaining such a system, the Index was disbanded in May 1997.

Key finding

With the demise of the HOAI, it has been argued that doctors in London will now face a greater problem than elsewhere in the country in checking for patients obtaining multiple prescriptions (Druglink, 1997). Given London's large and transitory population, local knowledge of known drug users amongst doctors is thought to be limited and it has been suggested that without *any* check on multiple prescriptions, a significant increase in the diversion of prescribed drugs onto the illicit market could occur.

Regional Drug Misuse Databases (1989 onwards)

In response to a perceived growth in the number of problem drug users, and an awareness of the HIV risk associated with injecting drug use, the Department of Health recommended in 1989 that all English Regional Health Authorities should establish a RDMD. By 1997, there were 12 RDMDs in England with one database in Scotland and Wales respectively. Northern Ireland, at the time of writing, does not have an RDMD.

Data

RDMDs collect data on any drug user who presents in person for treatment at a service. This treatment *episode* may either be the first time that an individual has attended treatment or where an individual re-contacts the same service after a break of at least six months. Therefore, an individual can have more than one *episode* of contact with treatment services. RDMDs also count the number of different individuals who present for treatment and help (this count is, of course, less than the number of episodes). At present, RDMD data cannot be used to calculate the total number or prevalence of individuals actually in treatment at any given time.

In contrast with the HOAI, full names and addresses are not collected by the RDMDs. Instead, 'attributors' such as an individual's initials, date of birth and gender are used. RDMDs receive reports from a wider range of sources than the HOAI and include information from statutory and non-statutory drug services, hospital units, as well as GPs. In addition, any drug that can be used problematically is recorded by the RDMDs - this includes alcohol, but only as a secondary drug

of misuse. A host of socio-demographic information is also collated.

Injecting and indicators

RDMDs primarily provide local epidemiological information on patterns of presenting drug use (Donmall, 1990). However, information on injecting and sharing of equipment is also collected. Such information is used to monitor the Government's Health of the Nation target to reduce the percentage of injecting drug misusers who report sharing injecting equipment (Department of Health, 1992). Furthermore, RDMDs also monitor specific indicators for the 27 Drug Action Teams in London relating to young people, health risks and problem drug use.

Regional Drug Misuse Databases in London

Prior to 1997, there were four RDMDs in London with each database collating reports within the then Thames Regional Health Authorities (Figure 12.2 opposite) Although each RDMD operated in a similar manner (with the exception of South-West Thames which used a different type of database) this geographic fragmentation made it difficult to co-ordinate and collate pan-London treatment data.

Two organisational changes, however, addressed this problem. In 1997, an attempt to reduce reporting overlap across the two North Thames RDMDs, resulted in the formation of a single North Thames database. This move was then mirrored in the recent decision to form a single South Thames database in 1998. From April 1998, The Centre for Research on Drugs and Health Behaviour will be responsible for all of the London RDMDs with the long-term aim of implementing a pan-Thames and pan-London RDMD.

Map 12.2 Areas covered by the Regional Drug Misuse Databases and the Home Office Addicts Index in London, before and after 1997/98 RDMD organisational changes

North-West Thames	North-East Thames
11 Hillingdon	6 Camden & Islington
8 Ealing, Hammersmith & Hounslow	9 East London and The City
4 Brent & Harrow	10 Enfield & Haringey
2 Barnet	16 Redbridge & Waltham Forest
12 Kensington & Chelsea and Westminster	1 Barking and Havering

South-West Thames	South-East Thames
13 Kingston & Richmond	14 Lambeth, Southwark & Lewisham
15 Merton, Sutton and Wandsworth	3 Bexley and Greenwich
7 Croydon	5 Bromley

Notes: In 1997, a single North Thames RDMD was formed by merging North-West and North-East Thames RDMDs. A single South Thames RDMD will be created during 1998, this will cover the South-East and South-West Thames RDMDs. The HOAI was unaffected by these changes.

Problem drug users and treatment demand in London

There are a number of indicators which provide information on the level of treatment demand in London. The two main reporting systems - the RDMDs and the HOAI - are detailed below and provide a good, if sometimes incomplete, guide to treatment demand. However, as shown later, it is possible to overcome some of their shortfalls and, using data from the RDMD reporting system, estimate the total number of London problem drug users in treatment.

How many notifications were made from London to the HOAI?

Table 12.3 illustrates both the number of new and all notifications made to the Home Office Addicts Index between 1991 and 1996. The number of new addicts notified from London doctors increased steadily until 1993, stabilising until the increase in 1996. In 1991, London doctors notified almost one-third of all new addicts in the UK (29%). However by 1996, this proportion declined to 19 per cent of all new notifications. A similar trend was noticed in all addicts notified. This is largely due to the notifications in other parts of the country (especially Northern and Yorkshire Health Authority) increasing at a greater rate than in London.

How many treatment episodes were reported to the London RDMDs?

The number of episodes and individuals reported by London services to RDMDs is shown in Table 12.4 (opposite).

There was a small increase of five per cent in the total episodes reported in 1995/96, followed by a two per cent drop in 1996/97. The largest numbers of episodes were reported from: Kensington & Chelsea and Westminster;

Table 12.3
Number of new and all notifications to the Home Office Addicts Index in London, 1991-1996

		New notifications					
		1991	1992	1993	1994	1995	1996
	London	2,310	2,404	2,870	2,823	2,881	3,397
	UK	8,007	9,663	11,561	13,469	14,735	18,281
London as a % of UK		29	25	25	21	20	19

		All (new and re-notifications)					
		1991	1992	1993	1994	1995	1996
	London	6,394	6,902	7,606	8,281	8,172	8,985
	UK	20,820	24,703	27,976	33,952	37,164	43,372
London as a % of UK		31	28	27	24	22	21

Source: Home Office Addicts Index (1996).

Notes: A new notification is where an individual is notified for the first time to the Home Office Addicts Index. Re-notified addicts are those who have been notified in a previous year and who have again been notified in the current year.

Table 12.4
Episodes and
individuals reported
by services to the
Regional Drug
Misuse Databases
by London health
authority, 1994-
1997

Health authority	1994/95	1995/96	1996/97
Hillingdon	106	131	117
Barnet	124	112	136
Ealing, Hammersmith & Hounslow	532	746	1,065
Kensington & Chelsea and Westminster	1,470	1,625	1,304
Camden & Islington	1,766	1,662	1,415
Brent & Harrow	412	524	416
Enfield & Haringey	124	385	396
Redbridge & Waltham Forest	164	208	182
East London and The City	2,015	1,492	1,632
Barking and Havering	216	304	272
Bexley and Greenwich	360	483	448
Lambeth, Southwark & Lewisham	2,611	2,644	2,829
Bromley	251	272	262
Croydon	248	368	323
Merton, Sutton and Wandsworth	954	1,085	1,006
Kingston & Richmond	485	409	455
Total episodes	11,838	12,450	12,258
Total individuals	11,536	12,419	10,972

Source: Regional Drug Misuse Databases (1997).

Camden & Islington; East London and The City; and Lambeth, Southwark & Lewisham.

Key finding
In 1996, London accounted for 8,985 of all notifications to the Home Office Addicts Index, compared to the United Kingdom total of 43,372. Approximately 21 per cent of all addicts therefore are reported in London.

The highest rate of drug users attending services per 100,000 population (Figure 12.6 overleaf) are reported in inner city areas such as: Camden & Islington (778); Lambeth, Southwark & Lewisham (771); and Kensington & Chelsea and Westminster (719). East London and The City (566) also has higher than average London reports. Outer London areas such as Redbridge & Waltham Forest (89), Barnet (96) and Hillingdon (105) have lower than average rates. However, these figures may be a reflection of higher or lower levels of service provision in the respective areas.

How many drug users are estimated to be in treatment in London?
Bearing in mind the caveats outlined in Box 12.5 (overleaf), estimations based on a recent study (Hickman et al, 1997) have indicated that there were approximately 16,000 individual problem drug users in contact with London treatment services in 1996/97 (Table 12.7 overleaf). In addition, it has been calculated that the annual volume of clients attending services was approximately 20,000 people (Table 12.7).

Box 12.5
Obstacles in
estimating the
number of drug
users in London in
treatment

Obstacles in estimating the number of drug users in London in treatment

There are three main considerations that need to be made:

Unknown overlap between the Addicts Index and RDMDs

Although in theory, the HOAI should be a subset of the data collected by the RDMDs - with general and private practitioners reporting to both systems - inconsistencies exist between the two reporting systems. This is partly explained by selective compliance by GPs and private practitioners towards the Index. However, assessing the extent of overlap of individuals recorded by both reporting systems is difficult, as direct comparisons are hindered by differing methodologies, geographical coverage, criteria for eligible cases, and time periods employed. In the only study of reporting system overlap (undertaken in the North West of England), nearly three-quarters of those individuals notified to the HOAI were also recorded by RDMDs (Mott et al, 1993). The extent of an equivalent overlap in London, however, is still unknown.

Non-compliance and under-reporting

As mentioned above, there will be doctors and agencies who should report to the HOAI and the RDMDs but either do this intermittently ('under-reporting') or fail to do so at all (non-compliance). The quality of reports received by the RDMDs in London tends to vary according to the type and philosophy of the service. For example, statutory services such as drug dependency units, who are likely to operate a detailed routine data collection procedure, are more compliant and less likely to under-report. However, other services may be unwilling to participate, particularly if they feel that providing client information could deter problem drug users from seeking treatment.

Therefore, whilst there are estimated to be approximately 150 services for problem drug users in London, around 89 services routinely report to the RDMDs. Of those services who are involved in face-to-face contacts with problem users, it is estimated that only 10 do not routinely report to the RDMDs. Those services not reporting include needle-exchanges, outreach schemes, criminal justice agencies and those other services presently outside of the RDMDs data collection remit. Furthermore, recent research by the RDMD in the North Thames region has indicated that under-reporting amongst these services may range between 25 to 32 per cent (Hickman et al, 1997).

Episodes versus caseload (prevalence of problem drug users)

RDMDs measure episodes as opposed to the prevalence of known problem drug users in treatment. Furthermore, since the databases only collect data on presenting drug misuse (those that involve face-to-face contact), other forms of service work such as telephone calls or third party contacts may be recorded locally, but for comparability are not included in database statistics.

**Figure 12.6
Rate of treatment
episodes reported
by services to
the Regional Drug
Misuse Databases
per 100,000 of the
population by
London health
authority, 1996/97**

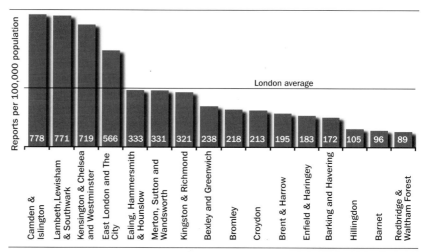

Sources: Thames Regional Drug Misuse Databases (1997), Office for National Statistics (1997).

Notes: Rates are calculated by relating the number of treatment episodes reported in each area to the 1995 mid-year population
estimates provided by the Office for National Statistics for the 15-44 age group. Mid-year population estimates should be
treated with caution as they are based on statistical assumptions which may not translate readily to the real world.

These estimations were achieved through applying a correction multiplier to existing RDMD data. This is a technique where data-sets are adjusted to accommodate known discrepancies in the data collection process. Further details of this procedure are given in the authors' report.

Key finding

For the six month period up to 31st March 1996, there were 5,867 individuals reported to the Regional Databases in London. This amounts to a quarter (25%) of all reports in England and a fifth (20%) of all reports from the United Kingdom (Department of Health, 1997a).

**Table 12.7
Estimations of the
volume and num-
ber of individual
drug users attend-
ing treatment ser-
vices in London,
1996/97**

	1996/97 London RDMD Figures	Correction multiplier
Individuals reported to London RDMDs	10,972	
Estimated volume of clients attending services in London	20,298	1.85
Estimated number of individual problem drug users	15,690	1.43

Source: Hickman et al (1997).

Notes: Volume of clients is the number of different individual drug users who are attending separate drug services in a year
(this figure may record more than once those individuals attending several different services). The number of
individual problem drug users is the total number of unique individuals reporting to North Thames services in a year.
The analysis excludes individuals in contact with services not currently recorded by the RDMD and does not take
into account GP reporting. There may be difficulties in translating generalisations from multipliers created from
research in the North Thames area, to services elsewhere in London and the UK.

Characteristics of problem drug users attending London treatment services

The RDMDs and HOAI can both provide socio-demographic profiles of problem drug users attending drug services in London. As not all drug services report to the RDMDs, a common criticism had, until recently, addressed the representativeness of these profiles for individuals in contact with non-reporting treatment centres. A study conducted in the North Thames area, however, confirmed that the characteristics of individuals attending treatment agencies who routinely report to the RDMD, actually differ little from those individuals - in terms of age, gender, area of residence, ethnicity and drug profile - attending agencies who do not partcipate (Hickman et al, 1997). Assuming this also holds for South Thames, North Thames RDMD data

can provide a roughly representative indicator of the social characteristics of drug users attending drugs agencies across London.

Age and sex

The RDMDs indicate that the modal age group for problem drug users attending treatment services is between 25 and 29 years (Figure 12.8). Nearly half are in their twenties, with 94 per cent being aged between 15 and 44 years. Approximately eight per cent are under twenty years of age (Table 12.9 opposite). This age profile is also reflected in HOAI data: in 1996, 97 per cent of 'new' drug addicts and 93 per cent of 'all' drug addicts notified to the Index were aged between 15 and 44.

The ratio of male to female drug users as reported to the RDMDs is roughly 70:30. With the exception of the 55 to 59, and 65 and over age groups (where the predominance of men is less pronounced), this is consistent across all

> **Key finding**
>
> The typical London problem drug user in treatment is male, white, aged mid-to-late twenties and unemployed.

Figure 12.8 Age and sex of problem drug users reported to the Regional Drug Misuse Databases in London, 1996/97

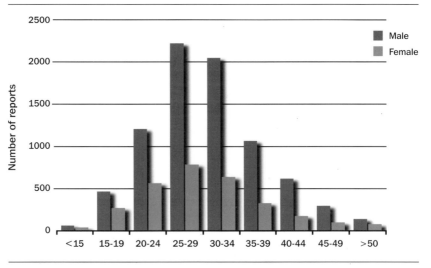

Source: Regional Drug Misuse Databases (1997).

Table 12.9	%	London	England
Percentage of	Under 15 years	1	1
problem drug	15-19	6	12
users reported to	20-24	16	28
Regional Drug	25-29	27	26
Misuse Databases	30-34	24	18
by age and	35-39	13	9
location, 1996	40-44	7	4
	45-49	4	2
	Over 50 years	2	1

Source: Regional Drug Misuse Databases (1997),
Department of Health (1997a).

Notes: London data cover the financial year 1996/97.
England data cover the period 1 October 1995
31 March 1996. Here, and elsewhere in this
chapter, England figures are inclusive of London.
Percentages may not add up to 100 as figures
have been rounded.

age groups. Similarly, in 1996, 77 per cent of new notifications to the Addicts Index were male as were 74 per cent of all notifications.

Ethnicity

The ethnic profile of users attending drug services in London is broadly similar to the wider London population (Table 12.10), with the large majority of

Key finding

Problem drug users attending services in London are slightly older than those in the rest of England (Table 12.9). London problem drug users are less likely to be aged between 15 and 24, but are more likely to be aged 30 years and above.

drug users attending services recorded as 'white'. However, based on comparisons with the proportion of individuals in the wider non-drug using London population, there are higher than expected numbers of 'black-other' problem drug users presenting for treatment in the London area. Meanwhile, the proportion of other ethnic groups such as black Africans, Chinese, Indian, Pakistani and Bangladeshi is lower. This could, however, imply that a proportion of problem drug users do not consider and self-report their ethnicity as falling within standard OPCS classification.

Employment

Nearly two-thirds of all problem drug users reported to the RDMDs are unemployed (Figure 12.11 overleaf). This compares with the 12 per cent of Londoners in the general population classified as unemployed (OPCS, 1993).

Table 12.10	Ethnicity	Drug users attending services	London population
Ethnicity of	(OPCS Classification)	%	%
individuals			
attending drug	White	79.7	79.8
treatment services	Black - Caribbean	4.5	4.4
reporting to London	Black - African	0.8	2.4
Regional Drug	Black - other	4.3	1.2
Misuse Databases	Indian	2.2	5.2
as compared to the	Pakistani	0.5	1.3
wider London	Bangladeshi	0.5	1.3
population,	Chinese	0.1	0.8
1996/97	Other	7.5	0.9

Source: Regional Drug Misuse Databases (1997), OPCS (1993).

Notes: Ethnic classification as defined by the OPCS. Percentages are not inclusive and may not total to 100%.

Figure 12.11
Employment status
of problem drug
users reported to
the Regional Drug
Misuse Databases
in London, 1996/97

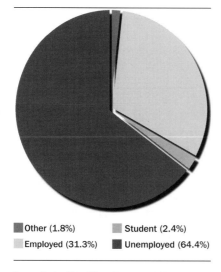

■ Other (1.8%)　　　■ Student (2.4%)
▨ Employed (31.3%)　■ Unemployed (64.4%)

Source: Regional Drug Misuse Databases (1997).

Problem drug use and social deprivation

There are notable differences between health authorities in the number of treatment episodes reported to the RDMDs. This may be for a number of reasons (ranging from levels of service provision to non-compliance), however, given the high proportion of unemployed drug users seeking treatment (Figure 12.11), it is not unreasonable to suggest the existence of a relationship between problem drug use and social deprivation.

Figure 12.12 (overleaf) illustrates in a regression line the correlation between Jarman Under Privileged Area (UPA) scores with the number of treatment episodes reported by each health authority during 1996/97. The UPA scores are based on eight census variables thought to indicate deprivation, which are weighted and standardised to produce a measure capable of indicating relative social deprivation or affluence. Using UPA scores, comparisons can be made between geographical areas, with a positive figure indicating areas of high social deprivation and a negative score indicating relative affluence (Jarman, 1983).

Correlation

There is a high correlation between reports to the RDMDs (categorised by health authority) and UPA scores ($R=0.776$, $p=0.0001$; $R2=0.605$). A link - at least at an aggregate level - may therefore exist between problem drug users attending treatment services and the wider level of social deprivation. A similar analysis using 'all' notifications made to the HOAI by health authority, suggests a slightly weaker correlation ($R2=0.391$, $p=0.01$). However, this could be accounted for by the proportionately more returns from GPs received by the Index. Generally, GPs tend to be located throughout the London area, unlike drug services which tend to be mainly based in poorer inner city areas. Furthermore, reports to the Addicts Index can also be made by private doctors who arguably tend to have a more affluent patient base.

Presently, the available RDMD data only reflect those areas where services are based - not where problem drug users actually live. Given the likely geographical mobility of those problem drug users seeking specialist treatment, a more valid analysis might attempt to consider the main place or area of residence of a problem drug user. In a collaborative report between the London RDMDs and the London Drug Policy Forum, this association was found to be statistically more significant than the actual district where treatment took place (Goldfinch et al, forthcoming).

Figure 12.12 Reports of problem drug use to the Regional Drug Misuse Databases per 100,000 of the London population by location and Jarman UPA scores, 1996/97

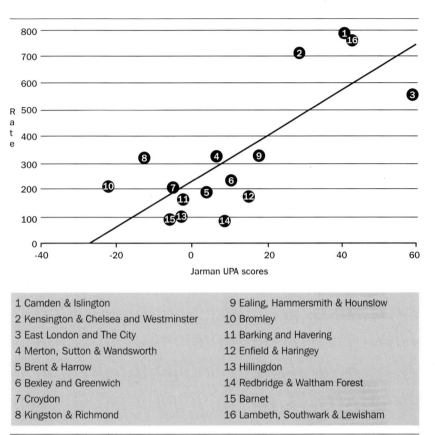

1	Camden & Islington	9	Ealing, Hammersmith & Hounslow
2	Kensington & Chelsea and Westminster	10	Bromley
3	East London and The City	11	Barking and Havering
4	Merton, Sutton & Wandsworth	12	Enfield & Haringey
5	Brent & Harrow	13	Hillingdon
6	Bexley and Greenwich	14	Redbridge & Waltham Forest
7	Croydon	15	Barnet
8	Kingston & Richmond	16	Lambeth, Southwark & Lewisham

Source: Regional Drug Misuse Databases (1997), Jarman (1983).

Notes: Each dot on the figure represents one of the 16 health authorities in London. The level of deprivation in that area is determined by two factors: the proximity of the dot to the regression line (the closer the dot, the more 'accurate' the description); and the UPA score the dot corresponds to. The eight census variables used to calculate UPA scores include: elderly living alone; children aged under five; residents in 'lone parent' households; residents in households with a head of household in the unskilled socio-economic group; unemployed; residents in overcrowded households; residents who changed address in previous year; residents in households headed by a person born in the New Commonwealth.

Which drugs are causing problems?

Regional Drug Misuse Database

Figure 12.13 (overleaf) illustrates the range of drugs used by individuals as reported to services in London in 1996/97. The 'main' drug is defined by the user as their most problematic substance of misuse. 'Any drug' refers to

up to five other drugs reported by the user as causing additional problems at the time of contact.

The majority of individuals report problems with heroin and methadone. However, as well as being indicative of prevalence, this may also be due to the opiate-based nature of many treatment services in London. Further caution

Figure 12.13
Drugs used by those reported to the London Regional Drug Misuse Databases, 1996/97

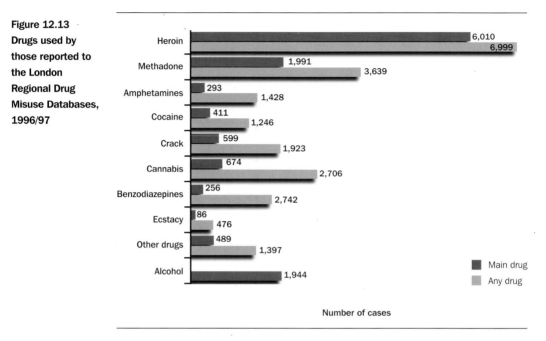

Number of cases

Source: Regional Drug Misuse Databases (1997).

Notes: One-hundred and sixty-three individuals stated that they were drug free. 'Any drug' totals will not equal the number of individuals as up to five drugs can be recorded on the database form.

should also be exercised where methadone is reported as a problem drug as individuals seeking treatment are often referred from another source where they were already being prescribed methadone. This could explain the relatively high number of problem methadone users reported.

Benzodiazepines, cocaine (including crack) and cannabis also feature strongly as secondary drugs (Table 12.14). Although alcohol is not recorded as a main drug by the RDMDs, it is recorded as a secondary drug due to it being problematically used in conjunction with other drugs.

Table 12.14
Comparison of 'main' and 'any' drug use reported to Regional Drug Misuse Databases by location, 1996/97

	Main Drug		Any Drug	
	London (incl. London)	England	London (incl. London)	England
	%	%	%	%
Heroin	56	54	65	63
Methadone	18	15	34	28
Benzodiazepines	2	3	25	20
Ampethamines	3	10	13	19
Cocaine (including crack)	9	4	29	15
Cannabis	6	7	25	27
Ecstasy	1	1	4	7

Source: Regional Drug Misuse Databases (1997), Department of Health Statistical Bulletin (1997a).

Notes: London data covers the financial year 1996/97. England data covers the period 1st October 1995 - 31st March 1996.

Table 12.15		1991	1992	1993	1994	1995	1996
New notifications							
in London to the	Heroin	1,927	1,959	2,262	2,156	2,179	2,658
Home Office	Methadone	514	535	809	834	904	962
Addicts Index by	Cocaine	384	428	601	589	662	729
drug type, 1991-	Others	50	44	48	44	37	38
1996	Total individuals	2,310	2,304	2,870	2,823	2,881	3,397

Source: Home Office Addicts Index (1997).

Notes: Drug totals will not add to the number of individuals as more than one drug per person can be notified.

Key finding

A higher proportion of clients in London report problems with heroin and methadone (Table 12.14 previous page); amphetamine is reported less in London, whilst cocaine and crack are nearly double the English average.

Home Office Addicts Index

The number of new heroin addicts notified to the Home Office Addicts Index increased from 1,927 addicts in 1991 to 2,658 addicts in 1996, a rise of 38 per cent (Table 12.15). Although there was a slight drop in the number of heroin notifications in 1994, there was an appreciable increase in the number of heroin notifications, with a 22 per cent rise between 1995 and 1996.

New methadone and cocaine notifications have both increased from 1991. In the five years from 1991 to 1996, the number of new notifications from London relating to problem methadone

use increased by 87 per cent (from 514 notifications to 962). However, the same caveats about interpreting methadone reports made to the RDMDs also apply to the Addicts Index. New cocaine notifications also increased by 90 per cent from 1991 to 1996 (from 384 new addicts to 729 addicts).

A similar pattern also applies to all notifications from 1991 to 1996 (Table 12.16). Although all heroin notifications slightly dipped in 1995, the number of heroin addicts notified in London increased by 27 per cent from 1991 to 1996. This constitutes a smaller increase than the number of new notifications of heroin users. Methadone notifications in London increased by 88 per cent from 1991 to 1996, whilst cocaine notifications rose by 94 per cent during this period. However, in comparison with the number of new notifications made in 1996, there has been a smaller increase in the percentage of all addict notifications (47% and 41% respectively).

Table 12.16		1991	1992	1993	1994	1995	1996
All notifications in							
London to the	Heroin	4,935	5,077	5,397	5,636	5,594	6,280
Home Office	Methadone	2,122	2,522	3,165	3,686	3,728	3,994
Addicts Index by	Cocaine	696	837	1,123	1,238	1,268	1,347
drug type, 1991-	Others	176	136	130	105	86	75
1996	Total individuals	6,394	6,902	7,606	8,281	8,172	8,985

Source: Home Office Addicts Index (1997).

Notes: Drug totals will not add to the number of individuals as more than one drug per person can be notified. All notifications include new notifications to the Addicts Index plus re-notifications.

How many individuals are injecting drugs?

The number of new notifications in London to the Addicts Index reported as injecting drugs has fluctuated from 1991 to 1996 (Table 12.17 opposite). However, the number of non-injectors has steadily increased from 1991 to 1995, with a 30 per cent rise in 1996. Furthermore, as a general trend, the number of non-injectors in London from 1991 to 1996 increased at a greater rate than those reported as injecting, resulting in the proportion of notified injectors falling to around half (50%) of all new addicts in 1996.

The proportion of all notified addicts reported to be injecting drugs has remained stable at around 58 to 63 per cent (Table 12.18 opposite).

The proportion of drug users reported to the RDMDs as injecting drugs in the last four weeks indicates a similar pattern to the rest of England, with nearly half of all users injecting drugs (Table 12.19 opposite). This is similar to the number of new notifications made to the Addicts Index, whilst slightly lower than all addicts notified.

The future

Presently, London has both a quarter of all the notified addicts in the UK and a quarter of those coming to treatment services in England. Estimates indicate that there are about 16,000 individuals attending treatment services in London (excluding GPs), with a total treatment volume in London of around 20,000 people. So what for the future?

Treatment

Although the most commonly reported drugs to the RDMDs and HOAI remain to be opiates such as heroin and methadone (although methadone statistics must be interpreted with caution), drugs such as benzodiazepine, crack and cannabis are increasingly reported. This reflects a wider shift amongst problem drug users away from a single drug of choice and towards poly-drug use. Furthermore, while an increase in the number of new heroin users notified to the HOAI in London occurred from 1991 to 1996, a rapidly increasing proportion of these users reported non-injecting as their preferred route of administration, perhaps reflecting another trend towards 'chasing' heroin (Strang et al, 1997).

Organisation

With the demise of the Addicts Index, RDMDs will have an even greater responsibility for information provision. Whilst the utility of the London RDMDs have been highlighted in the discussion above, debate now centres on how the RDMDs can both improve their reporting methodology and become a pan-Thames, pan-London resource for policy makers and planners (Chapter 14). Present indications are that the RDMDs will continue to routinely collect information on individuals attending drug services over time, however, improvements to their reporting system will allow new trends in the patterns of drug use to be quickly and accurately mapped.

Table 12. 17 Injecting status of new addicts in London notified to the Home Office Addicts Index, 1991-1996		1991	1992	1993	1994	1995	1996
	Injecting	1,331	1,224	1,565	1,485	1,358	1,565
	Not injected	789	880	944	1,010	1,181	1,534
	Valid Total	2,120	2,104	2,509	2,495	2,539	3,099
	Not recorded	190	300	361	328	342	298
	Total	2,310	2,404	2,870	2,833	2,881	3,397

Source: Home Office Addicts Index (1997).

Table 12.18 Injecting status of all addicts in London notified to the Home Office Addicts Index, 1991-1996		1991	1992	1993	1994	1995	1996
	Injecting	3,473	3,537	3,930	4,129	4,023	4,521
	Not injected	2,008	2,301	2,405	2,669	2,867	3,300
	Valid Total	5,481	5,838	6,335	6,798	6,890	7,821
	Not recorded	913	1,064	1,271	1,483	1,282	1,164
	Total	6,394	6,902	7,606	8,281	8,172	8,985

Source: Home Office Addicts Index (1997).

Table 12.19 Injecting status of problem drug users reported to Regional Drug Misuse Databases by location, 1996/97		London	London %	England (incl.) London %
	Injecting	4,642	48	49
	Not injecting	5,074	52	51
	Valid total	9,716	100	
	Not recorded	1,256		
	Total individuals	10,972		

Source: Regional Drug Misuse Databases (1997), Department of Health (1997b).

Notes: London data covers the financial year 1996/1997. England data covers the period 1st October 1995-31st March 1996.

References

Department of Health (1992). *The Health of the Nation*. London: HMSO.

Department of Health (1997a). *Drug Misuse Statistics 1997/9*. London: HMSO.

Donmall, M. (1990). *The Drug Misuse Database*: *Local Monitoring of Presenting Problem Drug Misuse*. London: Department of Health.

Druglink (1997). End of Index barely registers in drug field. *Druglink*, March/April 1997, 4.

Goldfinch, R., Sondhi, A., Edmond, I. et al (forthcoming). *Problem Drug Use in Greater London*. London: St. George's Hospital.

Hickman, M., Sutcliffe, H., Sondhi, A. et al (1997). Validation of a regional drug misuse database: implications for future policy and surveillance of problem drug use in the UK. *British Medical Journal,* 315,581.

Home Office Addicts Index (1996). Personal communication.

Home Office Addicts Index (1997). Personal communication.

Jarman, B. (1983). Identification of underprivileged areas. *British Medical Journal*, 289, 1587-1592.

Mott, J., Caddle, D. and Donmall, M. (1993). A comparison of doctors' practice in notifying addicts to the Home Office and reporting them to the North Western Drug Misuse Database. *Addiction*, 88, 249-256.

OPCS (1993). *1991 Census*. London: HMSO.

Office for National Statistics (1997). Personal communication.

Strang, J. and Shah, A. (1985). Notification of addicts and the medical practitioner: an evaluation of the system. *British Journal of Psychiatry*, 147, 195-198.

Strang, J., Griffiths, P. and Gossop, M. (1997). Heroin smoking by chasing the dragon origins and history. *Addiction*, 92 (6), 673-683.

Regional Drug Misuse Databases (1997). Personal communication.

PUBLIC HEALTH INDICATORS

Gerry V. Stimson and Gillian Hunter
The Centre for Research on Drugs and Health Behaviour

With additional contributions from: Di Bennett and Theresa Lamagni, Public Health Laboratory Service and Colin Taylor, National Addiction Centre.

Sections

Public health indicators

Any overview of public health problems arising from drug use in London will be selective and partial. There are better data on the consequences of more serious kinds of drug use such as injecting and opiate use, than on the consequences of more common forms of drug use.

There are relatively good data available on injecting risk behaviour, and its consequences for HIV and AIDS, hepatitis B and hepatitis C. However, data on the numbers of drug-related deaths and the mortality of drug users are currently inadequate. Furthermore, there are hardly any data on 'morbidity' (the physical and mental health consequences over time) associated with different kinds of drug use.

Injecting

The scale of exposure to health risk associated with injecting is higher in Inner London than in any other geographical area: some 4.7 per cent of men aged between 16 and 59 years in the National Survey of Sexual Attitudes and Lifestyles (NSSAL) self-reported injecting drugs at some time. In no other area was the prevalence for males higher than 1.7 per cent, and for Britain as a whole (including London) it was 0.8 per cent (Wadsworth et al, 1996; Hickman et al, 1997). The pattern is similar for women, although the proportion having injected is less at 1.2 per cent for Inner London, and 0.4 per cent for Britain as a whole.

Approximately one-third of men and 17 per cent of all women in Britain with a history of injecting drug use live in Inner London (although it has only about 5% of the population).

Hickman and colleagues have applied the NSSAL data to individual London health authorities in order to estimate the size of the population at risk of injecting drugs (Table 13.1 opposite) (Hickman et al, 1997). Because injecting is rare, the confidence intervals (or 'Lower' and 'Upper' estimates) in Table 13.1 are wide, and so the most likely values are underlined, based on information on the distribution of HIV infection. This table indicates the uneven distribution of injecting in the capital, with highest estimated numbers occurring in Inner London health authorities.

Syringe sharing

There is evidence that injecting drug users (IDUs) have made important changes in their injecting behaviour in response to the threat of HIV and AIDS. These changes have included: reductions in the overall proportion of IDUs reporting sharing syringes; decreased frequency of sharing; and increased discrimination regarding sharing partners.

Such reductions in injecting risk behaviour have been attributed to the relatively swift introduction of HIV prevention initiatives such as the distribution of

> **Key findings**
> Inner London has the highest proportion of men in Britain at risk of health problems associated with past or present injecting.
> London has about a third of all men in Britain who have injected drugs at some time.

Table 13.1	London health authority	Population	Estimated injecting drug use ever		
Estimated		aged 16-59	Lower	Central	Upper
populations at risk	**Males**				
of injecting drug	Brent & Harrow	140,900	0	420	1,120
use by sex and	Ealing, Hammersmith & Hounslow	207,400	1,340	2,900	4,760
London health	Kensington & Chelsea and				
authority, 1996	Westminster	115,700	3,000	5,430	7,860
	Barking and Havering	112,000	0	340	900
	Redbridge & WalthamForest	135,900	0	400	1,080
	East London and The City	178,900	4,660	8,410	12,160
	Enfield & Haringey	148,000	1,810	3,510	5,360
	Camden & Islington	114,500	2,980	5,380	7,790
	Bexley and Greenwich	127,600	0	390	1,020
	Lambeth, Southwark & Lewisham	226,400	5,890	10,650	15,400
	Merton, Sutton and Wandsworth	196,600	2,310	4,500	6,900
	Kingston & Richmond	97,100	0	290	780
	Barnet	93,000	0	280	740
	Hillingdon	75,800	0	230	610
	Bromley	86,500	0	260	690
	Croydon	100,600	0	300	800
	Females				
	Brent & Harrow	140,200	0	700	1,400
	Ealing, Hammersmith & Hounslow	206,400	160	1,410	2,710
	Kensington & Chelsea and				
	Westminster	115,800	350	1,390	2,550
	Barking and Havering	110,800	0	560	1,110
	Redbridge & Waltham Forest	134,300	0	670	1,350
	East London and The City	176,100	530	2,120	3,870
	Enfield & Haringey	145,300	210	1,200	2,270
	Camden & Islington	117,100	350	1,400	2,570
	Bexley and Greenwich	128,400	0	640	1,280
	Lambeth, Southwark & Lewisham	231,600	690	2,780	5,090
	Merton, Sutton and Wandsworth	196,600	270	1,610	3,050
	Kingston & Richmond	95,700	0	480	960
	Barnet	93,500	0	470	940
	Hillingdon	72,900	0	360	730
	Bromley	86,700	0	430	870
	Croydon	100,600	0	500	1,010

Source: Hickman et al (1997).

Notes: Details of the estimation techniques can be found in the authors' report.

sterile needles and syringes via syringe-exchange and pharmacy-based schemes, extensive local and national media HIV information campaigns, and the increased availability of methadone treatment. The British response to HIV among injectors has been hailed a 'public health success' (Stimson, 1995; 1996).

Research conducted prior to AIDS awareness in 1986/87 indicates that

Table 13.2
Syringe sharing in
London before and
after the introduc-
tion of HIV preven-
tion measures

	Sample location	Sharing rates
pre 1987		
1984-86	IDUs seeking treatment at drug agencies	59% had shared a syringe in the last four weeks
1985	Drug dependency unit	67% had shared with another person
1986	3 drug treatment agencies	34% shared in last 3 months
post 1987		
1987-88	Syringe-exchange	Last month sharing declined from 15% to 11%
1988-90	Syringe-exchange	In 1988, 27% of clients were 'sharing now'; but only 12% in 1990
1989	Drug dependency unit	31% had shared in the last month
1990-93	Community recruited	15% reported sharing in the last four weeks
1994-95	UAPMP surveys at drug agencies	26% of under 25s, and 16% of 25+ reported sharing in the last four weeks
1995	London Regional Drug Misuse Databases	11% shared in the last month

Source: Stimson and Hunter (1996).

Notes: UAPMP = Unlinked Anonymous Prevalence Monitoring Programme adminstered by PHLS.

syringe sharing in the UK was commonplace. However, as demonstrated in Table 13.2, studies completed after 1987 consistently report lower rates of syringe sharing (Stimson and Hunter, 1996).

Qualitative studies have also noted that IDUs have become increasingly discriminating about with whom they share needles and syringes (Power et al, 1995). The community-wide survey of IDUs in London conducted annually between 1990 and 1993 showed that among those who continued to share needles and syringes, the number of sharing partners was low (Hunter et al, 1995). Sharing was largely confined to intimates such as close friends and sexual partners, and IDUs reported a mean number of two sharing partners in the preceding six months.

The Unlinked Anonymous Prevalence Monitoring Programme (UAPMP) in England and Wales provides a useful tracking indicator of rates of sharing over time. This programme began in 1990, and it provides an indicator of the prevalence of, and risk factors for,

Table 13.3
Proportion of IDUs
that have shared
used needles or
syringes in the last
four weeks by age
group and loca-
tion, 1990-1995

Age		1990 - 91		1992 - 93		1994 - 95	
		N	%	N	%	N	%
16-24	London	7/30	23	36/119	30	32/125	26
	Elsewhere	60/192	31	285/1,194	24	245/1,048	23
25+	London	35/223	16	371/2,408	15	112/805	14
	Elsewhere	63/298	21	123/782	16	314/2,521	12

Source: UAPMP (1997).

Notes: Elsewhere includes England and Wales but not Greater London.

Table 13.4
Regional Drug
Misuse Database
reports of drug
injectors reporting
recent sharing of
needles or syringes
by location,
1995-1997

	N/Total	%
London IDUs	453/4,098	11.1
England IDUs	846/9,595	8.8

Source: Regional Drug Misuse Database (1997),
Department of Health (1997).

Notes: London IDUs data refer to the financial year
1996/97, while England IDUs data refer to the six
month period 1 October 1995 to 31 March 1996.

infection among adults whose behaviour may make them vulnerable to infection (Department of Health, 1996). The survey of adult IDUs, co-ordinated by the Public Health Laboratory Service (PHLS), collects specimens of saliva from current and former drug injectors attending drug treatment agencies, advice centres and syringe-exchange schemes, and asks IDUs to complete a questionnaire which measures risk behaviour. The specimens are later tested anonymously for antibodies to HIV and the hepatitis B virus.

The sharing results from this IDU survey suggest that no significant decrease has taken place in sharing among current injectors between 1990 and 1995 (Table 13.3 previous). Table 13.3 also indicates that younger injectors were at least two times more likely to share than older injectors in London.

Sharing data are also available from reports to the three London Regional Drug Misuse Databases (RDMDs) (North

Thames, South-East Thames and South-West Thames) (Table 13.4).

Most of the regional databases in England define recent sharing as sharing in the past four weeks, although South-West Thames defines it as sharing in the previous six months. Even with this broader definition of recent sharing for some parts of London, the London sharing rate is still similar to the average for England.

Key finding

Various studies show that syringe sharing has declined since about 1986, coinciding with the introduction of HIV prevention measures, and that it has been stable since about 1990.

Overall trends

However, a word of warning is necessary here. Whilst it is reasonable, on the above evidence, to conclude that syringe sharing is rarer now than 10 years ago, caution should be exercised regarding measures of the 'real' level of sharing. Research studies and routine surveillance systems which have examined injecting behaviour have varied in terms of design, behaviours investigated, wording of questions, and time frames for reports of behaviour. There have been few attempts to test the reliability and validity of the data. In the case of the RDMDs, information

Table 13.5
Indirect sharing
among injecting
drug users in
London,
1992-1993

	Sharing of filters or spoons		Front or backloading	
	%	N	%	N
1992				
Overall	52	257/496	37	180/493
Among people who did not share syringes	34	101/299	25	74/300
1993				
Overall	53	265/503	43	214/495
Among people who did not share syringes	32	96/303	34	101/299

Source: Hunter et al (1995).

is collected at point of first contact, and it is unclear what definitions of sharing staff use in practice. Recent work to develop a reliable and valid measure of risk behaviour using a new Injecting Risk Questionnaire indicates that precise and detailed questioning elicits higher reports of sharing (Stimson et al, 1997).

Continued risk behaviour - 'indirect sharing'

More recently, studies have identified the importance of sharing practices beyond those of sharing needles and syringes. Indirect sharing occurs through the shared use of filters and spoons during drug preparation, and via methods for dividing drug solutions such as 'frontloading' and 'backloading'. These practices are hypothesised to be associated with risk of HIV and hepatitis C transmission. Studies have found levels of indirect sharing to be high, even among those who did not report sharing needles and syringes (Table 13.5 previous).

Key finding
'Indirect sharing' of paraphernalia for the preparation of injections persists at a substantial level.

Prevalence of HIV infection among injecting drug users

HIV infection has been present in injectors in London since at least 1984. The prevalence of HIV infection among London injecting drug users is low by international standards (Stimson, 1995).

Number of reported HIV infections associated with IDU

In the Thames regions, a total of 1,298 injecting-related HIV infections were reported from voluntary confidential HIV testing to June 1997. This figure accounts for 68 per cent of the total injecting-related HIV infections for England (1,917), and 42 per cent of the total for the United Kingdom (3,060) (PHLS AIDS Centre, 1997).

These figures under-estimate the true total number of infections, because not all injectors have been tested. Surveys indicate that approximately 50 to 60 per cent of regular and long-term opiate injectors have been tested for HIV (Stimson et al, 1996). This testing rate is probably lower for people who inject occasionally, who have injected in the past, or who inject stimulants. The figures again under-estimate as they fail to count the number of people that have moved to London after a positive test. In contrast they also over-estimate, in that the total includes people who have moved away from London or have died.

Estimated total number of HIV infections associated with IDU

The 'real' number of infections can be estimated in various ways, including extrapolation from known AIDS cases (back-calculation models), and from HIV testing data combined with estimates of the numbers of known living cases.

Table 13.6
Estimated current
injecting-related
HIV infections by
location, 1996

Location	AIDS alive	HIV in contact with services	HIV not in contact with services	Total
Inner London	90	360	670	1,120
Rest of Thames region	30	130	130	290
Rest of England and Wales	100	450	460	1,010
Total	220	940	1,260	2,420

Source: Hickman et al (1997).

Using back-calculation from AIDS cases, adjusted for under-reporting and reporting delays, it has been estimated that in 1996 the actual number of current alive and resident people with HIV infections (including AIDS cases) related to drug injecting (past or present) was 2,420 in England and Wales, with a further 670 in Scotland (Hickman et al, 1997). Table 13.6 shows the estimates for Inner London, the rest of the Thames region, and the rest of England and Wales. 'In-contact' mainly means having had some engagement with a Genitourinary Medicine service in connection with HIV infection.

There are estimated to be 1,120 HIV infections from drug injecting in Inner London health authorities, which account for 46 per cent of the total for England and Wales. There were an estimated further 290 infections in the rest of the Thames Regions, which together with Inner London contributed 58 per cent to the total for England and Wales.

Table 13.7
Estimates of
current AIDS
cases, number of
HIV infected per-
sons, and cumula-
tive deaths from
AIDS, associated
with injecting drug
use by London
health authority, to
end of 1996

London health authority	AIDS alive	HIV alive	Total AIDS and HIV alive	Cumulative deaths
Brent & Harrow	<10	40	30	<10
Ealing, Hammersmith & Hounslow	10	150	160	30
Kensington & Chelsea and Westminster	20	190	210	40
Barking and Havering	<10	<10	<10	<10
Redbridge & Waltham Forest	<10	<10	<10	<10
East London and The City	10	140	140	30
Enfield & Haringey	<10	60	70	10
Camden & Islington	20	220	240	50
Bexley and Greenwich	<10	<10	<10	<10
Lambeth, Southwark & Lewisham	20	260	280	60
Merton, Sutton and Wandsworth	<10	80	80	20
Kingston & Richmond	<10	<10	20	<10
Barnet	<10	<10	<10	<10
Hillingdon	<10	20	20	<10
Bromley	<10	<10	<10	<10
Croydon	<10	<10	<10	<10

Source: Hickman et al (1997).

Notes: Estimates are rounded to the nearest 10, therefore totals do not always sum across the table. Details of the estimation techniques can be found in the authors' report.

Estimates of the number of injecting-related HIV infections, including AIDS cases, for each of the Thames health authorities, are shown in Table 13.7 (previous). The highest number of cases are in: Lambeth, Southwark & Lewisham; Camden & Islington; Kensington & Chelsea and Westminster; Ealing, Hammersmith & Hounslow; and East London and The City.

Key findings

For England and Wales as a whole, the HIV and AIDS epidemic among injecting drug users is concentrated in Inner London health authorities.

The total number of current injecting-related HIV infections in Inner London is estimated at about 1,120, and in the whole of the Thames regions is 1,410. This is low by international standards.

Estimated number of new infections associated with IDU

Another way to look at the problem is to ask how many new HIV infections occur over time. This can also be estimated using back-calculation models. Around 100 new HIV infections are estimated to occur each year from drug injecting in Inner London, with a further 20 or so in England and Wales (Figure 13.8) (Hickman et al, 1997).

The trend analysis depicted in Figure 13.8 is based on statistical modelling techniques, and should be approached with caution. It is not based on data collected whilst the HIV epidemic occurred, but rather it is a retrospective model based on back-calculation (statistical extrapolations from known AIDS case). Even so, the shape of the curve is of considerable interest. It suggests that there was a peak of new infections in London during 1984, followed by a substantial decline, and then a levelling off. Similarly, it suggests that the peak in the rest of England and Wales occurred during 1985 and 1986. This difference in epidemic peaks provides evidence that there may have been different epidemic dynamics in London compared with the rest of England and Wales. However, it is also possible that the earlier London peak is in part an artefact of the statistical modelling and reporting and testing behaviour.

Key finding

About two new HIV infections associated with injecting occur each week in London.

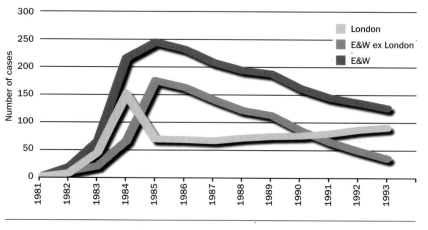

Figure 13.8
Estimated new cases of injecting-related HIV infection occurring each year by location, 1981-1993

Source: Hickman et al (1997).

Table 13.9
Prevalence of HIV
antibody amongst
injecting drug
users attending
treatment services
in London,
1990-1995

Year		HIV+/number tested	% HIV+
1990-91	Male	18/433	4.2
	Female	8/128	6.3
	Total	26/561	4.6
1992-93	Male	45/854	5.3
	Female	2/325	0.6
	Total	47/1,179	4.0
1994-95	Male	44/880	5.0
	Female	15/311	4.8
	Total	59/1,191	5.0

Source: UAPMP (1997).

What proportion of injectors are HIV positive?

A different way of looking at HIV infection is to ask what proportion of people who inject are HIV positive. Estimating the proportion with HIV infection is difficult because it is not possible to obtain true random samples of the injecting population. HIV prevalence estimates have therefore usually employed non-randomised 'convenience' samples. Such studies are described below, and, when taken together, provide the best estimates of HIV infection among IDUs in London.

Table 13.9 depicts HIV antibody prevalence levels for London IDUs gained from the 1990 onwards UAPMP survey. The prevalence of HIV infection amongst former and current injecting drug users attending treatment services in London was between four and five per cent for men, and one and six per cent for women. These prevalences among London injectors have been consistently higher than those of their counterparts in other areas of England and Wales. In 1995, for example, the overall prevalence of HIV infection among injectors outside South-East England was 0.45 per cent for men, with no infections among women (Department of Health, 1996).

Other studies have sought to recruit IDUs both from treatment services and community-based settings. For example, Strang and colleagues (1992) found an HIV prevalence of 12 per cent among current heroin injectors recruited from a variety of settings in South London.

Table 13.10
Prevalence of HIV
among community-
wide samples of
IDUs by location,
1990-1993

%		1990 N	1990 %	1991 N	1991 %	1992 N	1992 %	1993 N	1993 %
London	Male	37/317	11.7	29/327	8.9	19/297	6.4	25/341	7.3
London	Female	26/173	15.0	14/111	12.6	11/128	8.6	9/150	6.0
London	Total	63/490	12.8	43/438	9.8	30/425	7.0	34/491	6.9
Glasgow	Total	8/454	1.8	6/514	1.2	5/484	1.0	-	-
Edinburgh	Total	-	-	-	-	-	-	46/226	20.4

Source: Stimson et al (1996), Taylor et al (1994), Bath et al (1993).

Table 13.11 Prevalence of HIV antibody amongst current and former injecting drug users by year first injected and location, 1990-1995

Year first injected	Place	HIV+/number tested	% HIV+
up to 1985	London	124/1,744	7.1
	Elsewhere	69/5,581	1.2
1986+	London	13/1,020	1.3
	Elsewhere	6/6,538	0.1

Source: UAPMP (1997).

Notes: Elsewhere includes England and Wales, but not London.

The Centre for Research on Drugs and Health Behaviour (CRDHB) recruited IDUs from drug services and community settings mainly within North Thames Regional Health Authority between 1990 and 1993. Table 13.10 (previous) compares HIV prevalences from this London study with those from parallel studies in Edinburgh and Glasgow. These data suggest a decline and then stabilisation in the prevalence of HIV among London IDUs, from 13 per cent in 1990 to seven per cent in 1993.

Data from UAPMP also show marked variations in HIV prevalence by year first injected (Table 13.11). In London, among current and former injectors, those who started injecting before 1986 were six times more likely to be HIV positive than those who started injecting from 1986 onwards. Outside of London, pre-1986 injectors were 14 times more likely to be HIV positive than those starting later. The results are valid regardless of duration of injection.

Key findings

Taking the results of different studies, it is reasonable to assume that the prevalence of HIV infection among current injectors in London is between 5 and 7 per cent, and probably much lower in more recent injectors.

By international standards, the prevalence of HIV infection among London injectors is low.

AIDS related to injecting

In England 554 injecting-related AIDS cases were reported to the end of June 1997, and similarly 290 in Scotland, and 896 for the UK as a whole (PHLS AIDS Centre, 1997).

Most of the cases in England were in North Thames (226; 153 male and 73 female) and South Thames (129; 94 male and 35 female), making together 64 per cent of the cases in England and Wales, and 40 per cent of the cases in the UK. These data are based on residence at the time of diagnosis, and 'cases' here includes people who have died.

Key finding

The majority of AIDS cases associated with drug injecting in England and Wales have occurred in the Thames regions.

Current and projected AIDS cases

The total number of current injecting-related AIDS cases in 1996 (shown in Table 13.6 overall and 13.7 for Thames health authorities) was estimated at

120 in the Thames regions (90 in Inner London and 30 elsewhere). There were a further 100 cases in the rest of England and Wales (Hickman et al, 1997). The annual number of new injecting-related AIDS cases has been estimated to be about 60 in Inner London in 1997, rising to 80 by 2001, and 20 in the rest of Thames, remaining constant to 2001.

Prevalence of hepatitis B virus among injecting drug users

The presence of hepatitis B core antibody (known as anti-HBc) is an indicator of past or present exposure to the hepatitis B virus (HBV), but not of current infectiousness. Anti-HBc results from the UAPMP are depicted in Table 13.12. In London, the proportion of injectors testing anti-HBc positive has ranged between 22 and 40 per cent.

the prevalence of anti-HBc among IDUs between 1990 and 1995 for both London and the rest of England and Wales. Between 1991 and 1994, the prevalence was higher among London IDUs as compared to their counterparts in other parts of England and Wales.

Other surveys of syringe-exchange attendees and community recruited injectors have tended to find higher prevalences for anti-HBc than the UAPMP survey. In 1989, injecting drug users attending a central London syringe-exchange had an anti-HBc prevalence of 56 per cent (Hart et al, 1992). A community-wide sample of injecting drug users in London showed an anti-HBc

Key finding

Between a third and a half of London injectors have been exposed to the hepatitis B virus.

As can be seen from the table below, there has been some variation in

Table 13.12 Prevalence of HBV core antibody amongst injecting drug users by sex and location, 1990-1995	Year	Location	anti-HBc+/number tested	Total % anti-HBc+	% anti-HBc+ Male	Female
	1990	London	54/193	28	27	29
		Elsewhere	437/1,279	34	33	36
	1991	London	128/333	38	41	27
		Elsewhere	287/1,016	28	28	28
	1992	London	194/481	40	45	27
		Elsewhere	936/2,777	34	34	33
	1993	London	244/692	35	39	26
		Elsewhere	887/2,675	33	34	30
	1994	London	196/610	32	35	24
		Elsewhere	792/2,773	29	30	26
	1995	London	130/587	22	24	18
		Elsewhere	489/2,215	22	22	22

Source: UAPMP (1997).

Notes: Elsewhere includes England and Wales but not London.

frequency of 52 per cent in 1992 and 48 per cent in 1993 (Rhodes et al, 1996).

When the above UAPMP data are further analysed for differences by sex,

> **Key finding**
>
> The lower prevalences of anti-HBc for people who started injecting after 1985 supports the evidence for a decrease in injecting risk behaviour from the mid-1980s onwards.

prevalences for male IDUs peaked in London in 1992, and 'elsewhere' in 1992 and 1993, and have since fallen. Prevalences for female IDUs have generally declined from 1990 to 1995.

The prevalence of anti-HBc has been found to be associated with the year at which an injector first started injecting. The prevalence of anti-HBc is much higher among those who started injecting prior to 1986 (Table 13.13).

Table 13.13 Prevalence of HBV core antibody amongst injecting drug users who were tested between 1990 and 1995 by year first injected and location

Year first injected	Place	HIV+/number tested	% anti-HBc+
up to 1985	London	744/1,714	43
	Elsewhere	2,493/5,586	45
1986+	London	145/1,024	14
	Elsewhere	1,126/6,488	17

Source: UAPMP (1997).

Prevalence of hepatitis C virus among injecting drug users

The most comprehensive survey of the prevalence of hepatitis C virus (HCV) among drug users was conducted by Waller and Holmes (1996). This survey collated reports from various sources, with the London data originating from 28 different places. The results are shown in Table 13.14.

In both London and the UK, the HCV prevalence was extremely high at 71 per cent and 60 per cent respectively. Other studies measuring prevalences are few and far between, as testing was not available until relatively recently, but the evidence so far doesn't look good. The high rates for HCV, compared with the low rates for HIV and the declining rates for anti-HBc need investigation. It is likely that these rates are linked to various factors including: epidemic history in relation to behaviour change (it is possible that the prevalence of HCV was high before harm reduction measures were introduced); infectiousness; and viral transmissibility. Research on HCV and drug injecting is urgently needed.

Table 13.14 Prevalence of hepatitis C virus amongst injecting drug users by location, 1994

	Number of replies	HCV+/Number tested	% HCV+
London	28	295/416	71
UK	131	1,243/2,081	60

Source: Waller and Holmes (1996).

Drug-related deaths and mortality of drug users

Information on deaths connected with drug use come in two forms. Firstly there is the total number of drug-related deaths as recorded by the Office for National Statistics (ONS). Secondly are mortality figures for drug users where drug users are followed over time to see how many die and from what causes.

Drug-related deaths

Although many countries record contributory causes of death, the UK only records the underlying cause of death, which is 'the disease or injury that initiated the train of morbid events leading to death'. This is likely to include all cases where drug dependence or misuse is mentioned at death certification. When a death involves drugs, the person coding the death will first determine whether it was caused by suicide or homicide, and if so code it as such. Otherwise, if the coroner states that there was a history of drug dependence or other abuse of drugs it will be coded as 'drug dependence' or 'non-dependent abuse of drugs'. If the drug-related death does not fall under any of these codes, it is assigned to the

death by poisoning group, which is recorded either as accidental or undetermined. The assigned code for cause of death therefore depends both on the accuracy of the assessments contained within the death certificate and also the judgement of the coder. For example, a heroin overdose death may be coded as suicide, accident, drug dependence, drug abuse or undetermined cause.

There are no routinely published figures collating drug-related deaths for London. Information can be obtained from the ONS by request. Additionally, the Home Office has published figures on deaths associated with controlled drugs, and statistics on deaths associated with controlled drugs of addicts previously in treatment (as notified through the Home Office Addicts Index). These figures are only available on a national basis and up to 1996, and data relating to notified addicts are only available up to 1993.

ONS data
Figures for drug-related deaths in Greater London and the rest of England and Wales are available from the ONS database only since 1993 (Table 13.15).

Table 13.15 Number of drug-related deaths among 15 to 49 year olds by year of registration of death, underlying cause and location, 1993-1995

Underlying cause of death	1993 London	1993 E&W	1994 London	1994 E&W	1995 London	1995 E&W
Drug dependence	53	162	46	157	35	214
Non-dependent abuse of drugs	62	207	82	262	58	317
Deaths from poisoning where a drug was mentioned	123	506	111	592	119	632
Suicide by poisoning	57	433	59	435	46	417
Accident, suicide, homicide	140	897	176	980	193	1,140
Total	435	2,205	474	2,426	451	2,720

Source: Office for National Statistics (1997).

Notes: E&W = all England and Wales.

	1993		1994		1995	
	London	E&W	London	E&W	London	E&W
Males	291	1,539	354	1,751	328	1,965
Females	144	666	120	675	123	755
Male/female ratio	2.02	2.31	2.95	2.59	2.67	2.60
% of E&W deaths: Male	19%		20%		17%	
% of E&W deaths: Female	22%		18%		16%	

Source: ONS (1997).

Notes: E&W = all England and Wales.

The figures on drug-related deaths shown in Table 13.15 (previous) and Table 13.16 here are for all drugs, not only controlled ones, but exclude alcohol-related deaths. The figures therefore include people whose main or sole source of drugs would be medical prescriptions and products on sale in pharmacies and elsewhere.

The overall steady rise in the total number of deaths over the three years for England and Wales is contrasted with a possible peaking of the deaths in London in 1994. The suggestion of peaking is reinforced by the repeated peaking across most categories of death.

With the London trend in number of deaths presumably differing from the national trend, there is little of direct relevance to the London setting that can be identified from national figures alone, such as those published routinely by the Home Office (for example, Home Office Statistical Bulletin, 1996).

In particular, the recording of which of the different drugs caused the death is extremely limited.

As Table 13.16 shows there is a trend over the years shown for deaths to become more 'male dominated', both in London, and England and Wales. Male drug-related deaths outnumber female deaths by about two to one. The proportion of all deaths in England and Wales occurring in the London area amongst females has declined, although the trend is less evident amongst males. Nonetheless, it is likely that this could reflect a pattern of addiction spreading more broadly from the main metropolis as time progresses.

An analysis of drug-related deaths data serves then to raise as many questions about problem drug use in the capital as it offers answers. For example, it is unclear what proportion of deaths related to drug misuse are recorded as such, and the category assigned to any particular drug related

	Male	Female	Total
Deaths recorded	30	13	43
Numbers in study	93	35	128
Observed mortality rate per annum (%)	1.75	2.03	1.83
Expected deaths	2.67	0.93	3.60
Excess mortality ratio	11.2	13.9	11.9

Source: Oppenheimer et al (1994).

death appears somewhat arbitrary. In addition, increases or decreases in total deaths are only meaningful in relation to the total number of individuals exposed to risk, that is, the total number of drug consumers - which is unknown. Furthermore, the abandonment of the Home Office Addicts Index notification system has arguably reduced the availability of information at a national level, and resulted in a heavier reliance on the definitions and accuracy of the death certification codings used by the ONS database. This makes the calculation of rates of death (which require the numbers of individuals exposed to risk), a more difficult task, at least with respect to classified drugs.

Mortality of drug users

The longest running study of mortality of drug users started in 1969, taking a representative sample of all opiate users in treatment at London clinics (Stimson and Oppenheimer, 1982). This sample of 128 injectors has now been followed for 22 years (Oppenheimer et al, 1994).

After 22 years, 43 of the 128 were known to have died, giving an overall mortality rate of nearly two per cent per annum, and an excess mortality ratio of 11.9 (Table 13.17). Main causes of death (where known) were primarily associated with drug misuse (28/41, 68%), accidents and homicide (4/41, 10%) and natural causes (7/41, 17%).

Acknowledgements

The UAPMP is administered by the PHLS (HIV & STD Division, PHLS Communicable Disease Surveillance Centre, the Virus Reference Division, Central Public Health Laboratory) and the Institute of Child Health, London and supported by the Department of Health.

References

Bath, G.E., Dominy, N., Burns, S.M. et al (1993). Injecting drug users in Edinburgh. Fewer drug users share needles. *British Medical Journal*, 306, 693.

Department of Health (1996). *Unlinked Anonymous HIV Prevalence Monitoring Programme England and Wales*. London: Department of Health.

Department of Health (1997). Unpublished data.

Hart, G.J., Woodward, N., Johnson, A.M. et al (1992). Prevalence of HIV, hepatitis B and associated risk behaviours in clients of a needle-exchange in central London. *AIDS*, 5, 543-547.

Hickman, M., Bardsley M., De Angelis, D. et al (1997). *A Sexual Health Ready Reckoner: Summary Indicators of Sexual Behaviour and HIV in South East England*. London: East London and City Health Authority.

Home Office *(1996). Statistical Bulletin. Statistics of Drug Addicts Notified to the Home Office, United Kingdom, 1995*. London: Government Statistical Service.

Hunter, G.M., Donoghoe, M.C. and Stimson, G.V. (1995). Changes in the injecting risk behaviour of injecting drug users in London: 1990-1993. *AIDS*, 9, 493-501.

Office for National Statistics (1997). Personal communication.

Oppenheimer, E., Tobutt, C., Taylor, C. et al (1994). Death and survival in a cohort of heroin addicts from London clinics: a 22-year follow-up study. *Addiction*, 89, 1299-1308.

PHLS AIDS Centre - Communicable Disease Surveillance Centre, and Scottish Centre for Infection and Environmental Health (August 1997). *Unpublished Quarterly Surveillance Tables No 36.*

Power, R., Jones, S., Kearns, G. et al (1995). *Coping With Illicit Drug Use*. London: Tufnell Press.

Rhodes, T., Hunter, G.M., Stimson, G.V. et al (1996). Prevalence of markers for hepatitis B virus and HIV-1 among drug injectors in London: injecting careers, positivity and risk behaviour. *Addiction*, 91 (10), 1457-1467.

Stimson, G.V. (1995). AIDS and drug injecting in the United Kingdom, 1988 to 1993: the policy response and the prevention of the epidemic. *Social Science and Medicine*, 41 (5), 699-716.

Stimson, G.V. (1996). Has the United Kingdom averted an epidemic of HIV infection among drug injectors? *Addiction*, 91 (8), 1085-1088.

Stimson, G.V. and Hunter, G.M. (1996). Interventions with drug injectors in the UK: trends in risk behaviour and HIV prevalence. *International Journal of STD and AIDS*, 7 (suppl 2), 52-56.

Stimson, G.V., Hunter, G.M., Donoghoe, M.C. et al (1996). HIV-1 prevalence in community-wide samples of injecting drug users in London (1990-1993). *AIDS*, 10 (6), 657-666.

Stimson, G.V. and Oppenheimer, E. (1982). *Heroin Addiction: Treatment and Control in Britain*. London: Tavistock.

Stimson, G.V., Jones, S., Chalmers, C. et al (1998). A short questionnaire (IRQ) to measure injecting risk behaviour. *Addiction*, 93 (3), 337-346.

Strang, J., Gossop, M., Griffiths, P. et al (1992). HIV among south London heroin users in 1991. *Lancet*, 339, 1060-1061.

Taylor, A., Frischer, M., Green, S.T. et al (1994). Low and stable prevalence of HIV among drug injectors in Glasgow. *International Journal of STD and AIDS*, 5, 105-107.

Thames Regional Drug Misuse Databases (1997). Personal communication.

Unlinked Anonymous Prevalence Monitoring Programme (1997). Unpublished data.

Wadsworth, J., Hickman, M., Johnson A.M. et al (1996). Geographic variation in sexual behaviour in Britain: implications for sexually transmitted disease epidemiology and sexual health promotion. *AIDS*, 10, 193-199.

Waller, T. and Holmes, R. (1996) The sleeping giant awakes. *Druglink* 10 (5), 8-11.

THE FUTURE PUBLIC HEALTH SURVEILLANCE OF DRUG USE IN LONDON

Matthew Hickman and Chris Fitch
The Centre for Research on Drugs and Health Behaviour

Anna Bradley
Institute for the Study of Drug Dependence

Sections

Surveillance: revisiting the 'planner's nightmare'

'Planners' - be they policy makers, service purchasers from a range of different backgrounds, or members of multi-agency forums such as Drug Action Teams (DATs) - are all served by public health surveillance. The understanding gained from public health surveillance is useful to planners as it offers an overview of complex situations, assistance in identifying the priority health issues surrounding problem drug use, and help in making informed decisions about what action should be taken to address these. Surveillance systems may also be used to monitor changes in drug use over time, predict emerging trends and long-term problems, and evaluate the success of past decisions.

Although a wealth of public health data are potentially available in the capital, there is currently no systematic analysis and interpretation of these data with which to provide a coherent pan-London picture. This means that, despite some notable exceptions, surveillance is not playing the key role one would expect in tackling and reducing the harms of drug use in London - why is this?

Surveillance systems are only as effective as the networks and structures which inform them. In Chapter One, Alyson Morley noted that pan-London responses to problem drug use currently face a 'planner's nightmare'. The sheer number of bodies involved - with 33 local authorities, 16 health authorities, 63 Metropolitan Police Operational Command Units, 27 DATs, five Probation Service areas, and around 150 drug services - can make the simplest of organisational tasks instantly more difficult. The diverging agendas, funding bases and perceived responsibilities of each agency can repeatedly frustrate the co-ordination of potentially beneficial partnerships and information sharing. Furthermore, the distinct characteristics and idiosyncrasies which arguably still demarcate London's 'drug problem' from the rest of the UK, are mirrored within the capital itself: evident not only in the very different service needs of Inner and Outer London areas, but also in the varied institutional responses to collecting information about these problems.

This chapter reviews public health surveillance in London. It examines the reasons why surveillance should be an integral part of every London planner's thinking, evaluates the common problems encountered by national and London based approaches to the surveillance of problem drug use, and considers the development of a pan-London public health surveillance system in a 'five point agenda for change'.

What is surveillance?

Surveillance contributes to the evidence base of modern public health. This means that decisions can be made according to data collected about actual populations and their real health problems, rather than being based on hypotheses or abstract judgements. However, public health surveillance is not simply about collecting data: it is an ongoing process towards action. Surveillance is best defined then, as the systematic analysis and interpretation of data on specific health events for use in the planning and evaluation of health programmes (Thacker and Berkelman, 1988).

Although originally developed for the monitoring and control of infectious diseases, such as TB or smallpox, the basic concepts of public health surveillance can be usefully applied to other conditions. In 1968, the 21st World Health Assembly identified several suitable candidates for developing the surveillance of non-infectious diseases and problems, including cancer and 'drug addiction' (World Health Organization, 1968). More recently, surveillance systems have led to the identification of the HIV epidemic and the main routes of HIV transmission, secured funding for new health care services and prevention work, and provided the raw material for estimating the size of the HIV epidemic and future case-load (Day, 1996).

Why is surveillance useful to London's planners?

Surveillance systems can serve several objectives, although their acid test remains the same: if the information obtained does not help policy makers and planners to make decisions, the surveillance system is not working properly (Klauke et al, 1988). Consequently, before developing a surveillance system, a consensus needs to be established amongst policy makers and planners on what the 'key questions' actually are - a task made more difficult in London by the sheer number and diversity of agencies.

Box 14.2 (overleaf) matches a list of possible key questions (Stimson and Judd, 1997) against some of the traditional objectives of surveillance - it can be clearly seen that these are broadly in accordance with one another.

Does problem drug use merit a pan-London surveillance system?

Surveillance systems should be limited to important public health problems, as they can be expensive to maintain, and often rely upon the good will of health care and other workers to collect data (Box 14.1). Earlier chapters have outlined why drug use is an individual and public health problem in its widest sense with millions of pounds being spent each year on social services, education, health and criminal justice interventions (Chapters 10, 11, 12, and 13). Significantly, the successful prevention of the more harmful consequences of problem drug use

**Box 14.1
Main criteria to consider before establishing a surveillance system**

Main criteria to consider before establishing a surveillance system

- Frequency and severity of the problem.
- Cost of the problem to the health service and wider community.
- Consequences if current treatment programmes are not maintained or if no action is taken.
- Possibility for preventing or reducing the scale of the problem.

Box 14.2
Public health
surveillance: objec-
tives and potential
key questions for
policy making

Public health surveillance: objectives and potential key questions for policy making

Objectives of surveillance	Key questions for effective policy making
Describe health events in time, place and person (i.e. number of reports over time, geographical patterns, and socio-demographic characteristics).	What are the main characteristics of drug users in London? What drugs are they using? Does this differ between Inner and Outer London areas?
Estimate prevalence and incidence (i.e. total number of cases, and number of new cases).	How many new problem drug users are there, and is the number likely to increase in the future?
Identify 'at risk' groups and 'risk behaviours' associated with the problem.	What type of health and other problems are associated with drug use? Which Londoners are more likely to encounter these?
Mobilise resources for prevention and control.	How many drug users are in contact with services?
Target prevention.	What potential is there for intervention against the spread (i.e. diffusion) of drug use, against the harms associated with drug use; and where will investment achieve best results?
Evaluate prevention and control programmes.	What evidence is there that policy has worked?
Detect new epidemics (i.e. sudden departures from the normal number of cases, or different types of case).	Are new problem drug users on the increase? Are there any new drugs? Do these lead to any new drug problems?
Forecast future prevalence (the total number of a particular population) and their potential care needs.	What will be the future need for treatment and other social services. What effects will this have on the wider community?

through contact with treatment, outreach, and needle-exchange agencies has the potential to benefit both the individual and society. These benefits include: individual health gains from the improvement of a person's health and social circumstances; a reduction in the transmission of HIV and hepatitis; and a reduction in drug associated crime. Failure to provide sufficient services, to attract and retain people in treatment, and for services to stabilise and reduce problem drug use has equally wide implications for the general population.

Obstacles to pan-London surveillance: the 'jigsaw puzzle'

The Institute for the Study of Drug Dependence has suggested that interpreting existing information on drug use is similar to solving a complicated 'jigsaw puzzle' where each of the planner's key questions can be answered only by correctly putting a number of 'pieces' of data together (ISDD, 1997).

In most of the UK, and particularly in London, surveillance systems can currently only answer some of the questions thought to be most important to planners. This is due to a number of reasons including: difficulties in accessing and estimating 'hidden populations' of problem drug users; obstacles in co-ordinating data collection amongst a large number of institutions; or data pieces simply not being collected. The end result is that the larger picture of problem drug use still remains hidden.

What does the 'London jigsaw' look like?

Although there are a large number of data indicators potentially available, few are specific to London (Box 14.3 overleaf). Furthermore, in both the UK and London, many of these pieces of data have been developed with little strategic thought to their contribution towards uncovering the larger picture of problem drug use. Consequently, the effectiveness of public health drug surveillance systems is often hampered by the use of data indicators which were not designed to 'fit together' or complement one another.

The current absence of either a UK or pan-London information strategy - which can respond to planners' questions, oversee the development of complementary data sources, or identify which combination of indicators can provide the best answers - makes uncovering the larger picture of problem drug use even more difficult.

Population pieces

Whilst general population surveys, such as the British Crime Survey and school based surveys can still provide planners with good data on the proportion of the London population that has tried illicit drugs, these type of studies rarely yield much information about problem drug use. This is because problem drug use is too rare to be reliably estimated by even the largest population surveys (which sample over 10,000 people), and because numerous other biases can affect the findings of such surveys.

Table 14.3 Available drug-related data indicators, 1997

Indicator	Sample	Data collection	Frequency
General population survey			
Home Office British Crime Survey (BCS)	8,000 - 10,000 aged 16-59.	Self report - interview, assisted by direct entry onto portable computer.	Every 2 years from 1992.
National Survey Sexual Attitudes and Lifestyles (NSSAL)	19,000 aged 16-59.	Self report - interview.	One-off - 1990.
Office for National Statistics (ONS) Psychiatric Morbidity Survey	10,000 aged 16-64.	Self report - interview.	One-off - 1993-4.
Surveys of children and young people			
Health Education Authority (HEA) - National Drugs Campaign Survey	5,000 aged 11-35.	Self report - interview, assisted by direct entry onto portable computer.	One-off - 1995.
HEA - Tomorrow's Young Adults	11,000 aged 9-15.	Self-report.	One-off - 1989.
HEA - Today's Young Adults	4,000 aged 16-19.	Self report - interview.	One-off - 1990.
Schools Health Education Unit	25,000 to 50,000 aged 11-16.	Self-report - questionnaire.	Annual from 1994.
Routine reporting systems			
Home Office Addicts Index (HOAI)	Persons addicted to opiates or cocaine.	Report by medical practitioners.	1974 to 1997.
Regional Drug Misuse Database (RDMD)	All problematic drug-use (excluding alcohol only).	Report by agencies and other services in contact with drug users.	Ongoing from 1990.

Coverage	Relevance to drug taking	Comments
England and Wales representative sample of households plus booster sample of ethnic minority groups.	Drug use in general: type of drug, frequency of use, route of administration.	Good data on prevalence and trends in drug use in the population. However, identified few drug injectors/problem drug users.
UK representative sample of households.	Those who had ever injected.	Found very few injectors (<1%). Further geographical analysis showed Inner-London had much higher rates of people who had injected drugs at some time (4.7% for males, 1.2% for women).
England and Wales representative sample of households.	Those who had ever injected.	Found very few injectors (<1%). Not yet subjected to further geographical analysis.
England and Wales representative sample of households.	Drug use in general: type of drug, frequency of use, route of administration.	Good data on drug-taking in the population, and availability of drugs; identified few injectors/problem drug users.
England and Wales representative sample of schools.	Drug use in general: type of drug, frequency of use, route of administration.	-
England and Wales representative sample of households.	Drug use in general: type of drug, frequency of use, route of administration.	-
Volunteer - self-selected sample - of schools.	Drug use in general: type of drug, frequency of use, route of administration.	Very large sample - interesting data on drug-taking. Interpretation and generalistation difficult because sample not representative.
UK: notification system by doctors of first attendance and annual re-report if still in contact.	Opiate drug-use - including data on characteristics of drug user in contact with medical services.	Ceased in 1997. Useful data on trends in heroin users in contact with doctors. Area of residence not recorded. Unknown level of under-reporting. Did not count other problem drug users or drug agencies without doctors.
Regional reporting system by specialist drug agencies, medical practitioners and other services: first attendance and re-attendance after 6 month gap.	Problematic drug-use - including data on characteristics of drug user in contact with drug agencies and other services.	Recognises full gamut of problem drug-use, and agencies dealing with problem drug-use. Cannot measure annual case-load or prevalence of known users.

Table 14.3 Available drug-related data indicators, 1997 (continued)

Indicator	Sample	Data collection	Frequency
Home Office statistics on offences under Misuse of Drugs Act 1971	Cautions and prosecutions.	Paper based report by police, or data extracted from Crime Information System, and court statistics mentioning drugs offence.	Ongoing from 1972.
Home Office statistics on seizures	Drug seizures.	Report by police forces and Customs and Excise.	Ongoing from 1972.
Public health indicators			
Sharing needles and syringes	RDMD and unlinked anonymous surveys.	Self-report.	Ongoing from 1990.
AIDS/HIV statistics	AIDS diagnoses, HIV postive test results. Persons with HIV in contact with services.	Clinical, laboratory and health authority report.	Ongoing from 1982, 1984 and 1994 respectively.
Hepatitis B and C statistics	Positive tests for hepatitis B or C.	Laboratory report.	Hepatitis B from 1980, hepatitis C from 1990.
HIV prevalence	200-500 injecting drug users.	Unlinked anonymous sero-prevalence surveys - saliva tests for HIV antibody.	Public Health Laboratory Service (PHLS) and The Centre for Research on Drugs and Health Behaviour (CRDHB) from 1990.
Hepatitis B prevalence	200-500 injecting drug users.	Unlinked anonymous sero-prevalence surveys - saliva tests for hepatitis B core antibody.	i) (PHLS) ongoing from 1990; ii) (CRDHB) 1990 - 1993. 1995 women only.
Drug-related deaths, and mortality	ONS statistics and reports to HOAI.	Death certificates mentioning opiate or other drug use; record linkage between HOAI and ONS.	Mortality statistics from death certificates ongoing, record linkage ceased in 1994.

Coverage	Relevance to drug taking	Comments
Police forces and courts in UK, cautions introduced in England and Wales from 1982.	Possession and supply by type of drug.	Police statistics dominated by possession of cannabis. Area of residence not recorded. Event based.
Police forces and customs and excise in UK.	Frequency, amount and type of drug.	Trends in amount and purity difficult to interpret in relation to drug use in the population.
UK through RDMD, anonymous surveys in selected areas in England and Wales.	Reported levels of sharing (ever and in last month).	Single self-report questions under-estimate true level of sharing, and different modes of sharing.
England and Wales.	Reports identify number exposed through injecting drug use.	High levels of compliance with reporting systems. Reliable data for planning services. Interpretation hampered by lack of estimates of at-risk population.
Hospital laboratories in England and Wales.	Reports identify number exposed through injecting drug use.	Major under-reporting hampers interpretation of trends. Introduction of electronic systems may improve the data.
Specialist drug agencies in England and Wales, community-based sample in London.	Prevalence of HIV among current and recent injectors.	Best available data on impact of HIV on drug injectors. Main evidence showing that HIV prevalence is low. Samples may be biased. Trends difficult to interpret without knowledge of changes in the drug using population.
Specialist drug agencies in England and Wales, community-based sample in London.	Prevalence of hepatitis B.	Shows high proportions of injecting drug users previously or currently infected. Samples may be biased, and under-represent recent users.
UK.	Deaths associated with drug use; mortality rates in notified opiate users (up to 1994).	Drug-related deaths say little about person's drug use. Home Office data good indicators of mortality among long-term users, but may not be generalisable to new drug users or unnotified opiate users.

These biases include: an under-estimation of the frequency and type of drug use by self-report questionnaires (especially for more serious drugs and injecting behaviour); and the under-representation of 'difficult to reach' populations who may have higher rates of drug use (such as those living in deprived and Inner London areas, school truants and the homeless). Unfortunately, although ad-hoc surveys provide better instruments for looking at 'difficult to reach' populations, they cannot provide prevalence data over time or reflect changes in the incidence of drug use.

Public health pieces

Good data already exist on some of the associated harms of problem drug use, in particular those relating to HIV infection and hepatitis B (Chapter 13). Although the reliability of routine data on risk behaviour (such as sharing syringes) has still to be evaluated, this could be settled through the introduction of new studies which ask more detailed questions (Stimson, 1996).

However, data on drug-related deaths remain inconclusive and there are still no routine data sources, apart from ad-hoc surveys, on drug associated overdose. Equally, measures of the level of drug-related risk behaviour and its adverse health consequences will remain to be of limited value until the total number of problem drug users actually at risk in the population can be reliably estimated.

Treatment pieces

It is clear that problem drug use cannot be monitored simply by counting those people in contact with treatment agencies (Box 14.4).

Moreover, the Regional Drug Misuse Databases - which since the demise of the Home Office Addicts Index in May 1997 have become the primary source of information on drug users in contact with services - do not count the number of people in treatment (Chapter 12). Instead, data are collected on the number of treatment episodes (those individuals attending drug services for the first time or after a gap of six months). Therefore, we do not currently have sufficient evidence to either suggest what proportion of problem drug users in

Box 14.4
Problems with
treatment data
pieces

Problems with treatment data pieces

- Problem drug use arguably still has illicit, 'secretive' and sometimes 'marginalising' connotations. A proportion of the problem drug using population may therefore feel it is in their best interests to remain deliberately 'hidden'.
- Problem drug use is chronic - there are delays between a person starting drug use and first seeking treatment or help, and a person may also seek help several times and have different types of treatment during the time they are using drugs.
- The nature of problem drug use varies and includes ill-health, death, behavioural and psycho-social problems, and crime. Only some of these will be detected and dealt with by specialist drug agencies.
- Some of the harms associated with problem drug use, such as HIV infection, may be detected several years after a person has started using drugs, or after they have ceased drug use.

Source: Sutton and Maynard (1993), Hunt and Chambers (1976). .

London are in treatment, or to determine whether the growing number of problem drug users reporting to treatment is actually due to an increase in problem drug use in the population.

Criminal justice pieces

Although of considerable interest to planners and the media, the relationship between problem drug use and acquisitive crime is still a tentative one. In our current state of knowledge this relationship is often fuelled by 'back of the envelope calculations' involving assumptions about the income needed by problem drug users to buy drugs, the amount of problem drug use funded through acquisitive crime, the number of unreported crimes in an area, and the total number of problem drug users (Dorn et al, 1994; London Drug Policy Forum, 1997). Clearly, there is a need to replace such assumptions with more reliable indicators.

'New trend' pieces

Presently, neither the UK nor London operates a systematic reporting system to detect the use of new drugs, new drug problems or the potential for 'epidemics' of drug use to occur. Not all emerging drugs or apparent rises in drug use will become fully fledged 'epidemics', nor will such phenomena always lead to significant public health problems. Consequently, a system for detecting those new and developing drug trends which may have a public health impact, should provide a better evidence base for policy makers for both estimating future service demand and allocating appropriate responses.

Can the pieces be put together?

Previous attempts to provide estimates of the number of problem drug users have been undertaken by researchers in several cities elsewhere in the UK, Europe and world-wide, including Glasgow, Dundee, Liverpool, Barcelona, Toulouse, Amsterdam, Bangkok, New York, Sydney and Manipur in India (e.g. Frischer, 1992; Domingo-Salvany et al, 1995).

Most of these attempts have used 'capture-recapture' methods, which analyse the over-lap between a number of data sources to estimate the total number of cases in the population.

Box 14.5 Potential difficulties in solving the 'London jigsaw'

Potential difficulties in solving the 'London jigsaw'

- *Co-ordination* - London, until 1998, was the only major city in the UK with three Regional Drug Misuse Databases. This makes collaboration and data co-ordination more difficult.
- *Collection* - routine statistics from the Home Office and the Metropolitan Police Service are not collated by area of residence, meaning that London-wide estimation studies would require data to be extracted from over sixty different police divisions.
- *Comparison* - other potential sources of information for London (such as needle-exchanges, Probation Service and HIV testing programmes) are not part of any existing central reporting system. Furthermore, even if they were, it would be extremely difficult to compare and match these data sources ('record linkage') as such systems rarely share a core data-set permitting this.

Such methods are a growing feature of general surveillance systems and have been recommended by the European Monitoring Centre for Drugs and Drug Addiction for estimating the prevalence of problem drug users (EMCDDA, 1997)

Although useful, such capture-recapture methods are, again, more difficult to implement in the capital. Though some of the problems described in Box 14.5 (previous page) can be overcome in certain London districts, this process is usually extremely time consuming and often results in data-sets which are too small to generate reliable prevalence estimates.

Public health surveillance: what next?

Despite the apparent wealth of public health information collected, reported and potentially available for surveillance purposes, it is clear that few of the key policy questions for London can currently be answered. This is due partly to the nature of problem drug use and partly to the on-going 'planner's nightmare' in the capital. If a pan-London surveillance system is to be implemented, changes will be required in both the organisation and gathering of information. More critically, a consensus amongst planners about the key policy questions would need to be reached, and an information strategy developed to identify and manage potential information sources.

Ideally, such a surveillance system would be started from scratch, but this is simply not feasible. A more pragmatic alternative, however, might be an incremental process of development led by the main questions of concern to policy makers and planners.

The 'information and surveillance matrix' presented in Box 14.6 (overleaf) represents an initial attempt to do just this: combining those areas of potential interest to planners (shown in Box 14.1 as questions) with main data sources, methods and supplementary information. This matrix is based on the underlying assumption that rather than funding a series of separate routine reporting systems or ad-hoc studies, that these

should be planned, commissioned and integrated within a larger surveillance strategy. This strategy would include not only the monitoring of data from current routine information systems, but would also provide suggestions for new methods for monitoring drug use. Both of these would be clearly linked to the main questions of concern to policy makers and planners.

Five point agenda for change

Clearly, to move from the current situation to a fully integrated, pan-London public health surveillance system will require time and strong direction. This will not be achieved immediately, but will require development through a series of smaller steps.

1. Prevalence

Further estimates of the scale and type of problem drug use should be obtained and developed. Of particular importance to this process is the improved provision and collection of Metropolitan Police data on a London-wide basis. This is essential if capture-recapture studies linking RDMD and police data are to be used to produce estimates of the size of the problem drug using population. In addition, a core data-set of indicators needs to be agreed and used by those information systems collecting information on

Table 14.6 Public health information and surveillance matrix

Information pieces	Main data source/method	Supplementary information
Population pieces		
Prevalence estimates	Capture-recapture using RDMD, police and community-based sample and other sources.	Multiplier methods - standard questions incorporated into community-based samples, and/or RDMD samples.
Public health pieces		
Syringe-exchange	RDMD and monitoring reports from syringe outlets.	Community-based sample.
Sharing and other injecting behaviour	Community-based sample.	RDMD.
HIV	Clinical and laboratory reporting.	Mathematical modelling, unlinked sero-prevalence studies, community-based sample.
Hepatitis	Laboratory reporting.	Unlinked sero-prevalence studies, community-based sample.
Overdose	Accident & emergency (A&E) reports.	Community-based sample.
Death	Office for National Statistics mortality statistics.	Matching of deaths with known drug users (record linkage studies), cohort studies.
Treatment pieces		
Drug users in treatment (visible drug users)	Probation, police, social services, prison, A&E.	
Effectiveness of treatment and care	Audit/follow-up of sample of drug users reported to RDMD.	Survey of community-based sample of drug users.
Criminal justice pieces		
Supply	Customs and police statistics.	Economic modelling, mapping markets, trends in price and purity, community-based sample.
Possession	Police statistics of offences under Misuse of Drugs Act (1971).	Court and prison statistics, community-based sample.
Drug-related crime	Matching of offenders with known drug users (record linkage studies).	Community-based sample, case-control studies, prison statistics.
'New trends' pieces		
Incidence/new epidemics	New early warning system (e.g. accident & emergency reports, drug testing in police cells, or outreach reports) Analysis of RDMD, mathematical modelling.	

problem drug users in the capital, allowing data to be shared and compared across reporting systems.

2. RDMD

Regional Drug Misuse Databases are the biggest investment in regular surveillance and should be central to the goals of an improved public health information system. However, to sustain this investment, the current operation of the RDMD will require some modification.

Firstly, the RDMD needs to become an 'annual re-reporting system', recording both the incidence and prevalence of those individuals treated for problem drug use. This will enable estimates of the number of people seeking treatment, and those in treatment at any one time, to be produced. Secondly, RDMDs in South and North Thames should be merged to provide a single pan-Thames, London-wide database. Thirdly, greater use needs to be made of the RDMD databases as a research resource. In particular, the RDMD can be used to produce 'sampling frames' (lists from which research subjects can be drawn) for more detailed and focused studies.

3. Community samples

Community-based samples, where drug users are contacted and interviewed in the community, have emerged as an essential component in the monitoring of risk behaviour and contacting out of treatment users. Since 1990, there has been at least one community-based sample in London each year around issues such as HIV testing, syringe sharing, service utilisation, criminal activity, and sexual behaviour (Chapter 13).

A review of previous and current community-based studies should be undertaken to establish a common evidence base, identify areas presently under researched, recommend future arrangements for the organisation and funding of community-based samples, and produce a list of standard questions which can be used across these studies. Such a review will help to both improve the quality and range of information eventually provided to planners.

4. New trends

An assessment is also required of the feasibility and benefit of establishing a system for identifying new drugs, new epidemics, and new drug problems in London. This could be based on similar models in the United States where data on the incidence and changes in patterns of drug use are provided through: patients attending hospital accident and emergency units; and drug-testing in police cells.

Possible variations on these models for the London area include: further analysis of recent users reported to the RDMD; systematic reports from outreach workers; reports from hospital accident and emergency departments; and drug testing in police cells.

5. Crime

Tackling Drugs Together (HMSO, 1995) and local DATs in London have both stressed the importance of examining the relationship between drug use and crime, the need for reliable information on the level of crime associated with problem drug use, and the amount preventable through intervention and treatment. Currently, such measures are not available, and methods of evaluating drug-related crime need to be re-assessed. Options include: record linkage studies between known drug users and offenders; periodic surveys of offenders and problem drug users; and case-control studies between drug using and non-drug using offenders.

Can public health surveillance wake London from the 'planner's nightmare'?

Currently, the 'planner's nightmare' means that the surveillance of problem drug use in London is incomplete, based on information fragmented across numerous sources, and isolated in a variety of incompatible institutional forms. Consequently, policy makers often have to work extremely hard to accommodate insufficient and inappropriate evidence.

Clearly, changing this situation will not be easy. Although some short-term benefits may be accrued from the gradual improvement of individual datasources and indicators, a London-wide information strategy will also need to be developed to co-ordinate this process. Presently, it appears that a pan-London debate on the key questions for surveillance, the pieces of data and information this will require, and the body responsible for overseeing this process, appears to provide the most effective foundation for the future surveillance of drug use in London.

Significantly, although the conclusions reached in this chapter emanate from a discussion of public health surveillance in London, their principles equally apply to the development of other drug-related local, national and international information systems. Here, planner consultation and consensus, data compatibility and comparability, and sufficient co-ordination and vision are all essential in ensuring that such surveillance actually serves the needs of policy makers and planners. Consequently, if London does manage to wake from the planner's nightmare, it could find that the first voices it hears are from those seeking advice on implementing similar change elsewhere.

References

Day, N. E. (Chairman) (1996). The incidence and prevalence of acquired immune deficiency syndrome and other severe HIV disease in England & Wales for 1995-1999: projections using data to end of 1994. *Communicable Disease Report*, 6 (R1), 1-24.

Domingo-Salvany, A., Hartnoll, R.L., Maguire, A. et al (1995). Use of capture-recapture to estimate the prevalence of opiate addiction in Barcelona, Spain, 1989. *American Journal of Epidemiology*, 141, 567-74.

Dorn, N., Baker, O. and Seddon,T. (1994). *Paying For Heroin: Estimating the Financial Cost of Acquisitive Crime Committed by Dependent Heroin Users in England and Wales*. London: Institute for the Study of Drug Dependence.

European Monitoring Centre for Drugs and Drug Addiction (1997). *Estimating the Prevalence of Problem Drug Use in Europe*. EMCDDA Scientific Monograph Series No.1.

Frischer, M. (1992). Estimated prevalence of injecting drug use in Glasgow. *British Journal of Addiction*, 87, 235-243.

Hickman, M., Sutcliffe, H., Sondhi, A. et al (1997). Validation of a regional drug misuse database: implications for future policy and surveillance of problem drug taking. *British Medical Journal*, 315: 581.

HMSO (1995). *Tackling Drugs Together: A Strategy for England 1995-1998*. London: HMSO.

Hser, Y., Anglin, M.D., Wickens, T.D. et al (1992). *Techniques for the Estimation of Illicit Drug User Prevalence: An Overview of Relevant Issues*. New York: National Institute of Justice.

Hunt, L.D. and Chambers, C.D. (1976). *Heroin Epidemics: A Study of Heroin Use in the United States, 1967-75*. New York: Spectrum.

Institute for the Study of Drug Dependence (1997). *Drug Misuse in Britain 1996*. London: ISDD.

Klauke, D.N., Buehler, R.H.W., Thacker, S.B. et al (1988). Guidelines for evaluation surveillance systems. *Morbidity and Mortality Weekly Report*, S.5, 37, 1-20.

London Drug Policy Forum (1997). *Drug Users and the Criminal Justice System*. London: London Drug Policy Forum.

Stimson, G.V. and Judd, A. (1997). Estimating the scale and nature of drug problems: the relationship between science, policy and drugs strategy. In *EMCDDA - Proceedings of the 'Addiction Prevalence Estimation: Methods and Research Strategies' Conference (1996)*.

Stimson, G.V. (1996). Measuring the Health of the Nation target for injecting drug users: the Injecting Risk Questionnaire. *Executive Summary*, No. 54: November/December. London: Centre for Research on Drugs and Health Behaviour.

Sutton, M. and Maynard, A. (1993). Are drug policies based on fake statistics? *Addiction*, 88, 455-8.

Thacker, S. B. and Berkelman, R. L. (1988). Public health surveillance in the United States. *Epidemiologic Reviews*, 10, 164.

World Health Organization (1968). *Report of the Technical Discussions at the 21st World Health Assembly on National and Global Surveillance of Communicable Diseases*. WHO: Geneva.

Index

List of Boxes, Figures, Maps and Tables

Boxes

Figures

Maps

Tables